Editorial Director: Cynthia Tripp
Cover Designer and Illustrator: Matt Pollock
Illustrator: Sam Valentino
Photography Credit: wk1003mike/Shutterstock (front cover background)

ISBN 978-0-7609-9225-8
©2015—Curriculum Associates, LLC
North Billerica, MA 01862

Table of Contents

Family Letter available with every lesson.

Unit 4: Number and Operations—Fractions

Unit 5: Measurement and Data

Family Letter available with every lesson.

Unit 6: Geometry

Family Letter available with every lesson.

Dear Family,

This week your child is exploring place value in numbers.

Our number system is based on a pattern of tens. The value of a digit in a number is based on the place where the digit appears in the number.

A digit in one place has 10 times the value that the same digit would have in the place to its right.

Thousands Period			Ones Period		
Hundred Thousands	Ten Thousands	Thousands	Hundreds	Tens	Ones
4	6	7	8	8	2

This number is written in **standard form:**	467,882
This number is written in **word form:**	Four hundred sixty-seven thousand, eight hundred eighty-two
This number is written in **expanded form:**	400,000 + 60,000 + 7,000 + 800 + 80 + 2

Invite your child to share what he or she knows about place value by doing the following activity together.

NEXT

Place Value Activity

Do an activity with your child to practice exploring place value in real-life numbers.

The distance from Earth to the moon is about 238,855 miles.

This number is written in standard form.
238,855

- Have your child read the number aloud. (two hundred thirty-eight thousand, eight hundred fifty-five)

- Cover the standard form of the number above so that your child cannot see it. Read the number aloud and have your child write the number in standard form.

- Now, let your child make up a 6-digit number for you to write.

- Ask your child to check your work.

Look for other real-life opportunities to practice exploring place value of numbers with your child.

Name: _____

> **Prerequisite: How do you know the place value of each digit in a number?**

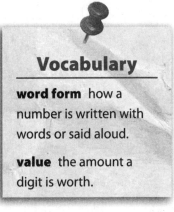

Study the example that shows how a place-value chart shows the value of each digit in a number. Then solve problems 1–8.

Example

The place-value chart shows the number 435.

Hundreds	Tens	Ones
4	3	5

Word form: *four hundred thirty-five*

The 4 in the hundreds place has a value of 400.
The 3 in the tens place has a value of 30.
The 5 in the ones place has a value of 5.

So, another way to write 435 is 400 + 30 + 5.

1 Show the number 762 in the following place-value chart.

Hundreds	Tens	Ones

2 What is the value of 7 in 762? _____

3 What is the value of the digit in the tens place in 762? _____

4 Use place value to show another way to write 762.

762 = _____ + _____ + _____

Vocabulary

word form how a number is written with words or said aloud.

value the amount a digit is worth.

Solve.

5 Use the place-value chart below to help you think about the value of each digit in the number.

Hundreds	Tens	Ones
5	2	2

   a. Write the number. _____

   b. Write the number in word form.

   Five _____ twenty-_____

   c. Write the number another way.

   _____ = _____ + _____ + _____

6 Look at the place-value chart in problem 5.

   a. The digit in the ones place is _____ .

   The value of the digit in the ones place is _____ .

   b. The digit in the tens place is _____ .

   The value of the digit in the tens place is _____ .

   c. 20 = _____ × 2

7 **a.** What is the value of 3 in 123? _____

   b. What is the value of 3 in 231? _____

   c. What is the value of 3 in 312? _____

   d. 30 = _____ × 3   300 = 10 × _____

8 Use the digits 4, 5, and 6 to write a number in which 4 has a value of 400. Explain your thinking.

_____

_____

_____

Name: _____

Use Place Value

Study how the example uses a place-value chart to show the value of the digits in a number. Then solve problems 1–8.

Example

Look at the place-value chart below. What is the value of the 3?

Then, use place value to explain the value of 3 if it were in the ten thousands place.

Hundred Thousands	Ten Thousands	Thousands	Hundreds	Tens	Ones
2	0	3	5	5	4

Standard form: 203,554
Expanded form: 200,000 + 3,000 + 500 + 50 + 4
Word form: *two hundred three thousand, five hundred fifty-four*

The 3 is in the thousands place, so it has a value of 3,000.
If 3 were in the ten thousands place, its value would be 30,000.

1 Write 70,681 in the following place-value chart.

Hundred Thousands	Ten Thousands	Thousands	Hundreds	Tens	Ones

2 Write 70,681 in expanded form and word form.

_____

_____

3 What would be the value of 8 if it were in the thousands place? _____

4 What is the value of the 6 in 70,681? Explain how you know.

_____

_____

Vocabulary

value the amount a digit is worth.

Solve.

5 What number is one thousand less than 921,438? Explain how you know.

_____

_____

_____

6 What number is one hundred thousand more than 75,000? Explain how you know.

_____

_____

_____

7 Show some different ways you can make 7,502.

_____ hundreds + _____ tens + _____ ones

_____ tens + _____ ones

_____ ones

8 What are three different ways to make the number 15,638 with only hundreds, tens, and ones?

_____

_____

_____

9 Solve the following base ten riddle:

I have 30 ones, 82 thousands, 4 hundred thousands,

60 tens, and 100 hundreds. What number am I?

Solution: _____

Name: _____

Reason and Write

Study the example. Underline two parts that you think make it a particularly good answer and a helpful example.

Example

Emma looked at the numbers 4,075 and 1,806. Her thinking is shown below.

The number 1,806 has more hundreds than 4,075 because 1,806 has 8 in the hundreds place, and 4,075 has 0 in the hundreds place. 8 hundreds is more than 0 hundreds.

Tell why Emma's thinking is incorrect. Then explain why there are more hundreds in 4,075 than in 1,806.

Show your work. Use a place-value chart, words, and numbers to explain your answer.

Hundred Thousands	Ten Thousands	Thousands	Hundreds	Tens	Ones
		4	0	7	5
		1	8	0	6

Emma looked only at the digits 0 and 8 in the hundreds place. She needed to also look at the digits in the thousands place.

4,075 has 4 thousands, or 40 hundreds, not 0 hundreds.

1,806 has 1 thousand, or 10 hundreds, plus 8 hundreds for a total of 18 hundreds, not 8 hundreds.

40 hundreds is more than 18 hundreds. There are more hundreds in 4,075 than in 1,806.

Where does the example . . .

- *use a chart to show the place value of digits?*

- *use words and numbers to explain?*

- *give details?*

Lesson 1 Understand Place Value   **7**

Solve the problem. Use what you learned from the model.

Tyler looked at the numbers 10,020 and 20,010. His thinking is shown below.

The number 10,020 has more tens than 20,010 because 10,020 has 2 in the tens place, and 20,010 has 1 in the tens place. 2 tens is more than 1 ten.

Tell why Tyler's thinking is incorrect. Then explain why there are more tens in 20,010 than in 10,020.

Show your work. Use a place-value chart, words, and numbers to explain your answer.

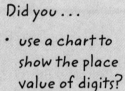
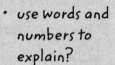

Did you . . .

- use a chart to show the place value of digits?

- use words and numbers to explain?

- give details?

Dear Family,

This week your child is learning how to compare whole numbers.

Your child can use a place-value chart to compare multi-digit numbers. For example, this place-value chart can be used to compare 23,643 and 23,987.

Ten Thousands	Thousands	Hundreds	Tens	Ones
2	3	6	4	3
2	3	9	8	7

To compare the two numbers in the place-value chart above, look down each column in the chart. Start at the left and compare the digits in each column.

The ten-thousands digits are the same.

The thousands digits are the same.

The hundreds digits are different.

6 hundreds is less than 9 hundreds, so the top number, 23,643, is less than the bottom number, 23,987.

Your child is learning to use a symbol to write the comparison: 23,643 < 23,987.

Invite your child to share what he or she knows about comparing whole numbers by doing the following activity together.

NEXT

Comparing Whole Numbers Activity

Use data from the real world to practice comparing real-life numbers with your child.

For example, famous mountains around the world have the following heights:

Mount Kilimanjaro: 19,341 feet

K2 (mountain in Asia): 28,251 feet

Mount Everest: 29,035 feet

Mount McKinley: 20,322 feet

- Have your child read aloud the mountain heights.
- Ask your child to compare the heights. Encourage your child to use comparison words and symbols as shown in the table below.

  Example: The height of Mount Everest is greater than the height of Mount McKinley. 29,035 > 20,322

symbol	<	>	=
meaning	is less than	is greater than	is equal to

Look for other real-life opportunities to practice comparing numbers with your child.

Compare Whole Numbers

Name: _____

Study the example that shows how to compare two three-digit numbers. Then solve problems 1–7.

Example

To compare numbers with the same number of digits, compare place by place. Start with the greatest place value.

Compare 790 and 728.

First, compare hundreds.
7 hundreds = 7 hundreds

Hundreds	Tens	Ones
7	9	0
7	2	8

Next, compare tens
9 tens > 2 tens
So, 790 > 728.

1 Write the numbers 465 and 483 in the place-value chart.

Hundreds	Tens	Ones

2 Complete the sentences to explain how to find which number is less, 465 or 483.

First, compare digits in the _____ place.

Next, compare the _____ place, because both

digits in the _____ place are the same.

_____ tens is less than _____ tens, so

_____ is less than _____.

3 Write the symbol (>, <, =) to compare 465 and 483.

465 ☐ 483

Vocabulary

greater than a comparison that says one number has greater value than another number.

9 > 2

less than a comparison that says one number has less value than another number.

2 < 9

Solve.

4 Write the symbol (>, <, =) that makes each statement true.

73 ☐ 95

184 ☐ 148

905 ☐ 950

5 Danny says 4 < 6, so 204 < 216. Is his reasoning correct? Explain.

_____

_____

_____

_____

6 Use numbers and words to explain why a two-digit number is always less than a three-digit number.

_____

_____

_____

_____

7 Write a digit (0–9) in the boxes below to make each comparison true.

4☐2 < 4☐2

☐30 > ☐60

60☐ = ☐05

9☐ < ☐81

☐60 > ☐50

Name: _____

Compare Multi-Digit Numbers

Study the example that shows how to compare multi-digit numbers. Then solve problems 1–6.

Example

Cara piloted two flights. On her first flight, she flew the airplane 30,825 feet high. On her second flight, she flew 30,750 feet high. Compare how high Cara flew on her two flights.

Hundred Thousands	Ten Thousands	Thousands	Hundreds	Tens	Ones
	3	0	8	2	5
	3	0	7	5	0

The ten thousands and thousands digits are the same.

The hundreds digits are different.

8 hundreds > 7 hundreds

30,825 > 30,750

1 In 2013, 50,266 runners finished the New York City Marathon and 38,879 runners finished the Chicago Marathon. Compare these numbers by lining up the place value. Explain which number is greater.

_____

_____

_____

2 Two numbers are shown in expanded form. Explain and show how to compare these numbers.

$$60,000 + 2,000 + 500 + 80 + 3$$
$$60,000 + 7,000 + 200 + 40 + 5$$

_____

_____

_____

Solve.

3 Circle all the numbers that are greater than 98,765.

    a. 100,100

    b. 89,975

    c. 99,132

    d. 987,650

4 Walnut Elementary raised $1,950 for new technology in their school. Grove Elementary raised $1,890. Which school raised more money? Explain how you know.

_____

_____

_____

_____

5 Write the symbol (>, <, =) that makes the statement true.

    8,035 ☐ 894

    62,999 ☐ 63,000

    142,073 ☐ 143,750

    501,348 ☐ 500,348

6 Tell whether each number sentence is *True* or *False*.

    a. 33,003 = 33,030   ☐ True ☐ False

    b. 524,980 > 52,498   ☐ True ☐ False

    c. 270,615 < 270,569   ☐ True ☐ False

    d. 100,000 < 99,999   ☐ True ☐ False

Name: _____

Compare Whole Numbers

Solve the problems.

1 Ethan read 901 pages this month. Henry read 1,002 pages. Maria read 1,020 pages. Kylie read 1,012 pages. Who read the least number of pages?

What place-value position do you need to compare?

A Ethan

C Maria

B Henry

D Kylie

2 A photographer has picture files saved in three online albums. The Wedding album has 2,073 files. The Birthday album has 1,860 files. The Pets album has 2,370 files. Which album has the most files?

Show your work.

You might want to use a place-value chart to compare these numbers.

Solution: _____

3 Which of these is equal to 25,973?

How could you write this number with only hundreds, tens, and ones?

A 25 thousands, 973 hundreds

B 259 hundreds, 7 tens, 3 ones

C 25 hundreds, 97 tens, 3 ones

D 25 ten thousands, 9 hundreds, 7 tens, 3 ones

Solve.

4 Circle the statement below that correctly compares 1,530 and 12,530.

A 1,530 > 12,530 because
5 thousands > 2 thousands.

B 1,530 = 12,530 because
5 hundreds = 5 hundreds.

C 1,530 < 12,530 because 1 < 2.

D 1,530 < 12,530 because
1 thousand < 12 thousands

Hannah wrote the numbers one above the other to compare them. She chose **A** as the correct answer. How did she get that answer?

_____

_____

_____

If you compare numbers by writing one above the other, how do you know that the numbers are lined up correctly?

5 Use the digits in the number 531,642 to write a number that is greater than and a number that is less than 531,642.

☐☐☐ , ☐☐☐ > 531,642

531,642 > ☐☐☐ , ☐☐☐

What could be the first step in solving this problem?

6 Use each of the digits 1–9 exactly once. Write a number in each box to create the greatest and least possible number.

Greatest Number ☐☐ , ☐☐☐

Least Number ☐ , ☐☐☐

What digit should you write in the greatest place value?

Dear Family,

This week your child is learning to add and subtract whole numbers.

One way your child is learning to subtract is to use place value in a subtraction problem such as 4,002 – 2,153.

In this problem, you need to regroup in order to subtract.
A place-value chart can show the regrouping.

Thousands	Hundreds	Tens	Ones
(4)	0	0	2

Thousands	Hundreds	Tens	Ones
3	(10)	0	2

4 thousands = 3 thousands + 10 hundreds

3	9	(10)	2

10 hundreds = 9 hundreds + 10 tens

3	9	9	10 + 2 = 12

10 tens = 9 tens + 10 ones

Now you can subtract.

	Thousands	Hundreds	Tens	Ones
	3	9	9	12
−	2	1	5	3
	1	8	4	9

Instead of using a place-value chart, your child is also learning to show the regrouping above the problem.

$$
\begin{array}{r}
{\scriptstyle 9\ 9} \\
{\scriptstyle 3\ \cancel{10}\cancel{10}12} \\
4,\cancel{0}\cancel{0}2 \\
-\ 2,153 \\
\hline
1,849
\end{array}
$$

Invite your child to share what he or she knows about adding and subtracting whole numbers by doing the following activity together.

Adding and Subtracting Whole Numbers Activity

Do an activity with your child to practice adding and subtracting numbers.

- **Adding Numbers:** Ask your child to come up with a four-digit number less than 5,000. This will be the "special" number.
  Example: Your child picks 3,854.

- Have your child ask a family member for a four-digit number less than 5,000.
  Example: The family member picks 2,093.

- Ask your child if he or she thinks the sum of the number and the "special" number will be greater than or less than 5,000.
  Example: Your child says it will be greater than 5,000.

- Have your child add the two numbers to check his or her answer.
  Example: 3,854 + 2,093 = 5,947; your child is correct!

- **Subtracting Numbers:** Now have your child pick a four-digit number less than 9,000. Make the "special number" 9,000 this time.

- Ask your child if he or she thinks the difference between 9,000 and his or her number will be greater than or less than 5,000.

- Have your child subtract the two numbers to check his or her answer.

Look for real-life opportunities to practice adding and subtracting numbers with your child.

Add and Subtract Whole Numbers

Name: _____

Prerequisite: Add and Subtract Three-Digit Numbers

Study the example showing how to subtract by breaking apart and combining numbers. Then solve problems 1–6.

Example

Solve $852 - 623$.

Use place value to write each number as hundreds, tens, and ones.	$852 = 800 + 50 + 2$ or **$800 + 40 + 12$** $623 = $ **$600 + 20 + 3$**
Subtract hundreds. Subtract tens. Subtract ones.	$800 - 600 = 200$ $40 - 20 = 20$ $12 - 3 = 9$
Combine the differences.	$200 + 20 + 9 = 229$ $852 - 623 = 229$

---

1 Show how to use place value to subtract $947 - 586$.

2 Show how to use place value to add $354 + 271$.

Solve.

3 Alice drove 235 miles on Saturday. On Sunday, she drove 68 more miles than on Saturday. How many miles did Alice drive altogether on Saturday and Sunday?

Show your work.

Solution: _____

4 Kayla solved a subtraction problem. She wrote 490 − 185 = 675. Explain what Kayla did wrong and correctly solve the problem.

Show your work.

Solution: _____

5 Ryan has 96 business cards. He buys 225 more cards. He hands out 248 cards at a conference. How many cards does Ryan have left?

Show your work.

Solution: _____

6 Write each digit in the correct box below. Use each digit only once.

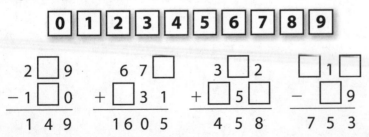

©Curriculum Associates, LLC   Copying is not permitted.

Name: _____

Add Whole Numbers

Study the example showing how to use addition to solve a word problem. Then solve problems 1–6.

Example

On Friday, 1,150 people saw the school play. On Saturday, 987 people saw the play. How many people saw the play on those two days?

```
  1,150
+   987
      7  ──→ 0 ones + 7 ones = 7 ones
    130  ──→ 5 tens + 8 tens = 13 tens or 1 hundred + 3 tens
  1,000  ──→ 1 hundred + 9 hundred = 10 hundreds or 1 thousand
+ 1,000  ──→ 1 thousand + 0 thousand = 1 thousand
  2,137
```

```
    1 1
  1,150
+   987
  2,137
```

2,137 people saw the play.

1 Show two ways to add 7,315 + 1,890.

2 Find the sum.

```
  1,025
+ 4,589
```

Solve.

3 Last summer, Mia's family drove 1,024 miles from Grand Canyon National Park to Mount Rushmore National Memorial. Then they drove 1,389 miles from Mount Rushmore to Yosemite National Park. How many miles did they drive in all?

Show your work.

Solution: _____

4 Use the tiles to create a number that makes each addition problem true. You may use a tile more than once.

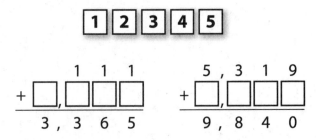

5 On Monday, Calvin ran 4,250 meters. On Tuesday, he ran 4,980 meters. How many meters did he run altogether on Monday and Tuesday?

Show your work.

Solution: _____

6 Sam added 6,152 and 379 and got a sum of 9,942. Explain why Sam's addition is incorrect and find the sum of 6,152 + 379.

_____

_____

_____

Name: _____

Subtract Whole Numbers

Study the example showing how to use subtraction to solve a word problem. Then solve problems 1–6.

Example

In one day, Pete took 7,192 steps. Joe took 5,210 steps. How many more steps did Pete take than Joe?

Regroup.

Thousands	Hundreds	Tens	Ones
7	1	9	2

Thousands	Hundreds	Tens	Ones
6	10 + 1 = 11	9	2

$$\begin{array}{r} {}^{6\ 11} \\ \cancel{7}\cancel{1}92 \\ -\ 5,210 \\ \hline 1,982 \end{array}$$

Subtract.

Thousands	Hundreds	Tens	Ones
6	11	9	2
− 5	2	1	0
1	9	8	2

Pete took 1,982 more steps than Joe.

---

1 Subtract.

$$\begin{array}{r} 3,008 \\ -\ 1,265 \\ \hline \end{array}$$

2 Find the difference.

$$\begin{array}{r} 1,640 \\ -\ 952 \\ \hline \end{array}$$

Solve.

3 The table below shows the number of seats in two basketball arenas. How many more seats does Arthur Arena have than Griffin Fieldhouse?

Number of Seats	
Griffin Fieldhouse	22,826
Arthur Arena	44,750

Show your work.

Solution: _____

4 A city has a population of 289,000 people. Ten years ago, the population was 259,500 people. How many more people does the city have now?

Solution: _____

5 Use the tiles below to create a number that makes each subtraction problem true. You may use a tile more than once.

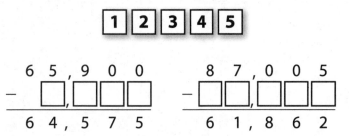

```
  6 5 , 9 0 0          8 7 , 0 0 5
−   □,□□□           − □□,□□□
  6 4 , 5 7 5          6 1 , 8 6 2
```

6 Peter listed his car for sale at $21,550. After a week, he dropped the sale price by $1,650. When the car sold, the sale price was another $1,955 less. What was the final sale price of the car?

Show your work.

Solution: _____

Name: _____

Add and Subtract Whole Numbers

Solve the problems.

1 Jake has 1,326 songs on his music player. Kyle has 795 more songs than Jake. How many songs does Kyle have?

Do you add or subtract to solve this problem?

A 2,021   **C** 2,121

B 631   **D** 531

2 A school's goal is to raise $5,000 to donate to charity. The school has raised $2,157. How much more money does the school need to raise?

What do you need to do before you can subtract ones?

A $2,843   **C** $2,953

B $7,157   **D** $3,843

Sonya chose **C** as the correct answer. How did she get that answer?

_____

_____

_____

3 Tell whether each number sentence is *True* or *False*.

What symbols tell you whether to add or subtract?

a. 908 + 1,725 = 2,633   ☐ True   ☐ False

b. 17,625 − 2,460 = 5,245   ☐ True   ☐ False

c. 112,950 + 32,408 = 45,358   ☐ True   ☐ False

d. 43,900 − 17,825 = 26,075   ☐ True   ☐ False

Solve.

4 Use the information below to fill in the missing data in the table.

The height of Willis Tower is 325 feet less than the height of One World Trade Center.

The height of Trump Tower is 139 feet more than the height of the Empire State Building.

The height of Bank of America Tower is 576 feet less than the height of One World Trade Center.

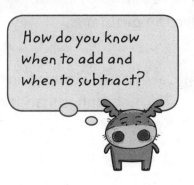

How do you know when to add and when to subtract?

Five Tallest Buildings in the U.S.

Rank	Name	Location	Height (ft)
1	One World Trade Center	New York City	1,776
2	Willis Tower	Chicago	
3	Trump Tower	Chicago	
4	Empire State Building	New York City	1,250
5	Bank of America Tower	New York City	

5 Use the information in the table below to answer the riddle. Write the the missing data in the table.

I am the tallest building in the world. If you add my height to the height of the next three tallest buildings, the total is 8,132 feet. How tall am I?

What operation do you need to do first?

Four Tallest Buildings in the World

Rank	Name	Location	Height (ft)
1	Burj Khalifa	United Arab Emirates	
2	Makkah Royal Clock Tower	Saudi Arabia	1,972
3	One World Trade Center	New York City	1,776
4	Taipei 101	Taipei, Taiwan	1,667

Show your work.

Dear Family,

This week your child is learning to round whole numbers.

You can use a number line to round a number such as 36,219 to the nearest thousand.

36,219

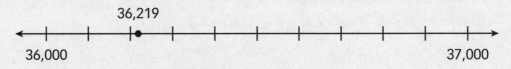

36,000   37,000

The number line shows the closest thousands less than and greater than 36,219.

The number 36,219 rounded to the nearest thousand is 36,000 because 36,219 is closer to 36,000 than to 37,000.

What if a number is exactly halfway between? Then, your child is learning to follow a rule: Round up.

- 36,500 is *exactly halfway* between 36,000 and 37,000, so round up to 37,000 when finding the nearest thousand.

Invite your child to share what he or she knows about rounding whole numbers by doing the following activity together.

Rounding Numbers Activity

Materials: 0–9 digit cards, scissors, bag, charts below

Do an activity with your child to practice rounding numbers. Cut out the digit cards below or write each digit from 0–9 on its own index card. Place the cards in a bag. Take turns. Play 5 rounds.

- Draw 5 digit cards and record them as a 5-digit number in the order drawn. Draw again if 0 is the first card drawn.

  Example: If you draw 2, 7, 4, 1, 9, record 27,419.

- Round the number to the nearest thousand.

  Example: 27,419 rounds to 27,000.

- Replace the cards in the bag. Now have your child draw 5 cards and follow the directions above to round to the nearest thousand.

Player 1

5-digit number	Rounded to the nearest thousand

Player 2

5-digit number	Rounded to the nearest thousand

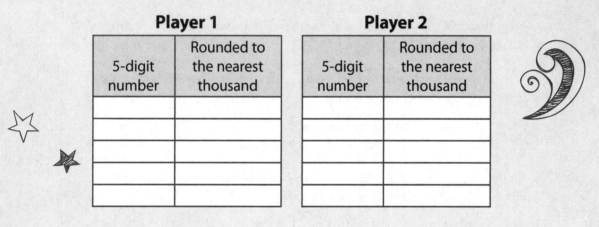

0	1	2	3	4
5	6	7	8	9

Round Whole Numbers

Name: _____

Prerequisite: Round Three-Digit Numbers

Study the example showing how to round a three-digit number. Then solve problems 1–6.

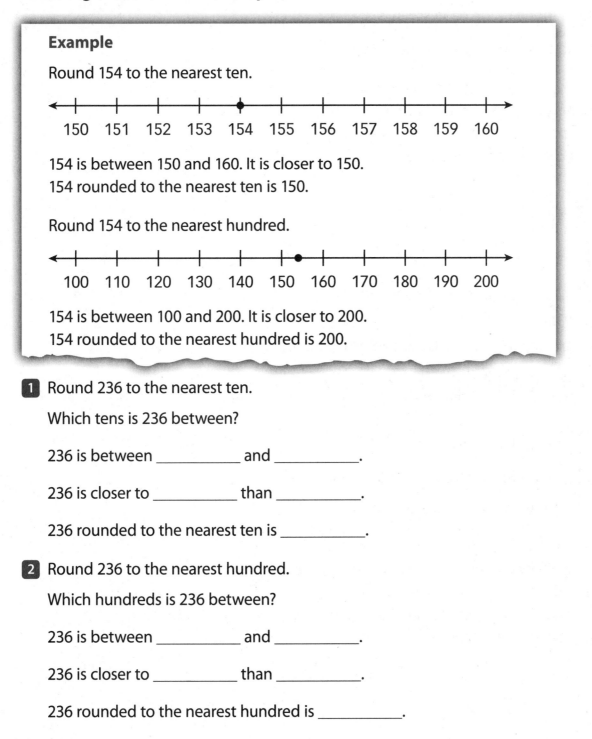

Example

Round 154 to the nearest ten.

150 151 152 153 154 155 156 157 158 159 160

154 is between 150 and 160. It is closer to 150.
154 rounded to the nearest ten is 150.

Round 154 to the nearest hundred.

100 110 120 130 140 150 160 170 180 190 200

154 is between 100 and 200. It is closer to 200.
154 rounded to the nearest hundred is 200.

1 Round 236 to the nearest ten.

Which tens is 236 between?

236 is between _____ and _____.

236 is closer to _____ than _____.

236 rounded to the nearest ten is _____.

2 Round 236 to the nearest hundred.

Which hundreds is 236 between?

236 is between _____ and _____.

236 is closer to _____ than _____.

236 rounded to the nearest hundred is _____.

Solve.

3 Round each number.

    a. 689 rounded to the nearest ten is _____ .

    b. 68 rounded to the nearest hundred is _____ .

    c. 945 rounded to the nearest ten is _____ .

    d. 945 rounded to the nearest hundred is _____ .

4 Rachel earned $164 babysitting last month. She earned $95 this month. Rachel rounded each amount to the nearest $10 to estimate how much she earned. What is each amount rounded to the nearest $10?

Show your work.

Solution: _____

5 Use the digits in the tiles to create a number that makes each statement true. Use each digit only once.

| 1 | 2 | 3 | 4 | 5 | 6 | 7 | 8 | 9 |

    ☐☐☐ rounded to the nearest 10 is 300.

    ☐☐☐ rounded to the nearest 100 is 500.

    ☐☐☐ rounded to the nearest 100 is 700.

6 There are 528 students. The school wants to order t-shirts for all the students. T-shirts come in packs of ten. Should the school round the number of students to the nearest ten or hundred so that each student gets a t-shirt? Explain.

_____

_____

_____

Name: _____

Round Whole Numbers

Study the example showing how to round multi-digit numbers to estimate a sum. Then solve problems 1–6.

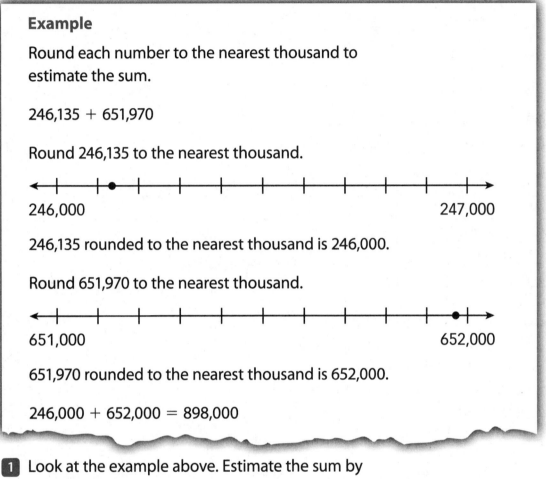

Example

Round each number to the nearest thousand to estimate the sum.

246,135 + 651,970

Round 246,135 to the nearest thousand.

246,000   247,000

246,135 rounded to the nearest thousand is 246,000.

Round 651,970 to the nearest thousand.

651,000   652,000

651,970 rounded to the nearest thousand is 652,000.

246,000 + 652,000 = 898,000

1 Look at the example above. Estimate the sum by rounding each number to the nearest hundred thousand. Write the number sentence.

_____

2 Round 45,621 to each place given below.

a. to the nearest ten _____

b. to the nearest hundred _____

c. to the nearest thousand _____

d. to the nearest ten thousand _____

Solve.

3 Round 452,906 to each place given below.

    a. to the nearest hundred thousand _____

    b. to the nearest ten thousand _____

    c. to the nearest thousand _____

    d. to the nearest hundred _____

    e. to the nearest ten _____

4 The table below shows driving distances between U.S. cities. Round each number to the nearest hundred.

	Actual distance (mi)	Rounded distance (mi)
Atlanta, GA to Los Angeles, CA	2,173	
Los Angeles, CA to Seattle, WA	1,135	
Atlanta, GA to Chicago, IL	716	
Chicago, IL to San Francisco, CA	2,131	

5 Look at the table in problem 4. Lisa drove from Atlanta to Los Angeles to Seattle. Alex drove from Atlanta to Chicago to San Francisco. Use the rounded numbers to show who drove farther and by about how many miles.

Show your work.

Solution: _____

6 Write numbers in the boxes below to show rounding on a number line. What place value are you rounding to?

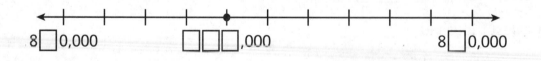

8☐0,000   ☐☐☐,000   8☐0,000

Solution: _____

Name: _____

Round Whole Numbers

Solve the problems.

1 Choose *Yes* or *No* to tell whether to round up to the greater hundred thousand.

Which place value should you look at?

a. 949,500   ☐ Yes   ☐ No

b. 503,817   ☐ Yes   ☐ No

c. 180,000   ☐ Yes   ☐ No

d. 352,625   ☐ Yes   ☐ No

2 Which numbers have been rounded correctly to the nearest hundred? Circle the letter for all that apply.

Which digit do you look at in each number to round to the nearest hundred?

A   38,753 ⟶ 38,800

B   38,503 ⟶ 39,000

C   38,910 ⟶ 38,900

D   38,960 ⟶ 39,000

E   38,109 ⟶ 38,110

3 A company spent $850,290 on advertising last year. The company spent $872,650 this year. Which of the following is the best estimate of how much more the company spent this year?

What do you do first to solve this problem?

A $100,000   C $22,000

B $30,000   D $22,400

Tyson chose **D** as the correct answer. Explain how he got his answer.

_____

_____

Solve.

4 Look at the table below. Round all the numbers to the same place value to complete the sentence below.

At what place value will the rounded numbers for female athletes be the same?

Olympic Athletes

Year	City	Total	Female	Male
2008	Beijing, China	10,942	4,637	6,305
2012	London, Great Britain	10,568	4,676	5,892

Each of the two Olympic games had about _____ total athletes, including about _____ female athletes, and about _____ male athletes.

5 Debbie looked at problem 4 and rounded the number of female athletes in 2008 to 5,000. She rounded the number of female athletes in 2012 to 4,700. She said that there were about 300 more female athletes in 2008. Explain why Debbie's estimate is incorrect and find a correct estimate.

What place value were the numbers rounded to?

_____

_____

_____

_____

6 In season one of *Sing Off*, 16,865 people tried out. In season two, 5,296 more people tried out. In season three, 1,834 fewer people tried out than in season two. Show two different ways to round and estimate the number of people who tried out in season three.

Show your work.

What place values can you choose to round to?

Solution: _____

Unit 1 Game

Subtraction Action

What you need: Recording Sheet, 3 sets of digit cards (0–9)

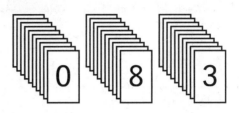

Directions

- Mix the digit cards and place them facedown in a stack. Each player takes 5 cards.

- Players each make two different 5-digit numbers using their 5 cards. The goal is to make two numbers that are as close in value to each other as possible.

- Both players subtract their lesser number from their greater number. The difference tells how close the two numbers are. Players write their subtraction problems on the Recording Sheet.

- Players compare their differences and write the comparison on the Recording Sheet. The player with the lesser difference made two numbers that are closer together. This player wins the round.

- Put all the cards back and remix. Play 5 rounds. The player with more wins after 5 rounds wins the game.

| 8 | 5 | 9 | 2 | 1 |
| 8 | 5 | 9 | 1 | 2 |

Subtraction Action Recording Sheet

Name: _____

_____Mike_____
Player A Name

1.
```
  8 5, 9 2 1
- 8 5, 9 1 2
          9
```

_____Sofia_____
Player B Name

1.
```
  7 6, 0 5 3
- 7 6, 0 3 5
      1 8
```

1. ___9___ < ___18___

> I subtracted 85,912 from 85,921. My difference of 9 is less than your difference of 18, so I win the first round.

Subtraction Action Recording Sheet

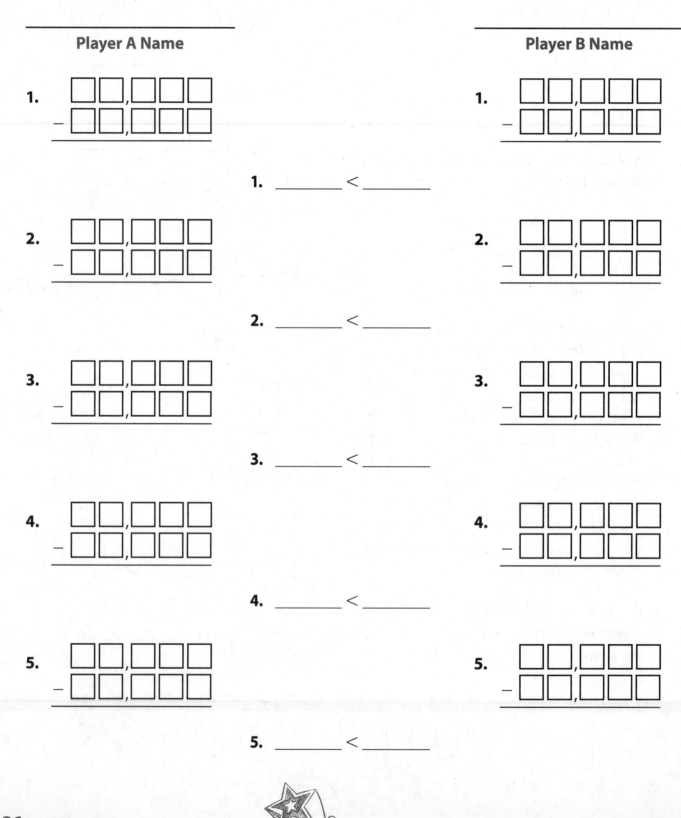

Player A Name

1.
2.
3.
4.
5.

1. _____ < _____
2. _____ < _____
3. _____ < _____
4. _____ < _____
5. _____ < _____

Player B Name

1.
2.
3.
4.
5.

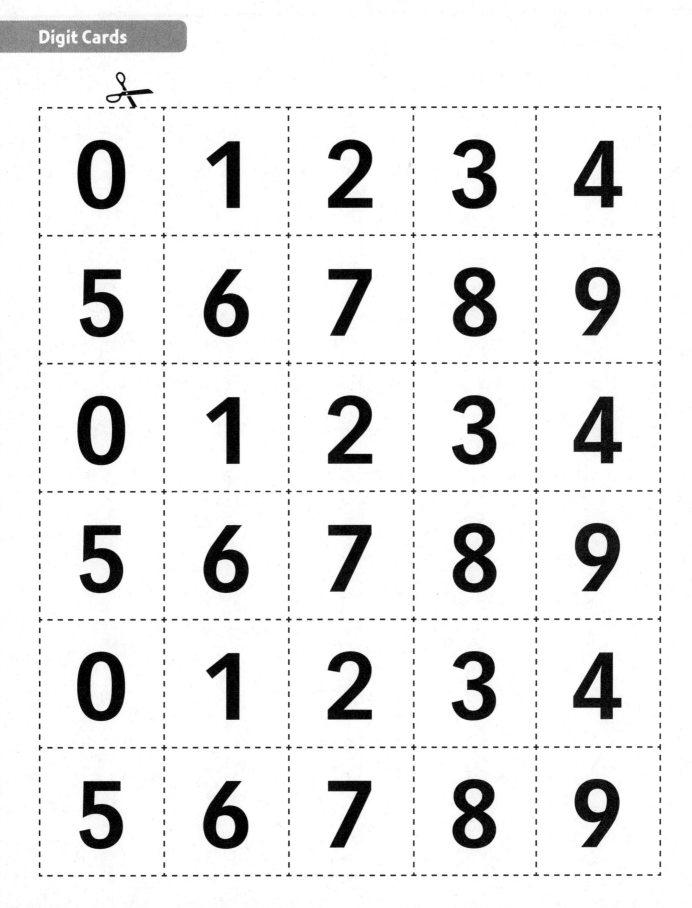

Number and Operations in Base Ten, Part 1

In this unit you learned to:	Lesson
read and write numbers using number names, for example: 495 is *four hundred ninety-five.*	1
read and write numbers using expanded form, for example: 352 = 300 + 50 + 2.	1
compare two multi-digit whole numbers, for example: 6,131 > 6,113.	2
add multi-digit whole numbers, for example: 3,966 + 7,550 = 11,516.	3
subtract multi-digit whole numbers, for example: 25,082 − 11,919 = 13,163.	3
round multi-digit whole numbers, for example: 528 rounded to the nearest ten is 530.	4

Use these skills to solve problems 1–6.

1 Use <, >, or = to complete each number sentence.

a. 790,599 ◯ 791,043

b. 52,180 ◯ 50,000 + 2,000 + 10 + 8

c. 99,999 ◯ 100,000

d. 55 hundreds + 2 tens ◯ 5,520

e. 200,000 + 10,000 + 300 + 50 ◯ 210,305

2 A publishing company printed 920,500 copies of a book. The company sold 843,255 copies. How many books did not sell?

Show your work.

Solution: _____

Solve.

3 The second longest bridge in the world, the Tianjin Grand Bridge, is 373,000 feet long. Its length is 167,700 feet less than the length of the longest bridge in the world. What is the length of the longest bridge?

Show your work.

Solution: _____

4 Use the clues below to guess the mystery number.

- The number is less than 190,000 and greater than 180,000.

- 5,000 more than the number has 187 thousands.

- 200 less than the number has 4 hundreds.

Solution: _____

5 Round each number in the table to the given place value. Then, write <, >, or = to compare the rounded numbers.

Round to . . .	95,498	Compare (>, <, or =)	95,607
Tens			
Hundreds			
Thousands			
Ten Thousands			

6 Juan's company spent $2,350 on an event. They spent about $1,500 on food and about $900 on entertainment. What could the actual cost of the food and entertainment be?

Show your work.

Solution: food _____ entertainment _____

Name: _____

Answer the questions and show all your work on separate paper.

The fourth-graders at Windy Hill Elementary School are collecting box tops to raise money for a robotics science program. The students need to collect 20,000 box tops in all to reach the goal.

The chart below shows how many box tops each fourth-grade class has collected in the first five months.

	Room 4A	Room 4B	Room 4C	Room 4D
Number of Box Tops	3,078	2,145	2,569	2,034

The science teacher wants to know how many box tops, to the nearest hundred, each class has collected and about how close the students are to reaching the goal of 20,000 box tops. Write an email to the science teacher describing how close the fourth-graders are to the goal and estimating how much more time the students need to reach the goal. In the email you should show your work and explain your reasoning.

Reflect on Mathematical Practices

After you complete the task, choose one of the following questions to answer.

1 **Reason Mathematically** How did you use the information in the table to estimate how close the fourth-graders are to the goal?

2 **Model** What equations did you write to solve the problem?

Checklist

Did you ...

☐ organize the information?

☐ use estimation in your calculations?

☐ write a clear explanation?

Word Bank Here are some words that you might use in your answer.

equal	sum	round
add	total	hundred
estimate	difference	about
halfway		

Models Here are some models that you might use to find the solution.

Thousands	Hundreds	Tens	Ones

←——|——|——|——|——|——|——|——|——|——|——→

Sentence Starters Here are some sentence starters that might help you write an explanation.

I rounded _____

I estimated the total by _____

The sum of _____

The difference between _____ is _____

To reach their goal, the classes need _____

Unit 1 Vocabulary

Name: _____

My Examples

value

the amount a digit is worth

word form

how a number is written with words
or said aloud

standard form

how a number is written with numerals

expanded form

how a number is written to show the
place value of each digit

period

    digits in groups of three in a large
number

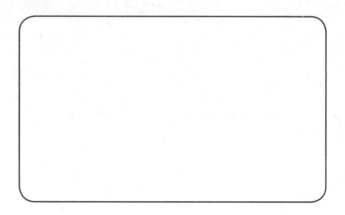

compare

    to decide if one number is greater than,
less than, or equal to another number

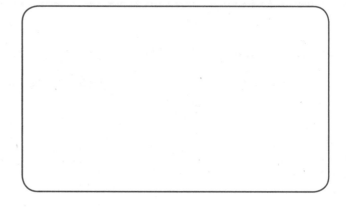

greater than (>)

    a comparison that says one number has
greater value than another number

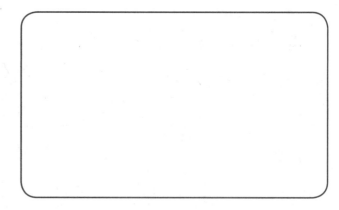

less than (<)

    a comparison that says one number has
less value than another number

Dear Family,

This week your child is exploring multiplication.

Your child is learning about multiplication as a way to compare two numbers.

This model shows that
15 is 3 times as many as 5.
You can write the comparison as
a multiplication equation:
$15 = 3 \times 5$

This model shows that
15 is 5 times as many as 3.
You can write the comparison as
a multiplication equation:
$15 = 5 \times 3$

Your child is also learning how to use bar models to help understand multiplication as a comparison.

| 2 |
| 2 | 2 | 2 | 2 |
8

This bar model shows that 8 is 4 times as many as 2: $8 = 4 \times 2$.

Invite your child to share what he or she knows about multiplication by doing the following activity together.

NEXT

Lesson 5 Understand Multiplication   **45**

Multiplication Activity

Do an activity with your child to explore multiplication as a way to compare two numbers.

Materials: 20 pennies or other small identical objects

With your child, arrange 10 pennies to show that 10 is 2 times as many as 5. The pennies should look like this:

- Now ask your child to arrange 10 pennies to show that 10 is 5 times as many as 2. (The pennies should be arranged in 5 rows with 2 pennies in each row.)

- Ask your child to arrange pennies to show other multiplication comparisons.

  Examples:
  14 is 7 times as many as 2.
  14 is 2 times as many as 7.
  12 is 4 times as many as 3.
  12 is 3 times as many as 4.

Look for real-life opportunities to practice multiplication as a comparison of two numbers with your child.

Name: _____

Study the example showing multiplication with an array and a number sentence. Then solve problems 1–5.

Example

In art class, 4 students each painted 6 tiles.

Draw an array to show the tiles.

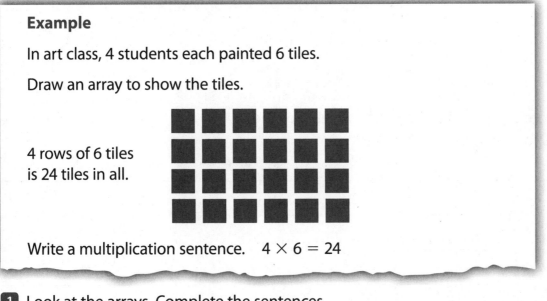

4 rows of 6 tiles
is 24 tiles in all.

Write a multiplication sentence. $4 \times 6 = 24$

1 Look at the arrays. Complete the sentences.

   a. 3 rows of _____ tiles

   is _____ tiles in all.

   $3 \times$ _____ = _____

   b. _____ rows of 8 triangles

   is _____ triangles in all.

   _____ $\times 8 =$ _____

   c. _____ rows of _____ stars

   is _____ stars in all.

   _____ $\times$ _____ = _____

Vocabulary

multiplication an operation used to find the total number of items in equal-sized groups.

Solve.

2 Each of 3 students in a book club read 7 books. Draw an array and write a multiplication sentence to show the number of books read.

3 Write a word problem that could be modeled by the multiplication sentence $6 \times 8 = 48$.

_____

_____

_____

_____

4 Leila's bookshelf has 4 shelves. Each shelf has 9 books. Write a multiplication sentence to tell about the books. Explain what each number in the multiplication sentence means.

_____

_____

_____

5 Look at problem 4. Suppose Leila moves her books onto a bookshelf with 6 shelves. She puts an equal number of books on each shelf. Describe what the array for this problem looks like and write a multiplication sentence.

_____

_____

Name: _____

Show Multiplication

Study the example showing how a bar model is used to show multiplication as a comparison. Then solve problems 1–7.

Example

Harris rides his bike 5 blocks to school. Daniel rides his bike 3 times as far as Harris. How far does Daniel ride his bike to school?

You can use a bar model to show multiplication as a comparison.

15 is 3 times as many as 5.
$15 = 3 \times 5$

Harris
| 5 |

Daniel
| 5 | 5 | 5 |

├──────── 15 ────────┤

---

1 Use the bar model to the right to describe the comparison and write an equation.

48 is _____ times as many as _____ .

_____ = _____ × _____

| 6 |

| 6 | 6 | 6 | 6 | 6 | 6 | 6 | 6 |

├──────────────── 48 ────────────────┤

2 Draw and label a bar model to show a number that is 5 times as many as 7.

3 Write a word problem that the bar model in problem 2 could represent.

_____

_____

_____

Solve.

4 Tara scored 6 times as many soccer goals as Leah during one season. Leah scored 3 goals. Draw a bar model and write an equation that represents the number of goals Tara scored.

5 What two comparisons does the equation $4 \times 2 = 8$ show?

a. _____ is _____ times as many as _____ .

b. _____ is _____ times as many as _____ .

6 Draw two different bar models to represent $2 \times 4 = 8$.

7 A pet caretaker walks dogs 9 times a day. He walks dogs from Monday to Friday, 5 days a week. Draw and label a bar model to show the total number of times the caretaker walks dogs in a week.

Name: _____

Reason and Write

Study the example. Underline two parts that you think make it a particularly good answer and a helpful example.

Example

Sylvie needs 2 cups of flour to make one loaf of bread. She wants to make 3 loaves of bread. She says she needs 5 cups of flour.

Is Sylvie correct? What did she do right? What did she do wrong?

Show your work. Use a bar model, an equation, and words to explain.

Sylvie is not correct. She used the numbers 2 and 3, but she added 2 + 3 instead of multiplying 2 × 3.

Sylvie needs 2 cups of flour for one loaf of bread, so she needs 3 times as many cups of flour for 3 loaves of bread.

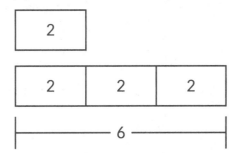

6 is 3 times as many as 2.
6 = 3 × 2

Sylvie needs 6 cups of flour to make 3 loaves of bread.

Where does the example . . .

- answer the questions?

- use a bar model to explain?

- use numbers in an equation to explain?

- use words to explain?

Solve the problem. Use what you learned from the model.

Victor needs 3 teaspoons of salt to make dough for one pizza. He wants to make dough for 8 pizzas. Victor says he needs 24 teaspoons of salt.

Is Victor correct? What did he do right? What did he do wrong?

Show your work. Use a bar model, an equation, and words to explain.

Did you . . .

• answer the questions?

• use a bar model to explain?

• use numbers in an equation to explain?

• use words to explain?

Dear Family,

This week your child is learning about multiplication and division in word problems.

Your child might see a problem like this:

> Market Street sells bags of 8 apples. Mark needs 5 times that amount. How many apples does Mark need?

You can use a bar model to help understand the problem.

Number in one bag

8

Number Mark needs

8	8	8	8	8

?

Then you can use the bar model to write an equation to help understand the problem.

5 × number of apples in one bag = total apples needed

5 × 8 = ☐

Solve the equation.

5 × 8 = 40

The answer to the problem is that Mark needs 40 apples.

Invite your child to share what he or she knows about multiplication and division in word problems by doing the following activity together.

Multiplication and Division in Word Problems Activity

Do an activity with your child to practice multiplication in word problems.

Materials: number cube, 40 counters such as pennies, beans, or paper clips

- Have your child roll the number cube first. Your child takes that number of counters and records the number.

  Example: Your child rolls a 4 and takes 4 counters.

- Then you roll the number cube. This number tells you how many times the number of your child's counters you take.

  Example: You roll a 3. You take 3 times as many counters as your child. You take 12 counters.

- Have your child count to check the number of counters you get in all. Then have your child tell or write a comparison multiplication sentence.

  Example: $3 \times 4 = 12$

- Finally, create a real-world story to match the multiplication sentence.

Tess has 4 seashells. I have 3 times as many seashells as Tess. I have 12 seashells.

Multiplication and Division in Word Problems

Name: _____

Prerequisite: Model Multiplication

Study the example showing how to use a model to solve a multiplication problem. Then solve problems 1–6.

Example

Lauren worked 4 hours last week. She worked 3 times as many hours this week as last week. How many hours did Lauren work this week?

Last week | 4 |

This week | 4 | 4 | 4 |
          |———— 12 ————|

12 is 3 times as many as 4.
12 = 3 × 4

Lauren worked 12 hours this week.

1. Nina picked 8 tomatoes last month. She picked 4 times as many tomatoes this month. How many tomatoes did Nina pick this month?

Label the bar model and complete the sentences.

Last month | |

This month | | | | |

_____ is _____ times as many as _____ .

_____ = _____ × _____

Nina picked _____ tomatoes this month.

2. Ben has 6 marbles. Tom has 3 times as many marbles as Ben. How many marbles does Tom have?

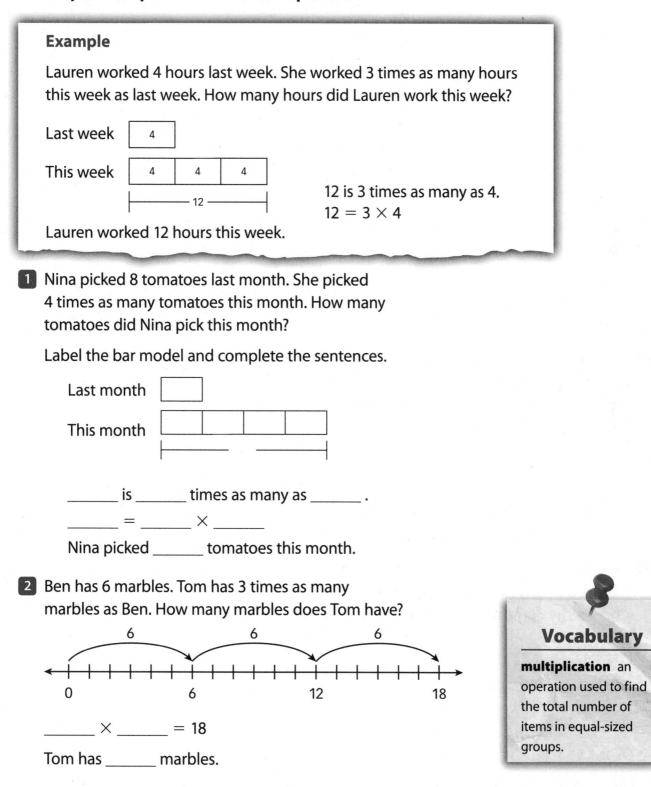

_____ × _____ = 18

Tom has _____ marbles.

Vocabulary

multiplication an operation used to find the total number of items in equal-sized groups.

Solve.

3 Yesterday Ruth scored 2 points at the game. Today she scored 8 times as many points as she did yesterday. How many points did Ruth score today?

Show your work.

Solution: _____

4 Matt planted 5 times as many flowers on Sunday as he planted on Saturday. Matt planted 7 flowers on Saturday. How many flowers did Matt plant on Sunday?

Show your work.

Solution: _____

5 Mr. Ash has 7 students in art class. Mr. Trent has double the number of students in his class as Mr. Ash. How many students does Mr. Trent have in his class?

Show your work.

Solution: _____

6 Which is more: 2 times as many as a number or 5 times as many as the same number? Explain. Choose any number to show how you know.

_____

_____

_____

_____

Name: _____

Use Multiplication in Word Problems

Study the example showing one way to use multiplication to solve a word problem. Then solve problems 1–5.

Example

Sue swam 4 laps in a pool. Andy swam 5 times as many laps as Sue. How many laps did Andy swim?

Number of laps Sue swam | 4 |

Number of laps Andy swam | 4 | 4 | 4 | 4 | 4 |

$5 \times 4 = \square$
$5 \times 4 = 20$
Andy swam 20 laps.

1 Adam has 9 pennies. Ryan has 3 times as many pennies as Adam. How many pennies does Ryan have?

Label the bar model.

Write an equation.

Use $\square$ for the unknown.   ____ $\times$ ____ = ____

Solve the equation.   _____

Write the answer.   Ryan has ____ pennies.

2 Jade picked 5 pounds of berries. She needs 3 times that amount to make jam. How many pounds of berries does Jade need to make jam?

Skip count to find the amount Jade needs:

5, _____, _____.

Jade needs _____.

Vocabulary

unknown a missing number in an equation.

$\square = 5 \times 4$

$\square$ is the unknown.

$6 \times 7 = P$
P is the unknown.

equation a mathematical sentence that uses an equal sign (=) to show that two expressions have the same value.

$5 \times 4 = 20$

Solve.

3 Look at how a student solved the problem below.

> A cook used 12 eggs at lunch. He used 3 times as many eggs at breakfast. How many eggs did the cook use at breakfast?
>
> Skip count: 12, 24, 36, 48
> The cook used 48 eggs at breakfast.

What did the student do wrong?

_____

_____

4 Look at problem 3. Draw a bar model. Use the model to write and solve an equation to find the correct answer.

Solution: The cook used _____ at breakfast.

5 Which problems can be solved using the equation $8 \times 2 = A$? Circle the letter of all that apply.

A In June, Ali read 8 books. In July, she read half as many books. How many books did Ali read in July?

B Cal is twice as old as his sister. Cal's sister is 8 years old. How old is Cal?

C A muffin costs $2. Dylan bought 8 muffins. How much did Dylan spend on muffins?

D Jordan has 8 apples and 2 oranges. How many pieces of fruit does she have altogether?

Name: _____

Use Division in Word Problems

Study the example showing a way to use division to solve a word problem. Then solve problems 1–5.

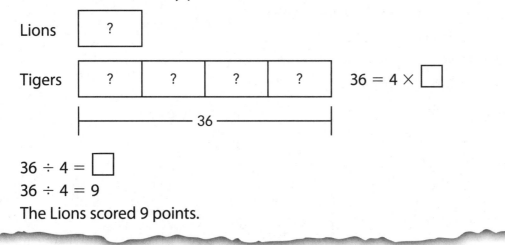

Example

The Tigers scored 36 points. They scored 4 times as many points as the Lions. How many points did the Lions score?

Lions [?]

Tigers [? | ? | ? | ?] $36 = 4 \times \square$

|———————— 36 ————————|

$36 \div 4 = \square$

$36 \div 4 = 9$

The Lions scored 9 points.

1 Charlie and Gabe collected cans to recycle. Charlie collected 5 times as many cans as Gabe. Charlie collected 50 cans. Draw a bar model you could use to compare the number of cans each boy collected.

2 Look at the model you drew in problem 1. Write and solve an equation to show how many cans Gabe collected.

Show your work.

Solution: _____

Solve.

3 Choose *Yes* or *No* to tell whether each equation is solved correctly.

a. $6 = 2 \times \square$ $\square = 12$ ☐ Yes ☐ No

b. $7 \times H = 28$ $H = 4$ ☐ Yes ☐ No

c. $2 = p \div 5$ $p = 10$ ☐ Yes ☐ No

4 James and Chris are in the school play. James has 42 lines to memorize. That is 6 times as many lines as Chris. Write and solve an equation to find the number of lines Chris has to memorize.

Show your work.

Solution: _____

5 Choose numbers from the tiles below to fill in the bar model. Then write and solve an equation using the model.

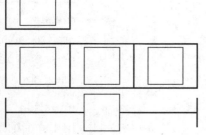

Equation: _____

Solution: _____

Name: _____

Multiplication and Division in Word Problems

Solve the problems.

1 Lin and Karla are planning a party. Lin spent $20 on invitations and decorations. Karla spent 4 times that amount on food and entertainment. How much did they spend altogether on the party?

Do you need to use more than one operation to find the answer?

A $20

C $100

B $80

D $120

2 Write and solve an equation for each problem below.

Darcy earned $5. Samantha earned $30. Samantha earned _____ times as much as Darcy.

You can write either a multiplication equation or a division equation for each problem.

Equation: _____

Solution: _____

Carey teaches twice as many fitness classes as Fran. If Fran teaches 7 classes, how many classes does Carey teach?

Equation: _____

Solution: _____

Joelle practices piano for 3 times as many minutes a day as Tran. Tran practices for 20 minutes a day. How many minutes a day does Joelle practice?

Equation: _____

Solution: _____

Solve.

3 There are 12 markers in a box. Mr. Ross needs 3 times that number of markers for his 4 math classes. How many markers does Mr. Ross need altogether?

Do you need to use all the numbers given to solve the problem?

A 4   **C** 36

B 12   **D** 48

Greg chose **A** as the correct answer. How did he get that answer?

_____

_____

4 Sofia and Tim are rolling marbles down a track. Sofia has 20 marbles. She has 4 times as many marbles as Tim. Tim has *m* marbles.

Is the number of marbles that Sofia has greater or less than the number Tim has?

Choose *Yes* or *No* to indicate whether the equation correctly indicates how to solve for *m*.

a. $m = 4 \times 20$ ☐ Yes ☐ No

b. $20 \div 4 = m$ ☐ Yes ☐ No

c. $m = 5 \times 4$ ☐ Yes ☐ No

5 Use the information in the table to answer the questions.

Does it make sense to multiply or divide?

Number of Basketball Free Throws Made

	Mariah	Lisa
Week 1	5	3 times Mariah
Week 2	4 times Lisa	4

How many free throws did Lisa make in Week 1? _____

How many free throws did Mariah make in Week 2? _____

Who made more total free throws? Explain. _____

_____

Dear Family,

This week your child is learning about multiples and factors.

> **factor pair:** two numbers that are multiplied together to give a product.
>
> **multiple:** the product of the number and any other whole number (0, 4, 8, 12, etc., are multiples of 4).
>
> **composite number:** a number that has more than one pair of factors.

Your child might see a problem like this:

> Monica is pasting 40 stars in rows on the wall. She wants to put the same number of stars in each row. Find all the ways she can arrange the stars.

One way to paste the stars is 5 rows of 8.
Another way is 8 rows of 5.
5 and 8 are a **factor pair**.

Other ways to paste the stars are:
10 rows of 4 or 4 rows of 10
2 rows of 20 or 20 rows of 2
1 row of 40 or 40 rows of 1

40 is a **composite number**. Factor pairs of 40 are:
5 and 8, 10 and 4, 2 and 20, 1 and 40.

40 is a **multiple** of 1, 2, 4, 5, 8, and 10.

Invite your child to share what he or she knows about multiples and factors by doing the following activity together.

NEXT ➡

Factors Activity

Do an activity with your child to practice finding factors of a number.

Materials: 2 number cubes

- One player rolls both number cubes and uses the numbers on the cubes to create a 2-digit number.

- The other player reverses the order of the digits to create another 2-digit number.

    Example:

Player 1: <u>21</u>   Player 2: <u>12</u>

- Each player finds all the factor pairs of his or her number.

    Example:
    Player 1: Factor pairs of 21 are 1 and 21, 3 and 7.
    Player 2: Factor pairs of 12 are 1 and 12, 2 and 6, 3 and 4.

- The player with the most factor pairs is the winner of the round.

- Play 5 rounds.

Player 2 wins the round because the number 12 has 3 factor pairs. Player 1's number, 21, has only 2 factor pairs.

Multiples and Factors

Name: _____

Study the example showing multiplication and division facts in a fact family. Then solve problems 1–6.

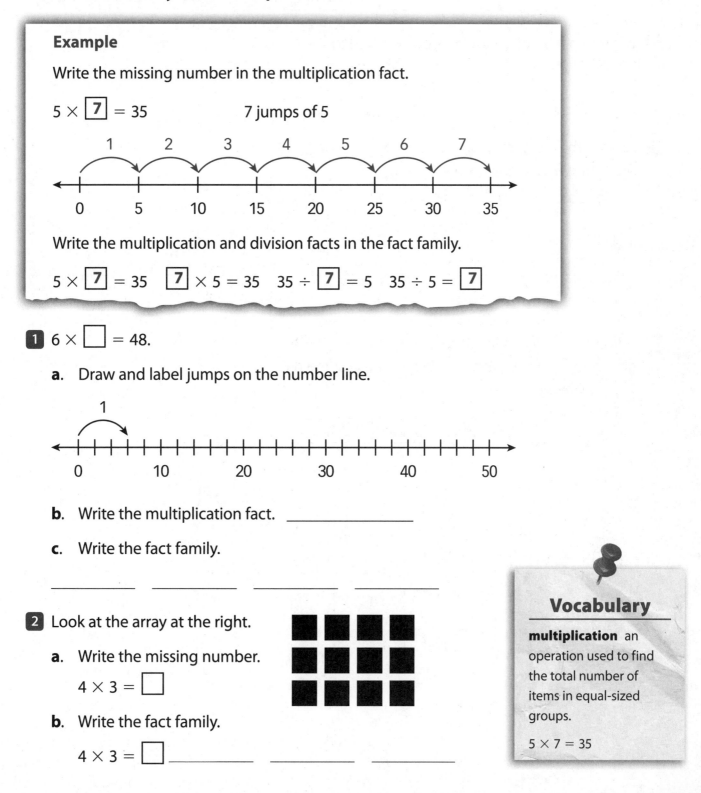

Example

Write the missing number in the multiplication fact.

$5 \times \boxed{7} = 35$ 7 jumps of 5

Write the multiplication and division facts in the fact family.

$5 \times \boxed{7} = 35$ $\boxed{7} \times 5 = 35$ $35 \div \boxed{7} = 5$ $35 \div 5 = \boxed{7}$

1 $6 \times \square = 48$.

a. Draw and label jumps on the number line.

b. Write the multiplication fact. _____

c. Write the fact family.

_____   _____   _____   _____

2 Look at the array at the right.

a. Write the missing number.

$4 \times 3 = \square$

b. Write the fact family.

$4 \times 3 = \square$ _____   _____   _____

Vocabulary

multiplication an operation used to find the total number of items in equal-sized groups.

$5 \times 7 = 35$

Solve.

3 Write the multiplication and division facts for the fact family with the numbers 5, 6, and 30.

_____   _____

_____   _____

4 What two multiplication facts can you use to solve

☐ ÷ 9 = 7?

_____   _____

5 Look at the multiplication and division facts below. Are they a fact family? Explain.

$4 \times 6 = 24$ $24 = 3 \times 8$ $24 \div 6 = 4$ $8 = 24 \div 3$

_____

_____

_____

6 Complete each fact family. Use the numbers in the tiles below to fill in each box. You may use some tiles more than once.

36 18 12 9 6 4 3 2 1

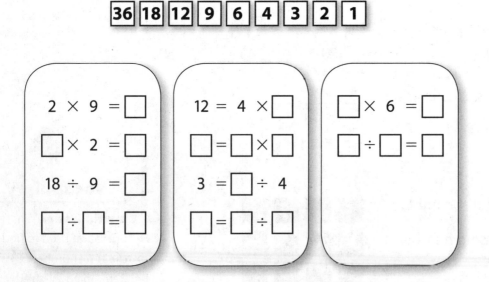

$2 \times 9 = \square$

$\square \times 2 = \square$

$18 \div 9 = \square$

$\square \div \square = \square$

$12 = 4 \times \square$

$\square = \square \times \square$

$3 = \square \div 4$

$\square = \square \div \square$

$\square \times 6 = \square$

$\square \div \square = \square$

Name: _____

Use Multiples

Study the example showing how to use multiples to solve a word problem. Then solve problems 1–6.

Example

Markers come in boxes of 5. Paul needs 40 markers for students in the art club. Can Paul buy exactly 40 markers in boxes of 5? How many boxes does he need to buy?

Find multiples of 5.

$5 \times 1 = \mathbf{5}$	$5 \times 4 = \mathbf{20}$	$5 \times 7 = \mathbf{35}$
$5 \times 2 = \mathbf{10}$	$5 \times 5 = \mathbf{25}$	$5 \times 8 = \mathbf{40}$
$5 \times 3 = \mathbf{15}$	$5 \times 6 = \mathbf{30}$	$5 \times 9 = \mathbf{45}$

40 is a multiple of 5.
Paul can buy exactly 40 markers in boxes of 5.
Paul needs to buy 8 boxes.

---

1 Skip count by 4s to find multiples of 4. Circle the multiples on the number line.

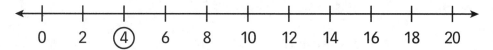

2 Complete the multiplication facts to find more multiples of 4.

$4 \times 6 =$ _____ $4 \times$ _____ $=$ _____

$4 \times$ _____ $=$ _____ $4 \times$ _____ $=$ _____

$4 \times$ _____ $=$ _____ $4 \times$ _____ $=$ _____

3 Look at problems 1 and 2. Are these the only multiples of 4? Use words and numbers to explain.

_____

_____

_____

Vocabulary

multiple the product of a number and any other whole number, for example, 3, 6, 9, 12, and 15 are multiples of 3.

Solve.

4 Max ordered 72 mugs. Mugs are packed 8 to a box. How many boxes of mugs did Max order?

Choose *Yes* or *No* to indicate whether the equation or statement could be used to solve the problem above.

a. $72 = 8 \times b$ ☐ Yes   ☐ No

b. $72 \div 8 = b$ ☐ Yes   ☐ No

c. List multiples of 8:
8, 16, 24, 32, 40, ...   ☐ Yes   ☐ No

d. $b = 72 + 8$ ☐ Yes   ☐ No

5 Cupcakes are packed 6 to a box. If Abby only buys full boxes of cupcakes, give two possible numbers of cupcakes that she could buy.

Show your work.

Solution: Abby could buy _____ cupcakes or _____ cupcakes.

6 Strawberries are sold in 1-pound, 2-pound, and 5-pound boxes. Stacy wants to buy exactly 10 pounds of strawberries. What are two ways that Stacy could buy exactly 10 pounds of strawberries? Tell which sizes of boxes she could buy and how many of each size box.

Show your work.

Solution: _____

Name: _____

Find Factors and Factor Pairs

Study the example problem about factors and factor pairs. Then solve problems 1–6.

Example

Mr. Kennedy is arranging the 16 chairs in his classroom for a presentation. He wants to put the chairs in rows with an equal number of chairs in each row. Find all the ways he can arrange the chairs.

1 row of	2 rows of	4 rows of	8 rows of	16 rows of
16 chairs	8 chairs	4 chairs	2 chairs	1 chair
$1 \times 16 = 16$	$2 \times 8 = 16$	$4 \times 4 = 16$	$8 \times 2 = 16$	$16 \times 1 = 16$

Factors of 16: 1, 2, 4, 8, 16.
Factor pairs: 1 and 16, 2 and 8, 4 and 4.
Mr. Kennedy can arrange the chairs in 5 ways.

1 Complete the list to show the factors of 12.

1, _____, 3, _____, 6, _____

2 Write the factor pairs of 12.

1 and _____, _____ and _____, _____ and _____

3 The 20 students in Amanda's class each carved a wooden plate to display on the wall. They want each row to have the same number of plates. Find all the ways to display the plates.

Show your work.

Solution: _____

_____

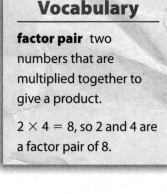

Vocabulary

factor pair two numbers that are multiplied together to give a product.

$2 \times 4 = 8$, so 2 and 4 are a factor pair of 8.

Solve.

4 Tell whether each sentence about the factors of 18 is *True* or *False*.

   a. All the factors of 18 are 2, 3, 6, 9, 18.   ☐ True   ☐ False

   b. 1 and 18 are a factor pair.   ☐ True   ☐ False

   c. 180 is a factor because $10 \times 18 = 180$.   ☐ True   ☐ False

   d. An array showing the factor pair of 3
      and 6 would have 3 rows of 6 objects.   ☐ True   ☐ False

5 Carlos arranged his building blocks into 2 rows of
12 blocks. Liz arranged her blocks into 6 rows of
4 blocks. If they each use the same number of
blocks, what two other ways could they arrange
their blocks?

Show your work.

Solution: _____

_____

6 Jonah has 100 flowers to arrange into vases. He wants
to put the same number of flowers in each vase. List
the factor pairs of 100. Then complete the table to
show the different ways to arrange the flowers.

Factor pairs of 100: _____

_____

Number of vases								
Number of flowers in each vase								

Name: _____

Identify Prime and Composite Numbers

Study the example showing how to identify prime and composite numbers. Then solve problems 1–6.

Example

Ms. Morris teaches a morning class with 13 students and an afternoon class with 14 students. Which class has a prime number of students?

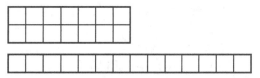

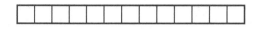

13 has one factor pair: 1 and 13
13 is a prime number.

14 has more than one factor pair: 2 and 7, 1 and 14
14 is a composite number.

The morning class has a prime number of students.

1 Is the number 2 prime or composite? Explain.

_____

_____

2 Kevin ran 23 laps around the track. Is the number 23 prime or composite? Explain.

_____

_____

3 Mae has more than 3 bracelets. She has an even number of bracelets. Is the number of bracelets a prime number or a composite number? Explain.

_____

_____

_____

_____

_____

Vocabulary

prime number a number that has only one pair of factors: itself and 1.

5 is a prime number; its factors are 5 and 1.

composite number a number that has more than one pair of factors.

8 is a composite number; it has the factors 1, 2, 4, and 8.

Solve.

4 Tell whether each sentence is *True* or *False*.

a. The number 9 is prime.   ☐ True   ☐ False

b. 2 is the only even prime number.   ☐ True   ☐ False

c. All the odd numbers between 1 and 10 are prime.   ☐ True   ☐ False

d. Some composite numbers have only two factors.   ☐ True   ☐ False

5 The area of a garden is 5 square feet.

The dimensions of the garden are
1 foot and 5 feet. 1 and 5 are factors
of the number 5.

```
┌─────────────────────────────────────┐
│                                      │ 1 foot
└─────────────────────────────────────┘
              5 feet
```

a. Is the number 5 a prime number? _____

b. If the area of a garden is 11 square feet, what
   could be the dimensions of the garden?

_____

6 Jordan and Mitchell are planning a graduation party
with 45 guests. They want to seat an equal number
of guests at each table. Each table should have more
than one guest. Answer the questions below.

a. List the different ways the guests and tables
   could be arranged. Tell how many tables are
   needed for each group of guests.

_____

_____

b. Jordan and Mitchell forgot to include themselves
   in the seating. They still want to have an equal
   number of guests at each table. List the ways the
   guests and tables could be arranged now.

_____

_____

Name: _____

Multiples and Factors

Solve the problems.

1 Raffle tickets at a fundraiser are $5 per ticket. Fiona spent $40 on tickets. How many tickets did she buy?

Show your work.

Which factor pair of 40 can help solve this problem?

Solution: _____

2 Which sentence(s) below are true about the numbers 1, 3, and 9?

Circle the letter for all that apply.

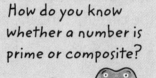

How do you know whether a number is prime or composite?

A Adding 1 to any of the numbers will make a composite number.

B Adding 2 to any of the numbers will make a prime number.

C 3 and 9 are prime numbers.

D All the numbers are factors of 9.

E All the numbers are factors of any multiple of 3.

3 The factors of 6 are also the factors of which number?

Which number also has 6 as a factor?

A 5   **C** 20

B 10   **D** 30

Mike chose **D** as the correct answer. How did he get that answer?

_____

_____

Solve.

4 If n = any number, what is one factor pair that you know n has?

> All numbers have 1 as a factor. What is the greatest factor any number can have?

Solution: _____

_____

5 Look at each number sentence below. Tell whether the circled number is a *factor* or *multiple*.

> Is the number multiplied by another number or is it a product of two numbers?

a. 1 ×④= 4   ☐ factor   ☐ multiple

b. 4 × 1 =④   ☐ factor   ☐ multiple

c. ⑤× 1 = 5   ☐ factor   ☐ multiple

d. ⑤= 5 × 1   ☐ factor   ☐ multiple

6 There are 56 fourth graders going on a field trip. The teacher wants to divide them evenly into groups of at least 4 students and no more than 8 students. What are the ways to divide the students evenly into groups?

> How can you use the factor pairs of 56 to find all the possible groups?

Show your work.

Solution: _____

Dear Family,

This week your child is learning about number and shape patterns.

Your child might see a number pattern like the one below. He or she is learning how to find the next numbers in the pattern.

3, 6, 9, 12, _____ , _____

The rule in the number pattern is "add 3." So the next numbers are 15, 18.

Another way to describe the pattern is to say that the numbers alternate in an odd/even pattern. The first number is odd, the second number is even, the third number is odd, and so on.

Your child is also learning about shape patterns like the one below.

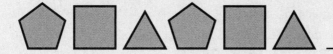

The pattern of shapes is:
    pentagon, square, triangle, pentagon, square, triangle.
So, the next two shapes in the pattern are pentagon, square.

Another way to describe the shape pattern is to say that the pattern has shapes with:
    5 sides, 4 sides, 3 sides, 5 sides, 4 sides, 3 sides, and so on.

Invite your child to share what he or she knows about patterns by doing the following activity together.

NEXT

Number Pattern Activity

Do an activity with your child to practice finding patterns in numbers.

- Look at the number pattern below with your child.

> 11, 22, 33, 44, 55, 66, 77, 88, 99, . . .

- Work together to identify the rule for the pattern (add 11).
- Talk about other patterns you notice in the numbers.

  Examples:

  The numbers alternate between odd and even: the first number is odd, the second number is even, and so on.

  The tens and ones digits are the same in each number.

  The tens and ones digits each go up by 1 in the next number in the pattern.

- Next, look at another number pattern and work together to identify the rule for the pattern.

> 12, 23, 34, 45, 56, 67, 78, 89, . . .

- Talk about other patterns you notice in the numbers. Discuss how this pattern and the first pattern are alike and different.
- Challenge your child to think about the kind of number pattern you would get using the rule "subtract 11."

Number and Shape Patterns

Name: _____

Study the example showing a number pattern.
Then solve problems 1–5.

Example

Leo noticed a pattern in the addition table.
What pattern did Leo notice?
What is the rule for the pattern?
What is the next number in the pattern?

Pattern: 0, 2, 4, 6, 8
  Rule: add 2

Use the rule to find the next number in the pattern:
$8 + 2 = 10$

10 is the next number in the pattern.

	0	1	2	3	4	5
0	0	1	2	3	4	5
1	1	2	3	4	5	6
2	2	3	4	5	6	7
3	3	4	5	6	7	8
4	4	5	6	7	8	9
5	5	6	7	8	9	?

1 Use the number line below to answer the questions.

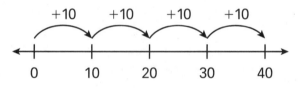

a. What pattern of numbers do you see on the number line?

0, _____, 20, _____, 40

b. What is the rule for the pattern? add _____

2 Use the number line below to answer the questions.

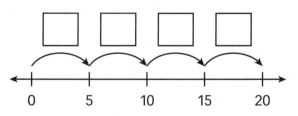

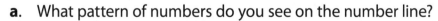

a. What pattern of numbers do you see on the number line?

_____, _____, _____, _____, 20

b. Label the number line to show the rule for the pattern.

Vocabulary

number pattern a series of numbers that follow a rule to repeat or change.

rule a procedure to follow to go from one number or shape to the next in a pattern.

Solve.

3 Fill in the missing numbers to show patterns with addends and sums.

Addend	Addend	Sum
100	10	110
90	20	
80		110
	40	110
60		

4 Look at problem 3.

a. What pattern do you see in the first Addend column?

_____

_____

b. What pattern do you see in the second Addend column?

_____

_____

c. When the sum remains the same, what do you notice about the two addends?

_____

_____

5 What is the same and what is different about the two patterns below?

Pattern A: 5, 10, 15, 20, 25, 30

Pattern B: 30, 25, 20, 15, 10, 5

Same: _____

Different: _____

Name: _____

Use Number Patterns

Study the example showing how to use a pattern on a number line to solve a word problem. Then solve problems 1–8.

Example

Riley wants to save $10 from her weekly babysitting job for the next 4 weeks. She has $50 in savings now. How much will Riley have in savings at the end of 4 weeks?

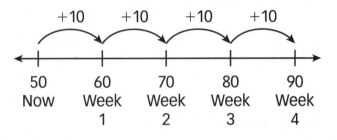

| +10 | +10 | +10 | +10 |

| 50 | 60 | 70 | 80 | 90 |
| Now | Week 1 | Week 2 | Week 3 | Week 4 |

Rule: add 10
Pattern: 50, 60, 70, 80, 90

Riley will have $90 in savings at the end of 4 weeks.

Eduardo practices the flute each weekday. His music teacher wants him to practice 5 minutes longer each day this week. Eduardo practices for 20 minutes on Monday. How many minutes will Eduardo practice on Friday?

1 Complete the table to show how many minutes Eduardo will practice each day this week.

Day	Monday	Tuesday	Wednesday	Thursday	Friday
Number of Minutes	20				

| | +5 | +5 | +5 | +5 |

2 Complete the sentence.

Eduardo will practice for _____ on Friday.

Solve.

3 Use the table below to answer the questions.

	Monday	Tuesday	Wednesday	Thursday	Friday
Jeff	1	2	3	4	5
Eric	2	4	6	8	10

   a. What is the rule for the pattern in Jeff's row? _____

   b. What is the rule for the pattern in Eric's row? _____

   c. Look at both Jeff's and Eric's numbers from day
      to day. What pattern do you see?

   _____

   _____

   d. If Saturday were shown in the table, what would
      be the numbers in Jeff's row and in Eric's row?

   _____

> Eve's soccer team has 48 water bottles in the locker
> room. Each of the 12 players takes a water bottle
> before a game.

4 Complete the table to show how many water bottles are left
in the locker room at the end of each of the first three games.

Game		1	2	3
Number of Bottles	48			

5 Use words and numbers to explain how you found the
number of bottles left after Game 1.

_____

_____

6 What is the rule for the pattern? _____

7 What number would come after 12 in the pattern? _____

8 What does this number mean? _____

Name: _____

Identify Shape Patterns

Study the example showing ways to describe a shape pattern. Then solve problems 1–7.

Example

A banner along a classroom wall has the shape pattern below.

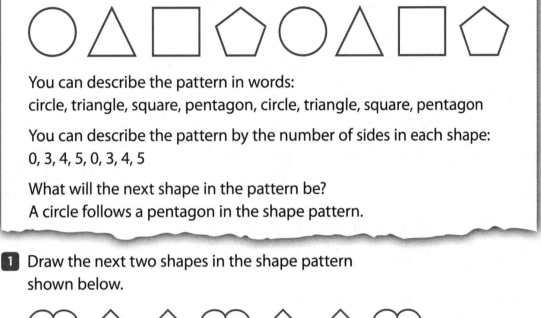

You can describe the pattern in words:
circle, triangle, square, pentagon, circle, triangle, square, pentagon

You can describe the pattern by the number of sides in each shape:
0, 3, 4, 5, 0, 3, 4, 5

What will the next shape in the pattern be?
A circle follows a pentagon in the shape pattern.

1 Draw the next two shapes in the shape pattern shown below.

 _____ _____

2 What two ways could you describe the shape pattern below?

_____

_____

3 Look at problem 2. The 3rd shape and the 6th shape are the same. Explain how to figure out what the 30th shape will be without drawing all 30 shapes.

_____

_____

Solve.

4 Sasha draws a shape pattern that goes back and forth between a 5-pointed star and 4-pointed star.

What is another way to describe the pattern?

_____

_____

5 Look at the shape pattern in problem 4. Choose *Yes* or *No* for each statement below.

a. The 7th spot has a 4-pointed star. ☐ Yes ☐ No

b. The 8th spot has a 5-pointed star. ☐ Yes ☐ No

c. The 99th spot has a 5-pointed star. ☐ Yes ☐ No

d. The 100th spot has a 4-pointed star. ☐ Yes ☐ No

6 Jamel used pattern blocks to make the shape pattern shown below.

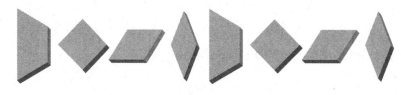

Draw the next 2 shapes in the pattern. _____ _____

7 Look at the shape pattern in problem 6. Choose *Yes* or *No* for each statement below.

a. ◆ will always be in an even spot. ☐ Yes ☐ No

b. ▱ will always be on a multiple of 3. ☐ Yes ☐ No

c. The 12th spot is ◆. ☐ Yes ☐ No

d. ◗ is in every 5th spot. ☐ Yes ☐ No

> **Vocabulary**
>
> **shape pattern** a series of shapes that follow a rule to repeat or change.

Name: _____

Number and Shape Patterns

Solve the problems.

1 How are the two number patterns below different?

Pattern A: 11, 22, 44, 88

Pattern B: 11, 22, 33, 44

_____

_____

_____

_____

_____

> What is the rule for each pattern?

2 Describe a rule you see in the shape pattern below.

B E C F D H G L

_____

_____

_____

_____

_____

> Look at how the letters are formed. What do some letters have in common? What do other letters have in common?

3 Use the letters T, P, J, and I to continue the pattern in problem 2.

_____

_____

_____

> How can you use the rule to find the next letter in the pattern?

Solve.

4 Vivian wrote the number pattern below.

8, 16, 32, 64, 128

Which of the following could be a rule for this pattern?

A Multiply by 2.

B Add 16.

C Double the number.

D Multiply by 4.

Tori chose **D** as the correct answer. How did she get that answer?

There may be several ways to describe a pattern.

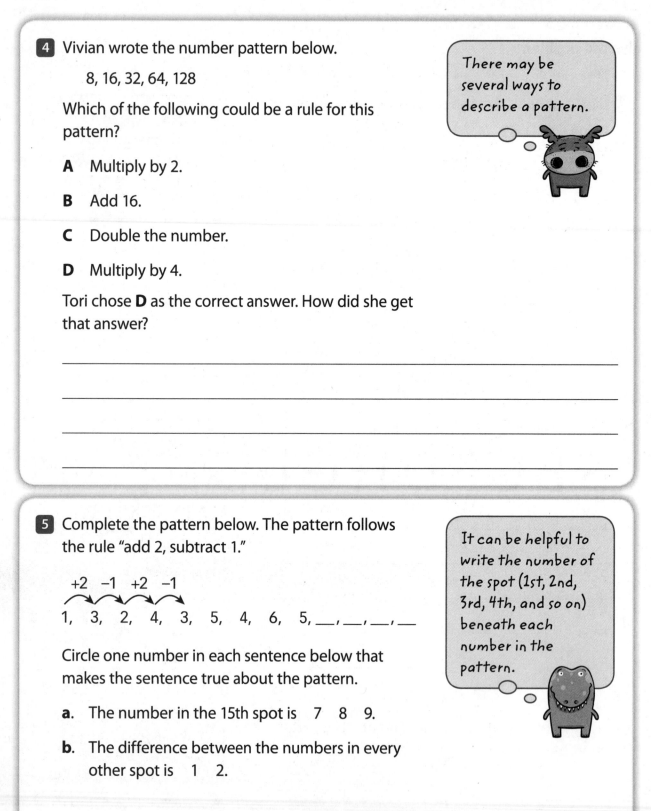

_____

_____

_____

_____

5 Complete the pattern below. The pattern follows the rule "add 2, subtract 1."

+2 −1 +2 −1

1, 3, 2, 4, 3, 5, 4, 6, 5, ___, ___, ___, ___

Circle one number in each sentence below that makes the sentence true about the pattern.

a. The number in the 15th spot is   7   8   9.

b. The difference between the numbers in every other spot is   1   2.

It can be helpful to write the number of the spot (1st, 2nd, 3rd, 4th, and so on) beneath each number in the pattern.

Dear Family,

This week your child is learning to model multi-step problems.

Your child might see a problem like this:

> Monty's family bought 3 pies and 4 muffins at the bake sale. The pies cost $5 each and the muffins cost $2 each. Write an equation that represents the amount of money Monty's family spent at the bake sale.

Your child is learning to model a problem like this with a bar model:

5	5	5	2	2	2	2

$\longmapsto$? $\longmapsto$

Looking at the bar model can help your child write an equation for the problem:

Money spent = (3 pies for $5 each) + (4 muffins for $2 each)
$M = (3 \times 5) + (4 \times 2)$

Your child could also write a different equation:

Money spent = ($2 each for 4 muffins) + ($5 each for 3 pies)
$M = (2 \times 4) + (5 \times 3)$

Both equations show the information in the problem. In each equation, the letter *M* stands for the amount of money that Monty's family spent at the bake sale.

Invite your child to share what he or she knows about modeling multi-step problems by doing the following activity together.

Multi-Step Word Problems Activity

Do an activity with your child to practice modeling word problems that have more than one step.

- Make up multi-step word problems using numbers you encounter in everyday life. Use ideas like the following:

  - Laurie has $25. Is that enough money to buy 3 books for $7 each and 2 folders for $2 each?

  - Mark wants to sell 40 tins of popcorn for the school fundraiser. He sold 8 tins of popcorn on Monday. On Tuesday he sold 3 times as many tins of popcorn as he did on Monday. How many more tins does Mark still need to sell?

- Have your child draw a bar model or write an equation that could be used to solve each word problem that you think of.

Look for real-life opportunities to practice modeling problems that have more than one step with your child.

Model Multi-Step Problems

Name: _____

Study the example showing how to model a two-step word problem. Then solve problems 1–9.

Example

Mr. Norman's fourth grade class held a pancake breakfast fundraiser. They bought 4 cartons of eggs to use for the pancakes. Each carton has 12 eggs. They have 7 eggs left over. How many eggs were used?

4 groups of 12 is 48.

$4 \times 12 = 48$

7 eggs are left over.

	48		
12	12	12	12
?			7

Subtract 7 from 48 to find how many eggs were used.

$48 - 7 = 41$

41 eggs were used.

1 Fiona has 6 garden boxes. She wants to plant 3 vegetable seeds and 3 flower seeds in each garden box. How many seeds does Fiona need in all? Draw a picture to model the problem. Then solve the problem.

Solution: Fiona needs _____ seeds in all.

2 Zander bought 3 hats for $7 each and 2 shirts for $9 each. How much did Zander spend? Draw and label jumps on the number line below to show how much Zander spent.

Zander spent _____ .

Lesson 9 Model Multi-Step Problems   **87**

Solve.

Nadia bought 4 bags of popcorn at the movies. She shared the popcorn with her 7 friends. Each bag held 6 cups of popcorn. If everyone had an equal amount, how many cups of popcorn did each person have?

3 Complete the bar model below to solve the problem.

4 What do the parts of the top bar represent?

_____

5 What do the parts of the bottom bar represent?

_____

6 Why are there more than 7 parts in the bottom bar?

_____

7 Explain how to find the number of cups of popcorn each person had. _____

_____

_____

Tom buys 5 packs of juice boxes for the class picnic. Each pack has 6 juice boxes.

8 At the picnic, 18 students take a juice box. How many juice boxes are left?

Show your work.

Solution: _____

Name: _____

Write Equations

Study the example showing how to model a multi-step problem and write an equation. Then solve problems 1–4.

Example

The table shows Eli's after-school activities. Write an equation to show how many hours a week Eli spends doing activities.

Activity	How long?	How often?
Volunteer at the library	2 hours	2 times a week
Work at the skate shop	2 hours	4 times a week
Swim practice	1 hour	5 times a week

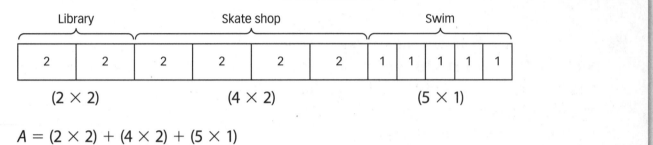

$A = (2 \times 2) + (4 \times 2) + (5 \times 1)$

Mia volunteered at the animal shelter on 7 weekends. On Saturdays, she volunteered for 3 hours. On Sundays, she volunteered for 2 hours.

1 Write an equation to find how many hours Mia volunteered.

a. Complete the bar model.

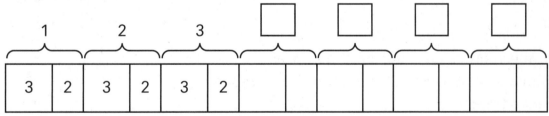

b. What do the numbers above the bar represent?

_____

c. What do the numbers in each part of the bar represent? _____

d. Write an equation. _____

Lesson 9 Model Multi-Step Problems   **89**

Solve.

2 A bike rental is $20 for a day and $3 for an hour. Caroline rented a bike for 2 days and 2 hours. Which equation could you use to find how much money, *M*, Caroline spent? Circle the letter for all that apply.

A $M = (2 \times 20) + (2 \times 3)$

B $M = (3 \times 20) + (2 \times 2)$

C $M = (20 \times 2) \times (3 \times 2)$

D $M = (20 \times 2) + (3 \times 2)$

3 Zara went to the book fair and bought 3 comic books for $5 each, 2 chapter books for $9 each, 4 posters for $2 each, and 1 picture book for $7. Write an equation that can be used to find how much Zara spent at the book fair.

Show your work.

Solution: _____

4 The table below shows clothing sales at a school fair. Use the information in the table to write an expression that equals *T*, the total amount of money spent on clothing.

Item	Price	Number sold
T-shirts	$12	100
Sweatshirts	$20	50

Solution: _____

Name: _____

Model Multi-Step Problems

Solve the problems.

1 Phillip earns $15 an hour at his tutoring job and $10 an hour babysitting. Last week, he worked 10 hours tutoring and 4 hours babysitting. Which equation shows how much Phillip earned, *E*?

Remember that parentheses tell what to do first.

A $E = (15 \times 10) + (10 \times 4)$

B $E = (15 + 10) \times (10 + 4)$

C $E = (15 \times 10) \times (10 \times 4)$

D $E = (15 \times 4) + (10 \times 10)$

2 The table below shows a cell phone plan.

	Cost per month
Phone	$22 each
Unlimited texting	$30 for a family
Unlimited data	$80 for a family
Insurance	$3 for each phone

What expressions can you write to show the cost of 4 phones and the cost of insurance for 4 phones?

Lola's family has 4 cell phones. They want to have insurance on each phone. They also want to have texting and data on each phone. Write an equation to show the monthly cost for Lola's family.

Show your work.

Solution: _____

_____

Solve.

3 There are 6 friends sharing 3 pizzas. Each pizza is cut into 8 slices. Which equation could be used to find the total number of slices, *P*, each friend will get?

First, how do you find how many slices there are in all?

A $(6 \times 3) \div 8 = P$

B $(3 \times 8) \div 6 = P$

C $8 \times (6 \div 3) = P$

D $(8 \times 6) \div 3 = P$

Sadie chose **B** as the correct answer. How did she get that answer?

_____

_____

_____

_____

_____

_____

4 Margaret received $20 each from 3 relatives and $50 from her parents at graduation. She spent $30. She saved half of the remaining money and donated the other half. Which equation(s) could you use to find how much money, *S*, she saved? Circle the letter of all that apply.

Another way to think of "half" is to think of dividing by 2.

A $S = (3 \times 20 - 50) - 30 \div 2$

B $S = (3 \times 20 + 50) - 30 \div 2$

C $S = (20 + 20 + 20 + 50 - 30) \div 2$

D $S = (3 \times 20 - 50 + 30) \div 2$

E $S = (3 \times 20 + 50 - 30) \div 2$

Dear Family,

This week your child is learning to solve multi-step problems.

Your child might see a problem like this:

> Max and Ross are making smoothies. Each batch of smoothies uses 3 bananas. Max has 5 bananas and Ross has 8 bananas. Write and solve an equation to find out how many batches of smoothies the boys can make.

Your child is learning to use a number line to help understand the problem and write an equation.

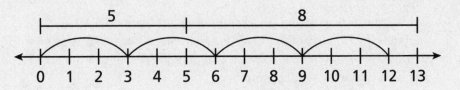

The number line shows the 5 bananas that Max has and the 8 bananas that Ross has. The curves above the number line show jumps of 3 since 3 bananas are needed to make each batch of smoothies. Looking at the number line can help your child write an equation like the one below.

$$(5 + 8) \div 3 = B$$

Your child can solve the equation for *B*, the number of batches of smoothies that the boys can make.

$$13 \div 3 = 4 \, R1$$

The answer to the problem is that the boys can make 4 batches of smoothies with 1 banana left over.

Invite your child to share what he or she knows about solving multi-step problems by doing the following activity together.

NEXT

Solving Multi-Step Problems Activity

Do an activity with your child to practice solving word problems that have more than one step.

- Work together with your child to look around the house or think about family activities that involve more than one of an item. Examples might be buying 6-packs of sports drinks or ordering an 8-slice pizza.

- Take turns. One person says a sentence about the item, that includes the number of the item (for example, 6 bottles of sports drink or 8 slices of pizza). The second person asks a question about the item that uses a 1-digit number.

  Example: There are 8 slices of pizza in a pizza pie. How many slices are in 2 pizzas?

- Work together with your child to answer the question. Then the first person asks how many of each item (sports drinks, slices of pizza, etc.) each person in your family would get if you divided the items evenly among the number of people in your family. Would there be any items left over?

- Work together with your child to solve the problem. Encourage your child to write an equation that shows the information in the problem. Then work together to solve the equation.

Look for real-life opportunities to practice solving problems that have more than one step with your child.

Solve Multi-Step Problems

Name: _____

Prerequisite: Solve Two-Step Problems

Study the example showing how to use a model to solve a two-step word problem. Then solve problems 1–5.

Example

Brian and his friends are doing a 200-piece jigsaw puzzle. Each of the 6 friends has placed 12 puzzle pieces. How many pieces have not been placed?

200	
6×12	p

$$(6 \times 12) \quad + \quad p = 200$$
$$72 \quad + \quad p = 200$$
$$p = 200 - 72$$
$$p = 128$$

128 pieces have not been placed.

---

1 Use estimation to check whether 128 is a reasonable answer in the example above.

$$p = 200 - 72$$

Round to the nearest ten. $p = $ _____ − _____

Subtract the rounded numbers. _____ = _____ − _____

_____ is close to 128 so 128 is a reasonable answer.

2 There are 8 students at each of 4 round tables in the cafeteria. There are 64 students at long tables. Use the bar model to write and solve an equation to find how many students there are in the cafeteria.

V	
4×8	64

Show your work.

Vocabulary

reasonable something that makes sense when the given facts are taken into account.

Solution: There are _____ in the cafeteria.

Solve.

3 The table below shows the cost of admission tickets at a museum. Write and solve an equation to find the cost of tickets for 1 child and 2 adults.

	Child	Adult
Cost of ticket	$6	$11

Show your work.

Solution: _____

4 Liz is training for a swim meet. Her goal is to swim 100 laps. She swam 12 laps in the pool on each of 3 days. Write and solve an equation to find how many more laps Liz needs to swim to reach her goal.

Show your work.

Solution: _____

5 Paperbacks sell for $2 and hardcover books sell for $4 at the library book sale. The library made $98 at the sale. There were 25 paperback books sold. Write and solve an equation to find how many hardcover books were sold.

Show your work.

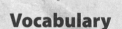

Vocabulary

equation a mathematical sentence that uses an equal sign (=) to show that two expressions have the same value.

Solution: _____

Name: _____

Solve Multi-Step Problems

Study the example showing how to model a multi-step problem with a remainder. Then solve problems 1–5.

Example

Mrs. Murray has 12 students in one science class and 14 students in another. She wants to combine both classes to do group work. Each table in the science room can seat 4 students. How many tables does Mrs. Murray need?

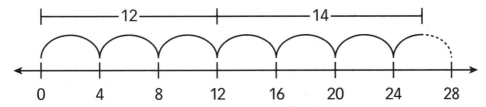

Let *T* equal the number of tables needed.

$T = (12 + 14) \div 4$

$\quad = 26 \div 4$

$\quad = 6 \text{ R2}$

6 R2 means:
- 6 tables with 4 students each
- 2 more students need another table

Mrs. Murray needs 7 tables.

1 Check the solution to the equation in the example.

_____ tables × _____ students per table +

_____ students = _____ total students

2 Leticia earns $8 each time she rakes the yard. She has earned $24 so far. Write and solve an equation to show how many more times Leticia needs to rake the yard to earn enough to buy a music player that costs $45.

Show your work.

Vocabulary

remainder the amount left over that will not divide equally into the given number of groups.

$26 \div 4 = 6 \text{ R2}$

Solution: _____

_____

Solve.

3 Meghan found 15 pieces of sea glass on the beach. The next day she found 4 more pieces than she found the day before. Write and solve an equation to find how many pieces of sea glass she found altogether.

Show your work.

Solution: _____

4 The table shows ticket prices at a movie theater. Ticket sales to an afternoon show were $146. There were 10 child tickets sold. Write and solve an equation to find how many adult tickets were sold.

Show your work.

	Child	Adult
Ticket price	$5	$12

Solution: _____

5 Ticket prices for 3-D movies are $10 for a child and $15 for an adult. One adult spent $55 to take a group of children to the movies. Write and solve an equation to find how many children went to the movies.

Show your work.

Solution: _____

Name: _____

Solve Multi-Step Problems

Solve the problems.

1 Jensen bought 10 boxes of granola bars. Each box has 8 bars. He wants to share the bars with 6 soccer teams. Which equation can be used to find how many bars each team gets?

What operation can you use to put the bars into equal-sized groups?

A $b = (8 \times 10) - 6$　　**C** $b = (6 + 8) \div 10$

B $b = (10 + 6) \div 8$　　**D** $b = (10 \times 8) \div 6$

2 Solve the equation in problem 1 to find how many granola bars each team gets. Are bars left over?

Show your work.

What does the remainder mean?

Solution: _____

3 The community center used 4 recycling bins one week, twice as many the next week, 7 bins the third week, and 5 bins the last week of the month. Which equation shows how many bins were used for the month?

Which numbers do you place in parentheses?

A $4 + (2 \times 7) + 7 + 5 = 30$

B $4 + (2 \times 4) + 7 + 5 = 24$

C $(1 \times 4) + (2 \times 4) + (3 \times 7) + 5 = 34$

D $4 + (4 \div 2) + 7 + 5 = 18$

Mia chose **A** as the correct answer. How did she get that answer?

_____

_____

Solve.

4 The table shows the results of a bake sale. The cost of renting tables for the bake sale was $100.

Write and solve an equation to show how much money the bake sale made.

How do you show the cost of renting the tables in the equation?

Baked item	Number sold	Price
Cookies	90	$1 each
Brownies	75	$1 each
Crispy treats	60	$2 each
Cupcakes	50	$3 each

Show your work.

Solution: _____

5 Look at the table in problem 4. If 10 fewer cookies and 10 more cupcakes were sold, how much would the bake sale have made?

Show your work.

Which numbers in the equation you wrote in problem 4 do you need to change?

Solution: _____

Unit 2 Game

Factor Finder

What you need: Recording Sheet, Game Board, 2 sets of digit cards (1–9), 40 counters (2 different colors)

Directions

- Mix the digit cards and place them facedown in a stack.

- Player A picks a card and writes the digit on that card in the list at the top of the Recording Sheet to make a two-digit number.

- Player A writes that two-digit number and all the factors for that two-digit number on the Recording Sheet.

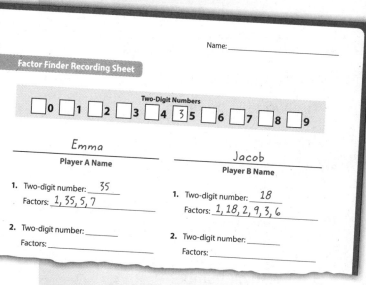

Factor Finder Recording Sheet

Two-Digit Numbers

0 □ 1 □ 2 □ 3 □ 4 | 3 | 5 □ 6 □ 7 □ 8 □ 9

Emma
Player A Name

Jacob
Player B Name

1. Two-digit number: ___35___
   Factors: _1, 35, 5, 7_

1. Two-digit number: ___18___
   Factors: _1, 18, 2, 9, 3, 6_

2. Two-digit number: _____
   Factors: _____

2. Two-digit number: _____
   Factors: _____

- Player A places counters on the Game Board to cover the factors for that two-digit number. Not all factors are on the Game Board, and some factors appear more than once. Cover a factor only once.

- Player B takes a turn, following the same steps as Player A. Player B uses different color counters on the Game Board.

- The first player to have 5 counters in a row on the Game Board wins.

- If no player has 5 counters in a row, the player with the most counters on the board after 5 rounds wins the game.

> I picked 3 and made the two-digit number 35. The factors of 35 are 1, 35, 5, and 7. I put counters on the 5 and 7 on the Game Board because they are both factors of 35.

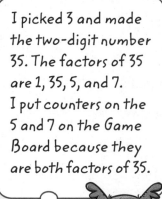

Name: _____

Factor Finder Recording Sheet

Two-Digit Numbers

☐0 ☐1 ☐2 ☐3 ☐4 ☐5 ☐6 ☐7 ☐8 ☐9

_____
Player A Name

_____
Player B Name

1. Two-digit number: _____

Factors: _____

1. Two-digit number: _____

Factors: _____

2. Two-digit number: _____

Factors: _____

2. Two-digit number: _____

Factors: _____

3. Two-digit number: _____

Factors: _____

3. Two-digit number: _____

Factors: _____

4. Two-digit number: _____

Factors: _____

4. Two-digit number: _____

Factors: _____

5. Two-digit number: _____

Factors: _____

5. Two-digit number: _____

Factors: _____

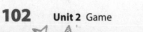

Factor Finder Game Board

2	8	7	6	5
3	6	5	8	11
12	2	10	4	12
6	9	8	3	4
5	4	3	9	2

✂

1	2	3	4	5	6
7	8	9	1	2	3
4	5	6	7	8	9

Name: _____

Operations and Algebraic Thinking

In this unit you learned to:	Lesson
multiply and divide to solve comparison problems, for example: 28 is 4 times as many as 7.	5, 6
identify factor pairs for a number, for example: 4 and 5 are a factor pair for 20.	7
identify multiples of a number, for example: 42 is a multiple of 6.	7
identify prime and composite numbers, for example: 16 is composite.	7
generate and describe patterns, for example: every other number is odd in 3, 10, 17, 24, … .	8
model and solve multi-step word problems using equations, for example: $(6 \times 3) - 11 + 2 = 9$.	9, 10

Use these skills to solve problems 1–4.

1 Extend the pattern below by drawing a shape on each blank. Use each shape in the box once.

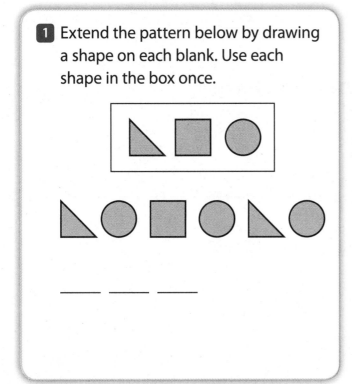

2 Gwen, Alex, and Manny are playing a game as a team. Gwen has scored 2 times as many points as Manny. Alex has scored 7 more points than Manny. Manny has scored 15 points. Which equation shows how many points their team has scored altogether?

A $T = 15 + (2 \times 7) + (15 + 7)$

B $T = 15 + (2 + 15) + (2 \times 7)$

C $T = 15 + (2 \times 15) + (15 + 7)$

D $T = 15 + (2 + 7) + (15 \times 7)$

Solve.

3 Extend the number pattern below. Then write the number that would be the 100th number in the pattern. Explain how you figured out what the number would be.

100th

5, 10, 15, 20, 25, 30, _____, _____, _____, ..., _____

_____

_____

_____

4 Ken is building an outdoor walking path with pavers. Pavers are sold $8 for 10 pavers or $1 per paver.

Part A

The walking path needs 52 pavers. What is the least amount that 52 pavers cost?

Show your work.

Solution: _____

Part B

How much more would it cost to buy 52 pavers individually?

Show your work.

Solution: _____

Part C

What is the greatest number of pavers Ken can buy for $60?

Show your work.

Solution: _____

Name: _____

Answer the questions and show all your work on separate paper.

The Pet Club is raising money for the local animal shelter. The club members want to make fundraising posters that tell how a donation helps the animals in the shelter. Each poster will have a statement like the following:

A donation of $_____ helps _____ cats, _____ small dogs, and _____ large dogs for one day.

The chart below shows the amount that the shelter spends caring for animals.

Animal	Cost per Day
Cat	$3
Small dog	$4
Large dog	$5

Decide on three different donation amounts for the posters. Complete a statement for each donation amount. Write how many of each kind of animal the donation helps. Explain how you decided which numbers to use in your three statements.

Reflect on Mathematical Practices

After you complete the task, choose one of the following questions to answer.

1 Persevere How did you use the information in the table to help you decide on donation amounts?

2 Reason Mathematically How do factors and multiples help you solve this problem?

Checklist

Did you . . .

☐ check your calculations?

☐ write three statements?

☐ explain how you chose the numbers you used?

Performance Task Tips

Word Bank Here are some words that you might use in your answer.

multiply	each	expression
product	factor	equation
total	multiple	equals

Models Here are some models that you might use to find the solution.

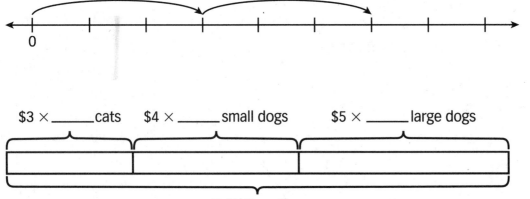

$3 × _____ cats $4 × _____ small dogs $5 × _____ large dogs

Total Donation

Sentence Starters Here are some sentence starters that might help you write an explanation.

The cost per day for _____ is _____

Multiples of _____ are _____

An expression that represents the number of _____ is _____

An equation that represents a donation of $_____ is _____

Unit 2 Vocabulary

Name: _____

My Examples

multiplication

an operation used to find the total number of items in equal-sized groups

product

the result of multiplication

factors

numbers that are multiplied together to get a product

factor pair

two numbers that are multiplied together to give a product

My Examples

multiple

the product of a number and any other whole number; for example, 3, 6, 9, 12, and 15 are multiples of 3

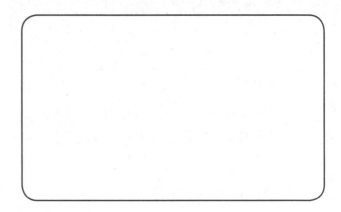

division

an operation used to separate a number of items into equal-sized groups

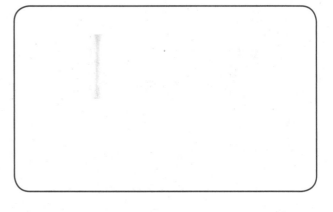

remainder

the amount left over that will not divide equally into the given number of groups

reasonable

something that makes sense when the given facts are taken into account

symbol

> an object used to stand for an unknown number in an equation

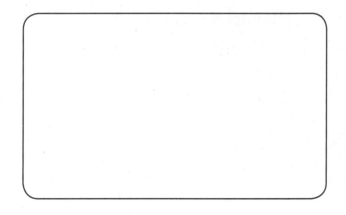

unknown

> a missing number in an equation

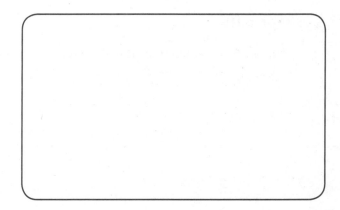

equation

> a mathematical sentence that uses an equal sign (=) to show that two expressions have the same value

expression

> a group of one or more numbers, unknowns, and operations that represents a quantity, for example, $5 \times h$

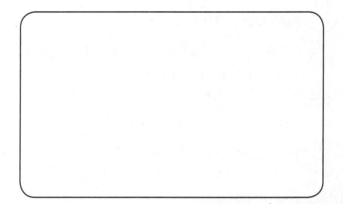

My Examples

composite number

a number that has more than one pair of factors

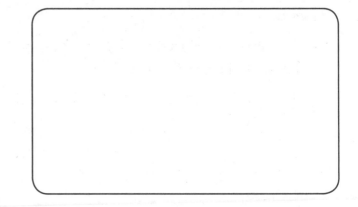

prime number

a number that has only one pair of factors: itself and 1

shape pattern

a series of shapes that follow a rule to repeat or change

number pattern

a series of numbers that follow a rule to repeat or change

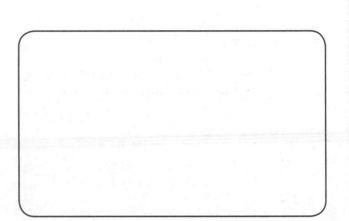

rule

a procedure to follow to go from one number or shape to the next in a pattern

My Words

_____

_____

_____

_____

_____

_____

_____

_____

_____

My Words

My Examples

Dear Family,

This week your child is learning to multiply whole numbers.

Your child is learning to multiply two-digit numbers, such as 16 × 28.

One way your child can multiply two-digit numbers is by using an area model. With this strategy, your child multiplies using the place value of each digit.

The area model below shows the number 16 as 10 + 6 along the top, and the number 28 as 20 + 8 at the left. Your child finds the individual products, then adds the products together to find the total product of the multiplication.

	10	+	6
20	20 × 10 2 tens × 1 ten = 2 hundreds **200**		20 × 6 2 tens × 6 = 12 tens **120**
+ 8	8 × 10 8 × 1 ten = 8 tens **80**		8 × 6 = **48**

200 + 80 + 120 + 48 = 448

16 × 28 = 448

Invite your child to share what he or she knows about multiplying whole numbers by doing the following activity together.

NEXT

Multiplying Whole Numbers Activity

Do an activity with your child to practice multiplying two-digit numbers.

Materials: timer or watch with a second hand

- Together with your child, think of things that can be counted in one minute, such as the number of times you clap your hands or the number of steps you walk.

- Choose one idea. Have one person do the activity while the other person times the activity for one minute.

- The person doing the activity counts how many. Count carefully. Stop counting when the person with the timer says "Stop!"

    Example: Clap your hands for one minute, counting each clap. Count 92 hand claps.

- Have your child use that number to figure out how many could be counted in 15 minutes.

    Example: $15 \times 92 = ?$

- Have your child multiply to find the answer.

- Switch roles and repeat the activity.

Look for other real-life opportunities to practice multiplying two-digit numbers with your child.

Multiply Whole Numbers

Name: _____

Prerequisite: Multiply by a Multiple of 10

Study the example showing how to multiply by a multiple of 10. Then solve problems 1–7.

Example

Roy swims for 20 minutes a day, 6 days a week. How many minutes does Roy swim in a week?

Use base-ten blocks.

6 groups of 2 tens is
6 × 2 tens, or 12 tens.
12 tens = 120

Roy swims 120 minutes in a week.

Use factors and grouping to multiply.	6 × 20
Break down 20 into factors 2 and 10.	6 × (2 × 10)
Change grouping and multiply.	(6 × 2) × 10 12 × 10 = 120

1 The base-ten blocks below show 4 × 30.

Fill in the blanks to find the product.

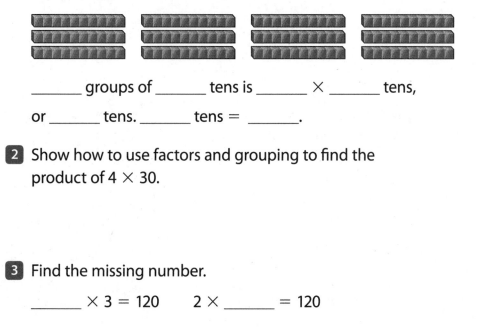

_____ groups of _____ tens is _____ × _____ tens,

or _____ tens. _____ tens = _____.

2 Show how to use factors and grouping to find the product of 4 × 30.

3 Find the missing number.

_____ × 3 = 120   2 × _____ = 120

Vocabulary

factors numbers that are multiplied together to get a product.

product the result of multiplication.

6 × 20 = 120

factors   product

Solve.

4 Saundra has 8 folders on her computer. Each folder has 50 files. How many files are on Saundra's computer?

Show your work.

Solution: _____

5 There are 5 ten-pound bags and 8 twenty-pound bags of rice on a shelf. How many pounds of rice are on the shelf?

Show your work.

Solution: _____

6 Lola gets two 20-minute breaks at work each day. She works 5 days a week. How much time does she spend on break each week?

Show your work.

Solution: _____

7 Andrew wants to buy 3 video games that are $50 each. He earns $80 a week. In how many weeks will he have enough money to buy the games?

Show your work.

> First find the total cost of the video games. Then compare the cost to the amount he earns in a week.

Solution: _____

Name: _____

Multiply by a One-Digit Number

Study the example showing one way to multiply by a one-digit number. Then solve problems 1–5.

Example

Jesse's family has 4 music players. Each music player can hold 8,352 songs. What is the total number of songs all 4 music players can hold?

Use an area model.

	8,000	+	300	+	50	+	2
4	4 × 8,000		4 × 300		4 × 50		4 × 2

$$4 × 8,352 = (4 × 8,000) + (4 × 300) + (4 × 50) + (4 × 2)$$
$$= 32,000 + 1,200 + 200 + 8$$
$$= 33,408$$

All 4 music players can hold 33,408 songs.

---

1 Look at the multiplication above. Use partial products to multiply 4 × 8,352. Fill in the blanks.

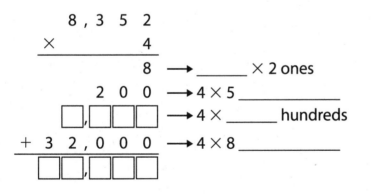

```
      8 , 3  5  2
    ×           4
  ─────────────────
              8  ⟶ _____ × 2 ones
        2  0  0  ⟶ 4 × 5 _____
     □,□□□  ⟶ 4 × _____ hundreds
  + 3 2 , 0  0  0  ⟶ 4 × 8 _____
     □□,□□□
```

2 Show how to use partial products to multiply 5 × 1,643.

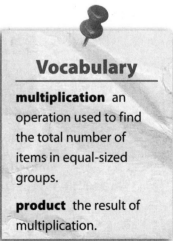

Vocabulary

multiplication an operation used to find the total number of items in equal-sized groups.

product the result of multiplication.

Solve.

3 Write $4 \times 3,569$ in expanded form to show the place value of each digit. Then find the product.

_____

_____

_____

4 Lee earns $1,075 each month. How much does he earn in 6 months?

Show your work.

Solution: _____

5 Look at Callie's work for solving $3 \times 9,423$.

a. Explain what Callie did wrong.

_____

_____

_____

_____

_____

_____

_____

$$
\begin{array}{r}
9,423 \\
\times \quad\quad 3 \\
\hline
9 \\
60 \\
120 \\
+\ 2,700 \\
\hline
2,889 \\
\end{array}
$$

b. What is the correct answer for $3 \times 9,423$?

_____

Name: _____

Multiply Two-Digit Numbers by Two-Digit Numbers

Study the example showing how to multiply a two-digit number by a two-digit number to solve a word problem. Then solve problems 1–6.

Example

Aaron's guitar lesson is 35 minutes a week.
He has been taking lessons for 12 weeks.
How many minutes has Aaron spent at lessons?

Use an area model to multiply 35 × 12.

	30 $+$	5
10	10 × 30 1 ten × 3 tens = 3 hundreds **300**	10 × 5 1 ten × 5 = 5 tens **50**
$+$ 2	2 × 30 2 × 3 tens = 6 tens **60**	2 × 5 = **10**

300 + 60 + 50 + 10 = 420 minutes
Aaron has spent 420 minutes at lessons.

1 Look at the example above. Use partial products to multiply 35 × 12. Fill in the blanks.

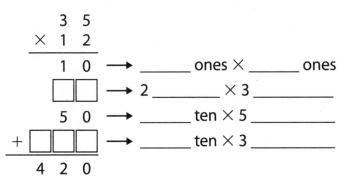

```
      3  5
   ×  1  2
   ─────────
      1  0  ⟶ _____ ones × _____ ones
   ☐☐       ⟶ 2 _____ × 3 _____
      5  0  ⟶ _____ ten × 5 _____
 + ☐☐☐      ⟶ _____ ten × 3 _____
   ─────────
   4  2  0
```

2 Show how to use an area model to multiply 71 × 48.

71 × 48 = _____ + _____ + _____ + _____ = _____

Solve.

3 Show how to use partial products to multiply 48 × 71.

$$48 \times 71 = \underline{\hspace{3cm}}$$

4 Tell whether each number sentence is *True* or *False*.

a. $18 \times 42 = (10 \times 40) + (10 \times 2) + (8 \times 40) + (8 \times 2)$ ☐ True ☐ False

b. $60 \times 15 = (6 \times 10) + (6 \times 5)$ ☐ True ☐ False

c. $37 \times 22 = (30 \times 20) + (30 \times 20) + (7 \times 20) + (7 \times 20)$ ☐ True ☐ False

d. $99 \times 11 = (1 \times 9) + (1 \times 90) + (10 \times 9) + (10 \times 90)$ ☐ True ☐ False

5 Mr. Greene is preparing 28 bags of materials for his art class. Each bag needs 40 glass tiles. How many glass tiles are needed?

Show your work.

Solution: _____

6 Stephanie has 6 classes a day at school. Each class is 52 minutes long. She goes to school 5 days a week. How much time does she spend in class each week? Show two different ways to solve this problem.

Show your work.

Solution: _____

Name: _____

Multiply Whole Numbers

Solve the problems.

1 One mile is 5,280 feet. How many feet are in 6 miles?

  A 30,068   **C** 31,248

  B 30,168   **D** 31,680

What would an area model for 6 × 5,280 look like?

2 Which of the following are equal to 420 × 3?

Circle the letter for all that apply.

  A (3 × 400) + (3 × 20)

  B 420 + 420 + 420

  C (3 × 400) + (3 × 2)

  D 1,260

How many hundreds, tens, and ones are in 420?

3 The bell on a clock tower rings every 15 minutes. If the bell has rung 24 times, how many minutes have passed?

  A 220 minutes

  B 342 minutes

  C 360 minutes

  D 380 minutes

Amber chose **A** as the correct answer. How did she get that answer?

_____

_____

_____

What are the partial products of 15 × 24?

Solve.

4 The multiplication problem 5 × 3,000 can be written in many different ways. One way is 5 × 3 × 1,000. Write 3 more ways.

_____

_____

_____

You can also write 3,000 as 3 × 10 × 100. What other ways can you think of?

5 A distance race is 42 kilometers. Kylie has completed 16 distance races. How many kilometers has she run?

Show your work.

How many tens and ones are in each number?

Solution: _____

6 Fourth graders are taking a field trip. The cost is $15 for each student and $18 for each chaperone. There are 94 students and 16 chaperones on the field trip. What is the total cost for all students and chaperones?

Show your work.

How much does it cost for all the students? All the chaperones?

Solution: _____

Dear Family,

This week your child is learning to divide whole numbers.

Here are some vocabulary words your child is using to communicate about division.

> **quotient:** the answer to a division problem.
> **dividend:** the number you divide in a division problem.
> **divisor:** the number you divide by in a division problem.

Your child is learning to divide three-digit or four-digit numbers by a one-digit number. One way your child can solve a division problem is to find partial quotients. With this strategy, your child divides using place value. The division problem below shows how to divide 2,125 by 4.

```
      6
     25
    500
 4)2,125  →  1. How many groups of 4 in 2,000? 500
 − 2,000  →  2. Subtract 500 groups of 4.
      125  →  3. How many groups of 4 in 100? 25
    − 100  →  4. Subtract 25 groups of 4.
       25  →  5. How many groups of 4 in 25? 6
     − 24  →  6. Subtract 6 groups of 4.
        1
```

The sum of the partial quotients is 531. The remainder is 1.

Altogether there are 500 + 25 + 6, or 531 groups of 4 in 2,125, with one extra left over. 2,125 ÷ 4 = 531 R1

Invite your child to share what he or she knows about dividing whole numbers by doing the following activity together.

NEXT

Dividing Whole Numbers Activity

Do an activity with your child to practice dividing a three-digit number by a one-digit number.

Materials: book with a number of pages in the hundreds

- With your child, choose a favorite book and look at the number of pages it has.

- Suppose you want to read the entire book in a week. How many pages would you need to read each day in order to finish the book in a week (7 days)?

- Have your child use division to find the answer.

    Example: The book has 157 pages.
    $157 \div 7 = 22 \text{ R}3$

- You and your child can check the answer to the division problem by using multiplication. If you have a remainder, remember to add the remainder to the product.

- Decide what to do if you have a remainder. Will you read one page each day for the number of days shown by the remainder or will you read all the remaining pages on the last day?

You and your child can repeat the activity with other favorite books.

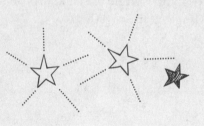

Divide Whole Numbers

Name: _____

Study the example showing how to use multiplication to solve a division problem. Then solve problems 1–7.

Example

The Lin family spent $800 on 4 airplane tickets. Each ticket was the same price. How much did each ticket cost?

Divide 800 by 4. $800 \div 4 = ?$

Use the related multiplication equation.
$4 \times 200 = 800$
So, $800 \div 4 = 200$

Each ticket cost $200.

	800		
200	200	200	200

1 Look at the model below. Write a division equation and a related multiplication equation.

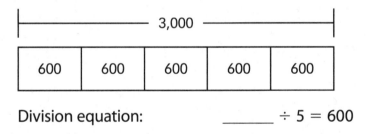

		3,000		
600	600	600	600	600

Division equation: _____ $\div$ 5 = 600

Multiplication equation: _____ $\times$ _____ = _____

2 Multiply.

$4 \times 700 =$ _____

$6 \times 300 =$ _____

$3 \times 900 =$ _____

3 Write the missing numbers in the equation.

$5 \times 743 = ($ _____ $\times 700) + ($ _____ $\times 40) + ($ _____ $\times 3)$

$=$ _____ $+$ _____ $+$ _____

$=$ _____

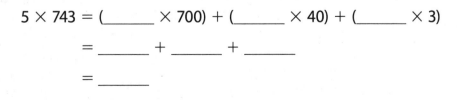

Solve.

4 Write numbers in the area model below to show 6 × 925. Then complete the equation.

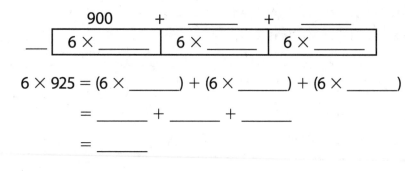

900 + _____ + _____

| 6 × _____ | 6 × _____ | 6 × _____ |

6 × 925 = (6 × _____) + (6 × _____) + (6 × _____)

= _____ + _____ + _____

= _____

5 Multiply. 3 × 213 = ?

Show your work.

Solution: 3 × 213 = _____

6 For each division equation below, write a related multiplication equation. The first one is done for you.

900 ÷ 3 = ? **3 × 300 = 900**

600 ÷ 3 = ? _____

30 ÷ 3 = ? _____

9 ÷ 3 = ? _____

7 Heidi drove to visit her grandparents last weekend. She drove 215 miles each way. This weekend she drove to her friend's house. It was 174 miles each way. How many miles did she drive altogether on both weekends?

Show your work.

You can multiply by 2 to find the distance Heidi drove each weekend.

Solution: Heidi drove _____ miles.

Name: _____

Divide Three-Digit Numbers by One-Digit Numbers

Study the example problem showing how to divide a three-digit number by a one-digit number. Then solve problems 1–6.

Example

Muffins are packed and sold in boxes of 4.
How many boxes are needed to pack 260 muffins?

$260 \div 4 = ?$

Use an area model.

$260 \div 4 = 65$

	50	**+**	**10**	**+**	**5**	**= 65**
4	(4 × 50 = 200)		(4 × 10 = 40)		(4 × 5 = 20)	
	260		60		20	
	− 200		− 40		− 20	
	60		20		0	

65 boxes are needed.

Use multiplication to check:

$4 \times 65 = (4 \times 60) + (4 \times 5)$
$= 240 + 20$
$= 260$

1 Use the example above. Show how to subtract partial products to divide 260 by 4.

2 Identify the dividend, divisor, and quotient.

a. $900 \div 3 = 300$

dividend: _____ divisor: _____ quotient: _____

b. $120 = 600 \div 5$

dividend: _____ divisor: _____ quotient: _____

Vocabulary

dividend the number you divide in a division problem.

divisor the number you divide by in a division problem.

quotient the answer to a division problem.

dividend ÷ divisor = quotient
260 ÷ 4 = 65

$$\overset{\text{quotient}}{\text{divisor}\,\overline{)\text{dividend}}} \qquad \overset{65}{4\overline{)260}}$$

Solve.

3 A health center raised $476. The money was divided equally among 7 programs. How much did each program get? Use an area model to solve the problem.

Show your work.

Solution: _____

4 Mike has 876 building pieces to share among himself and 2 friends. He wants each person to have an equal number of pieces. How many pieces does each person get?

Show your work.

Solution: _____

5 Look at how you solved problem 4. Explain how you could have used estimation before you divided so that you would know whether your answer was reasonable.

_____

_____

_____

6 Explain how to use multiplication to check your answer in problem 4.

_____

_____

Name: _____

Divide Four-Digit Numbers by One-Digit Numbers

Study the example problem showing how to divide a four-digit number by a one-digit number. Then solve problems 1–5.

Example

A group of hikers plan to take 8 hours to hike a mountain trail 5,380 meters long. If they hike the same distance each hour, how many meters should they hike in an hour?

5,380 ÷ 8 = 672 R4

The hikers should hike 672 meters each hour. Then they will need to hike 4 more meters to reach the end of the trail.

The sum of the partial quotients is 600 + 70 + 2 , or 672. The remainder is 4.

```
        2
       70
      600
   8)5,380  ──→ There are 600 groups of 8 in 5,000.
   − 4,800  ──→ Subtract 600 groups of 8; 8 × 600.
      580   ──→ There are 70 groups of 8 in 580.
   −  560   ──→ Subtract 70 groups of 8; 8 × 70.
       20   ──→ There are 2 groups of 8 in 20.
   −   16   ──→ Subtract 2 groups of 8; 8 × 2.
        4
```

1 Complete the division problem.

8,236 ÷ 5 = _____

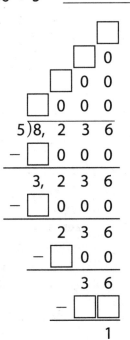

2 Complete the division problem.

4,507 ÷ 4 = _____

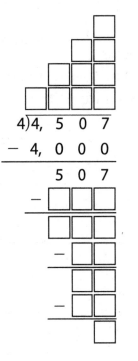

Solve.

3 One week has 7 days. How many weeks do 1,230 days make? What does the remainder mean?

Show your work.

Solution: _____

4 Mugs are packed 6 to a box. How many boxes are needed to pack 1,524 mugs?

Show your work.

Solution: _____

5 Tyson used a calculator to find the quotient for each of the problems below. Use estimation to tell whether each quotient is *Correct* or *Incorrect*.

a. $4,960 \div 2 = 9,920$ ☐ Correct ☐ Incorrect

b. $7,095 \div 5 = 1,419$ ☐ Correct ☐ Incorrect

c. $9,621 \div 3 = 230$ R7 ☐ Correct ☐ Incorrect

d. $3,875 \div 6 = 645$ R5 ☐ Correct ☐ Incorrect

6 Explain how you used estimation to tell which quotients were incorrect in problem 5.

_____

_____

_____

_____

_____

_____

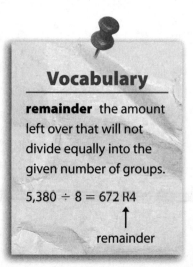

Vocabulary

remainder the amount left over that will not divide equally into the given number of groups.

$5,380 \div 8 = 672$ R4
↑
remainder

Name: _____

Divide Whole Numbers

Solve the problems.

1 Find the quotient.

$$3{,}752 \div 6$$

A 652   **C** 625

B 652 R2   **D** 625 R2

> To check the quotient, multiply it by the divisor and add any remainder.

2 Carter has a pack of 800 rubber bands. Alicia has twice as many rubber bands as Carter. They combine their rubber bands so that they can make bracelets. Each bracelet needs 100 rubber bands. Which equation below can be used to find how many bracelets they can make?

> Drawing a model or picture can help make sense of this problem.

A $(800 \times 2) \div 100$ **C** $(800 \div 100) \times 2$

B $(800 \times 3) \div 100$ **D** $(800 \times 100) \div 3$

Jon chose **A** as the correct answer. How did he get that answer?

_____

_____

3 Tell whether each sentence is *True* or *False*.

a. $5{,}497 \div 4 = 1{,}374$ ☐ True ☐ False

b. $4{,}806 \div 6 = 81$ ☐ True ☐ False

c. $955 \div 5 = 191$ ☐ True ☐ False

d. $642 \div 8 = 82$ ☐ True ☐ False

> What does it mean to have a zero place value in the dividend?

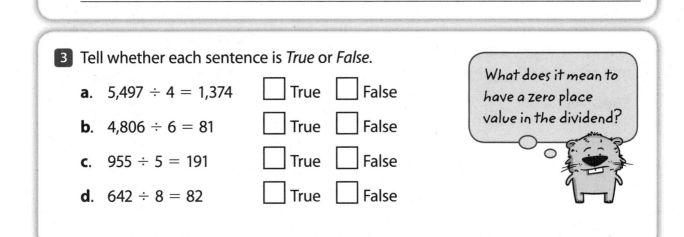

Solve.

4 Chloe and Ingrid are packing boxes with books. They have 238 books. Each box will fit 8 books. Chloe says 29 boxes is enough to pack all the books. Ingrid thinks they need 30 boxes. Explain who is correct.

What does the remainder mean in this problem?

Show your work.

Solution: _____

5 Carolyn has 1,090 photos that she wants to organize into an album. Each album page holds 6 photos. How many pages can she fill with 6 photos each?

Divide each place value in the dividend, 1,090, by the divisor, 6.

Show your work.

Solution: _____

6 In 4 weeks, a school raised $2,560 for Health and Fitness awareness. Students collected donations 5 days each week. The principal agreed to make one donation that was the same as the amount collected in a day. If an equal amount was collected each day, how much did the principal donate?

This looks like a multi-step problem. To start, what number do you divide 2,560 by?

Show your work.

Solution: _____

Unit 3 Game

Multiplication Products

What you need: Recording Sheet, 2 sets of digit cards (0–9)

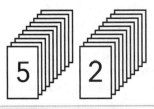

$$6\,4 \times 3\,9$$

Directions

- Mix the cards and place them facedown in a stack. (Before each new round, you'll need to place the cards back in the stack and shuffle them again.)

- In Rounds 1 and 2, each player draws 4 cards. Players use the numbers on their cards to make 2 two-digit numbers. Players record their numbers on the Recording Sheet and multiply them. In Round 1, the player with the greater product wins the round. In Round 2, the player with the lesser product wins the round.

- In Rounds 3 and 4, each player draws 5 cards. Players use the numbers on their cards to make a four-digit and a one-digit-number. Players record their numbers on the Recording Sheet and multiply them. In Round 3, the player with the greater product wins. In Round 4, the player with the lesser product wins.

- In Round 5, players choose a round from Rounds 1–4 to repeat.

- The winner is the player with more wins after 5 rounds.

Multiplication Products Recording Sheet

Name: _____

⭐ ☆

Rosa
Player A Name

Henry
Player B Name

Round 1: Multiply a two-digit number by a two-digit number. Circle the _greater_ product.

1. __64__ × __39__ = (2,496)   1. __71__ × __28__ = _1,988_

Round 2: Multiply a two-digit number by a two-digit number. Circle the _lesser_ product.

2. ____ × ____ = _____   2. ____ × ____ = _____

> I multiplied 64 by 39 and got a product of 2,496. My product is greater than your product of 1,988, so I win the first round.

Multiplication Products Recording Sheet

_____   _____
Player A Name   **Player B Name**

Round 1: Multiply a two-digit number by a two-digit number. Circle the <u>greater</u> product.

1. _____ × _____ = _____   1. _____ × _____ = _____

Round 2: Multiply a two-digit number by a two-digit number. Circle the <u>lesser</u> product.

2. _____ × _____ = _____   2. _____ × _____ = _____

Round 3: Multiply a four-digit number by a one-digit number. Circle the <u>greater</u> product.

3. _____ × _____ = _____   3. _____ × _____ = _____

Round 4: Multiply a four-digit number by a one-digit number. Circle the <u>lesser</u> product.

4. _____ × _____ = _____   4. _____ × _____ = _____

Round 5: Choose Round 1, 2, 3, or 4 to repeat.

5. _____ × _____ = _____   5. _____ × _____ = _____

Final Score Player A _____   **Final Score Player B** _____

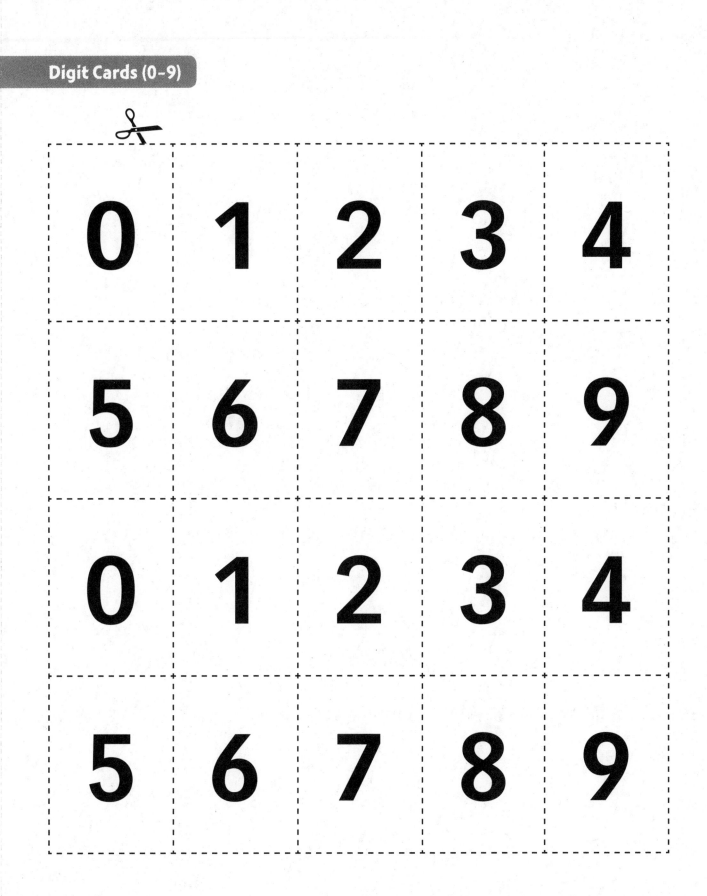

Unit 3 Practice

Name: _____

Numbers and Operations in Base Ten, Part 2

In this unit you learned to:	Lesson
multiply a 4-digit number by a 1-digit number, for example: 2,810 × 3 = 8,430.	11
multiply a 2-digit number by a 2-digit number, for example: 62 × 33 = 2,046.	11
divide a 4-digit number by a 1-digit number, for example: 6,328 ÷ 4 = 1,582.	12
use area models and equations to explain calculations, for example: 7 × 240 = (7 × 200) + (7 × 40).	11, 12

Use these skills to solve problems 1–5.

1 Write numbers in each section of the area model to complete the model. Then write the product to complete the equation. Use numbers from the gray number bank at the right to complete the model and the equation.

4	8	10
20	30	32
40	50	68
160	272	432

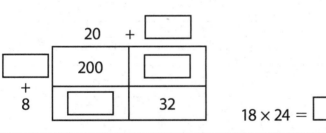

$18 \times 24 = \boxed{}$

2 Use numbers from the gray number bank in problem 1. Write numbers in each section of the area model to complete the model. Then write the quotient to complete the equation.

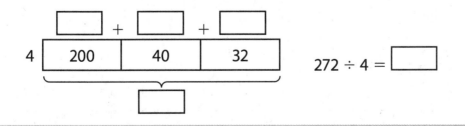

$272 \div 4 = \boxed{}$

For problems 3–5, circle the error in the student work. Then find the correct solution to the problem.

3 Circle the error.	Find the correct solution.
3,490 × 5 = (3,000 × 5) + (400 × 9) + (90 × 5)	3,490 × 5

4 Circle the error.	Find the correct solution.
$$\begin{array}{r} 61 \\ \times\ 23 \\ \hline 3 \\ 18 \\ 20 \\ +\ 1,200 \\ \hline 1,159 \end{array}$$	$$\begin{array}{r} 61 \\ \times\ 23 \\ \hline \end{array}$$

5 Circle the error.	Find the correct solution.
$$\begin{array}{r} 6 \\ 30 \\ 300 \\ 8\overline{)2,494} \\ -\ 2,200 \\ \hline 294 \\ -\ 2400 \\ \hline 54 \\ -\ 48 \\ \hline 6 \end{array}$$	$8\overline{)2,494}$ 2,494 ÷ 8 = _____

Name: _____

Answer the questions and show all your work on separate paper.

Wooddale Summer Camp has 250 campers. Dan, the arts and crafts counselor, is planning two art projects.

For the paper project, each camper needs 8 sheets of paper and 3 bottles of paint. For the yarn project, each camper needs 2 balls of yarn and 9 wooden beads.

Dan has $4,000 to spend. The table below shows the cost of supplies. Use the information in the table to create a plan. In your plan, tell how many campers can do each art project and the total cost. Explain how you know that Dan can use your plan.

Supplies	Quantity in Package	Cost
Paper	5,000 sheets	$115
Paint	6 bottles	$8
Yarn	9 balls	$74
Beads	1,000 beads	$33

Reflect on Mathematical Practices

After you complete the task, choose one of the following questions to answer.

1 **Model** How did you use equations to solve the problem?

2 **Make Sense of Problems** How did you find how many supplies were needed for the number of campers you chose?

> **Checklist**
>
> Did you . . .
>
> ☐ create a plan?
>
> ☐ check your calculations?
>
> ☐ give a clear explanation?

Performance Task Tips

Word Bank Here are some words that you might use in your answer.

product	multiply	divide
remainder	quotient	need
each	total	compare

Model Here is a model that you might use to find the solution.

Supplies	Number for Each Camper	Number of Campers	Packages Needed	Cost
Paper				
Paint				
Yarn				
Beads				

Sentence Starters Here are some sentence starters that might help you write an explanation.

In my plan, _____ campers do _____

For each art project, I multiply _____

To find how many packages are needed, I divide _____

I compare the total cost to _____ in order to _____

Unit 3 Vocabulary

Name: _____

My Examples

multiplication

> an operation used to find the total number of items in equal-sized groups

product

> the result of multiplication

factors

> numbers that are multiplied together to get a product

multiple

> the product of a number and any other whole number; for example, 3, 6, 9, 12, and 15 are multiples of 3

My Examples

quotient

the answer to a division problem

dividend

the number you divide in a division problem

divisor

the number you divide by in a division problem

remainder

the amount left over that will not divide equally into the given number of groups

Dear Family,

This week your child is exploring equivalent fractions.

equivalent fractions: two or more fractions that name the same amount of a whole.

numerator: the top number in a fraction; it tells the number of parts in a whole that are being described.

denominator: the bottom number in a fraction; it tells the total number of equal parts in a whole.

You can show the equivalent fractions $\frac{1}{3}$, $\frac{2}{6}$, and $\frac{4}{12}$ with models.

The model at the right is divided into 3 equal parts. The shaded section shows the fraction $\frac{1}{3}$.

$\frac{1}{3}$

The same model can be divided into 6 equal parts. It has 2 times as many parts shaded and 2 times as many equal parts. The shaded section shows the fraction $\frac{2}{6}$.

$\frac{2}{6}$

The same model can be divided again into 12 equal parts. Now it has 4 times as many parts shaded and 4 times as many equal parts. The shaded section shows the fraction $\frac{4}{12}$.

$\frac{4}{12}$

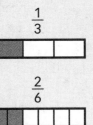

Another way to find equivalent fractions is to multiply both the numerator and denominator of a fraction by the same number. This is the same as multiplying by 1 because $\frac{2}{2} = 1$ and $\frac{4}{4} = 1$.

$\frac{1 \times 2}{3 \times 2} = \frac{2}{6}$

$\frac{1 \times 4}{3 \times 4} = \frac{4}{12}$

Invite your child to share what he or she knows about equivalent fractions by doing the following activity together.

NEXT

Equivalent Fractions Activity

Do an activity with your child to explore equivalent fractions.

Materials: recipe ingredients, $\frac{1}{8}$-cup measuring cup, and soup pot (all optional)

Look at the recipe below for Mexican Bean Soup. Then follow the steps below to find equivalent fractions.

- Suppose the only measuring cup available is a $\frac{1}{8}$-cup measuring cup. Rewrite the recipe so all the ingredients can be measured using only the $\frac{1}{8}$-cup measuring cup. (This means that you will find equivalent fractions with 8 as the denominator.)

- Discuss how the numerator relates to using the $\frac{1}{8}$-cup to measure each ingredient. (The numerator is the number of times the measuring cup is filled.)

- Make the recipe for your family to enjoy.

Recipe for
Mexican Bean Soup

Ingredients:

$\frac{4}{4}$ cup stewed tomatoes

$\frac{3}{4}$ cup canned black beans with liquid

$\frac{1}{2}$ cup cooked rice

$\frac{1}{4}$ cup salsa

Directions:

Mix all the ingredients together in a soup pot.

Stir. Heat and serve. Enjoy!

Understand
Equivalent Fractions

Name: _____

> **Prerequisite: How do you know when fractions are equivalent?**

Study the example showing one way to find equivalent fractions. Then solve problems 1–6.

Example

Find a fraction equivalent to $\frac{4}{6}$.

The number line shows both thirds and sixths.

$\frac{4}{6}$ and $\frac{2}{3}$ are at the same point on the number line.

$$\frac{4}{6} = \frac{2}{3}$$

0      $\frac{1}{3}$ $\frac{2}{3}$ 1

0   $\frac{1}{6}$ $\frac{2}{6}$ $\frac{3}{6}$ $\frac{4}{6}$ $\frac{5}{6}$ 1

1 Look at the number line in the example above. Write a fraction equivalent to $\frac{2}{6}$.

$$\frac{2}{6} = \text{_____}$$

2 Fill in the missing fractions on the number line.

0     $\frac{1}{4}$ _____ $\frac{3}{4}$ $\frac{4}{4}$

0   $\frac{1}{8}$ ___   ___ $\frac{4}{8}$ $\frac{5}{8}$ ___ $\frac{7}{8}$ $\frac{8}{8}$

3 Look at the number line in problem 2.

Write equivalent fractions.

$$\frac{1}{4} = \text{_____} \qquad \text{_____} = \frac{4}{8} \qquad \frac{3}{4} = \text{_____}$$

Solve.

4 Look at the models below. Shade the models to show two fractions equivalent to $\frac{3}{4}$. Then write the fractions.

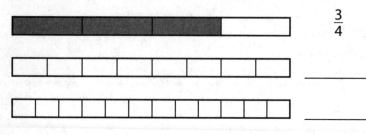

$\frac{3}{4}$

_____

_____

5 Use the models below to complete the sentences. The models show wholes and parts. There are 3 wholes, each divided into fourths.

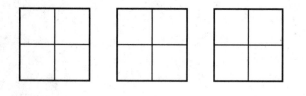

Each part is _____ of a whole.

There are _____ fourths in all. $\dfrac{\boxed{}}{\boxed{}} = 3$

6 Look at the models below. Write the fractions they represent. Are the fractions equivalent? Explain.

_____

_____

_____

_____

_____

Name: _____

Show Equivalent Fractions

Study the example showing one way to model equivalent fractions. Then solve problems 1–8.

Example

A model can show equivalent fractions.

The model has 5 equal parts. It shows $\frac{3}{5}$.

Divide the model into 10 equal parts to show an equivalent fraction.

The model shows $\frac{6}{10}$.

$\frac{3}{5} = \frac{6}{10}$

1 Divide the model below to show $\frac{1}{2} = \frac{5}{10}$.

2 Draw a model to show $\frac{1}{6}$. Then divide the model into twice as many parts to find an equivalent fraction.

$\frac{1}{6} =$ _____

3 Multiply the numerator and denominator of $\frac{1}{6}$ by 2.

$\frac{1 \times 2}{6 \times 2} =$ _____

4 Why does it make sense that the fraction you wrote in problems 2 and 3 is the same?

_____

_____

Solve.

5 Fill in the missing numbers to find two equivalent fractions to $\frac{4}{5}$.

$$\frac{4 \times \boxed{}}{5 \times 2} = \frac{\boxed{}}{10} \qquad \frac{4 \times 20}{5 \times 20} = \frac{\boxed{}}{100}$$

6 Look at problem 5. Explain how $\frac{8}{10} = \frac{80}{100}$.

_____

_____

_____

_____

_____

_____

_____

7 Shade the model below to show $\frac{1}{5}$. Then show 10 equal parts and write an equivalent fraction.

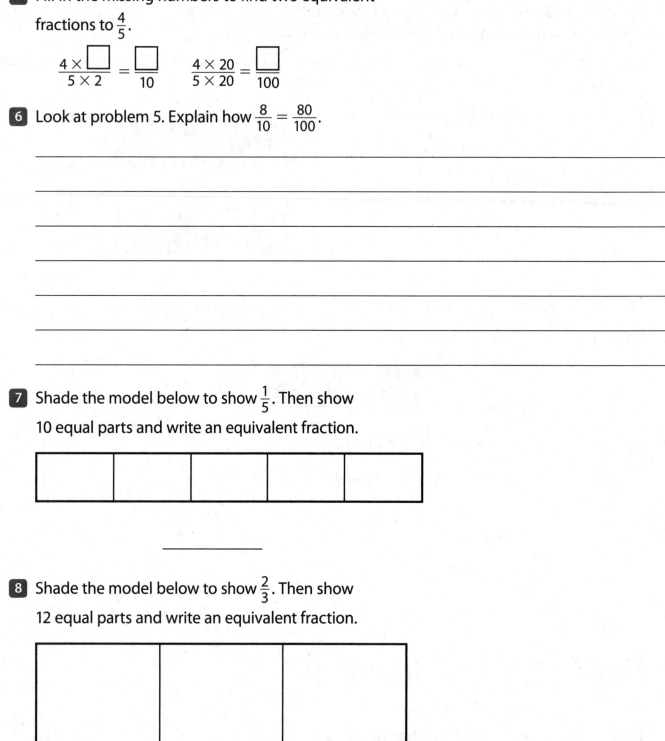

_____

8 Shade the model below to show $\frac{2}{3}$. Then show 12 equal parts and write an equivalent fraction.

_____

Name: _____

Reason and Write

Study the example. Underline two parts that you think make it a particularly good answer and a helpful example.

Example

Find a fraction equivalent to $\frac{1}{2}$ that has a denominator of 12.

Show your work. Use models, words, and numbers to explain your answer.

I draw a model that shows $\frac{1}{2}$.

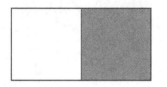

To find an equivalent fraction with a denominator of 12, I divide the model into 12 equal parts. The model shows $\frac{6}{12}$. So $\frac{1}{2} = \frac{6}{12}$.

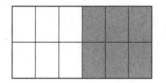

I can also multiply both the numerator and denominator of $\frac{1}{2}$ by 6 to find an equivalent fraction with a denominator of 12.

$$\frac{1 \times 6}{2 \times 6} = \frac{6}{12}$$

> Where does the example . . .
>
> • use models to show equivalent fractions?
>
> • use numbers to write equivalent fractions?
>
> • use words to explain?

Lesson 13 Understand Equivalent Fractions **153**

Solve the problem. Use what you learned from the example.

Find a fraction equivalent to $\frac{2}{5}$ that has a denominator of 20.

Show your work. Use models, words, and numbers to explain your answer.

Did you . . .

• use models to show equivalent fractions?

• use numbers to write equivalent fractions?

• use words to explain?

Dear Family,

This week your child is learning to compare fractions.

There are different ways to compare fractions.

One way to compare fractions like $\frac{2}{4}$ and $\frac{2}{5}$ is to use models. You must use the same-size whole for both. If the wholes are different sizes, it doesn't make sense to compare the parts. Each whole model below is the same size.

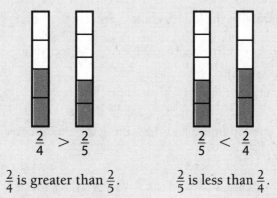

$$\frac{2}{4} > \frac{2}{5} \qquad \frac{2}{5} < \frac{2}{4}$$

$\frac{2}{4}$ is greater than $\frac{2}{5}$. $\qquad$ $\frac{2}{5}$ is less than $\frac{2}{4}$.

Another way to compare fractions is to write equivalent fractions with the same denominators. Using the same denominators means that there are the same number of parts in each whole. Then you can compare the numerators to find which fraction has a greater number of parts.

$$\frac{2 \times 4}{5 \times 4} = \frac{8}{20} \qquad \frac{2 \times 5}{4 \times 5} = \frac{10}{20}$$

$$\frac{8}{20} < \frac{10}{20}, \text{ so } \frac{2}{5} < \frac{2}{4}$$

Your child might also use a number line to compare fractions by comparing each fraction to a benchmark fraction, such as $\frac{1}{2}$.

Invite your child to share what he or she knows about comparing fractions by doing the following activity together.

NEXT

Lesson 14 Compare Fractions   **155**

Comparing Fractions Activity

Do an activity with your child to compare fractions.

Materials: 4 same-size clear glasses, colored liquid

- Fill one glass to the top with colored liquid. This glass represents 1 whole. Fill another glass half full to represent $\frac{1}{2}$. Leave a third glass empty to represent 0.

- Pour any amount of liquid into the fourth glass. Compare the fourth glass to the full glass and the empty glass to determine if the amount of liquid is closer to 0 or to 1. Then determine if the amount of liquid in the fourth glass is greater than or less than $\frac{1}{2}$.

- You can check your answer by comparing the fourth glass to the glass that is half full.

- Now empty the fourth glass. Take turns filling it with various amounts of colored liquid and describing the quantity as greater than or less than $\frac{1}{2}$.

- Talk with your child about why it is important that the four glasses are the same size and shape. (Half of a tall glass is a different amount of liquid than half of a short glass.)

©Curriculum Associates, LLC   Copying is not permitted.

Compare Fractions

Name: _____

Prerequisite: Model Comparing Fractions

Study the example problem showing ways to compare fractions. Then solve problems 1–9.

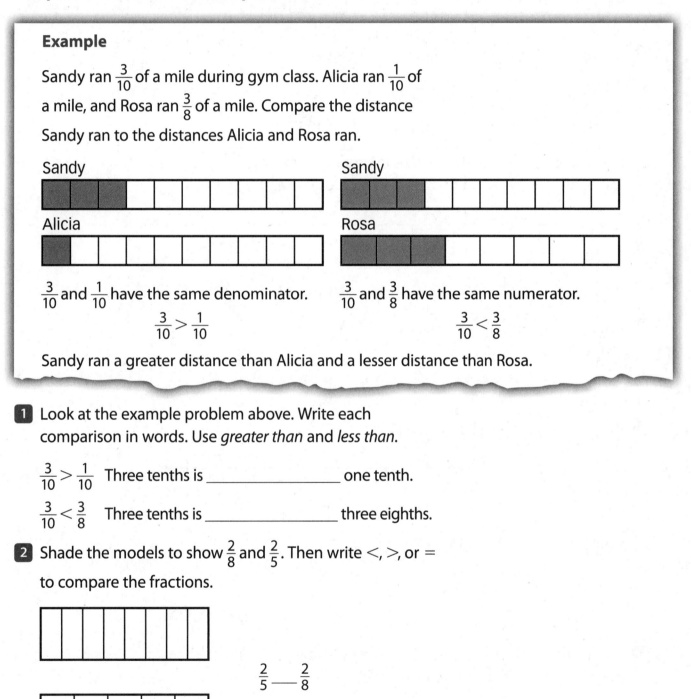

Example

Sandy ran $\frac{3}{10}$ of a mile during gym class. Alicia ran $\frac{1}{10}$ of a mile, and Rosa ran $\frac{3}{8}$ of a mile. Compare the distance Sandy ran to the distances Alicia and Rosa ran.

Sandy

Alicia

Sandy

Rosa

$\frac{3}{10}$ and $\frac{1}{10}$ have the same denominator.

$$\frac{3}{10} > \frac{1}{10}$$

$\frac{3}{10}$ and $\frac{3}{8}$ have the same numerator.

$$\frac{3}{10} < \frac{3}{8}$$

Sandy ran a greater distance than Alicia and a lesser distance than Rosa.

1 Look at the example problem above. Write each comparison in words. Use *greater than* and *less than*.

$\frac{3}{10} > \frac{1}{10}$ Three tenths is _____ one tenth.

$\frac{3}{10} < \frac{3}{8}$ Three tenths is _____ three eighths.

2 Shade the models to show $\frac{2}{8}$ and $\frac{2}{5}$. Then write <, >, or = to compare the fractions.

$$\frac{2}{5} \underline{} \frac{2}{8}$$

Solve.

3 Shade the models to show $\frac{5}{12}$ and $\frac{7}{12}$.

4 Compare $\frac{5}{12}$ and $\frac{7}{12}$ using symbols and words.

$$\frac{5}{12} \underline{\hspace{1cm}} \frac{7}{12}$$

Five twelfths is _____ seven twelfths.

5 Explain how you used the models in problem 3 to show how the two fractions compare in problem 4.

_____

_____

_____

6 Label $\frac{7}{8}$ on the number line below.

0   1

7 Label $\frac{7}{12}$ on the number line below.

0   1

8 Compare $\frac{7}{8}$ and $\frac{7}{12}$ using symbols and words.

$$\frac{7}{8} \underline{\hspace{1cm}} \frac{7}{12}$$

Seven _____ is _____ seven twelfths.

9 Explain how you used the number lines in problems 6 and 7 to show how the two fractions compare in problem 8.

_____

_____

Name: _____

Find a Common Numerator or Denominator

Study the example problem showing how to compare fractions by finding a common denominator. Then solve problems 1–7.

Example

A length of ribbon is $\frac{3}{4}$ foot. Another length of ribbon is $\frac{5}{6}$ foot. Compare the lengths using a symbol.

Find a common denominator. $\quad \frac{3 \times 3}{4 \times 3} = \frac{9}{12} \qquad \frac{5 \times 2}{6 \times 2} = \frac{10}{12}$

Write the equivalent fractions. $\qquad \frac{3}{4} = \frac{9}{12} \qquad\qquad \frac{5}{6} = \frac{10}{12}$

Compare the numerators. $\qquad\qquad\qquad \frac{9}{12} < \frac{10}{12}$

$9 < 10$ so $\frac{9}{12} < \frac{10}{12}$

$\frac{3}{4} < \frac{5}{6}$

1 Shade the models below to show $\frac{3}{4}$ and $\frac{5}{6}$.

Fill in the blank to show the comparison. $\frac{3}{4}$ ___ $\frac{5}{6}$

2 Divide each model in problem 1 into 12 equal parts to show an equivalent fraction. Write the equivalent fractions and symbol to show the comparison.

$\dfrac{\square}{12}$ ___ $\dfrac{\square}{12}$

3 Compare $\frac{2}{3}$ and $\frac{9}{12}$ by finding a common denominator.

a. Write a fraction equivalent to $\frac{2}{3}$ with a denominator of 12.

$\dfrac{2 \times \square}{3 \times \square} = \dfrac{\square}{12}$

b. Compare the fractions. $\dfrac{\square}{12}$ ___ $\dfrac{9}{12}$. So, $\dfrac{2}{3}$ ___ $\dfrac{9}{12}$.

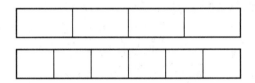

Solve.

4 Compare $\frac{1}{5}$ and $\frac{2}{12}$ by finding a common numerator.

a. Write a fraction equivalent to $\frac{1}{5}$ with a numerator of 2.

$$\frac{1 \times \boxed{}}{5 \times \boxed{}} = \frac{2}{\boxed{}}$$

b. Compare the fractions. $\frac{2}{\boxed{}}$ —— $\frac{2}{12}$. So, $\frac{1}{5}$ —— $\frac{2}{12}$.

5 Compare the fractions. Use the symbols $<$, $>$, and $=$.

a. $\frac{2}{5}$ —— $\frac{8}{10}$

b. $\frac{5}{12}$ —— $\frac{1}{3}$

c. $\frac{3}{5}$ —— $\frac{60}{100}$

d. $\frac{9}{100}$ —— $\frac{9}{10}$

6 Tell whether each sentence is *True* or *False*.

a. $\frac{2}{3} > \frac{5}{6}$ ☐ True ☐ False

b. $\frac{4}{10} < \frac{4}{5}$ ☐ True ☐ False

c. $\frac{70}{100} = \frac{7}{10}$ ☐ True ☐ False

d. $\frac{1}{3} > \frac{3}{1}$ ☐ True ☐ False

e. $\frac{3}{4} < \frac{2}{3}$ ☐ True ☐ False

7 Can two fractions with the same numerator and different denominators be equal? Use words and numbers to explain.

_____

_____

_____

_____

_____

Name: _____

Use a Benchmark to Compare Fractions

Study the example problem using 1 as a benchmark to compare fractions. Then solve problems 1–4.

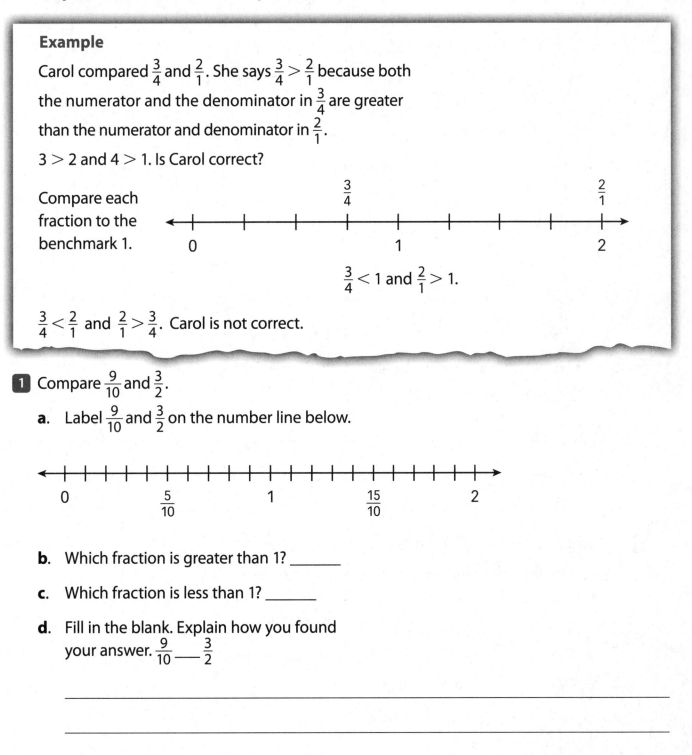

Example

Carol compared $\frac{3}{4}$ and $\frac{2}{1}$. She says $\frac{3}{4} > \frac{2}{1}$ because both the numerator and the denominator in $\frac{3}{4}$ are greater than the numerator and denominator in $\frac{2}{1}$.

$3 > 2$ and $4 > 1$. Is Carol correct?

Compare each fraction to the benchmark 1.

$\frac{3}{4} < 1$ and $\frac{2}{1} > 1$.

$\frac{3}{4} < \frac{2}{1}$ and $\frac{2}{1} > \frac{3}{4}$. Carol is not correct.

1 Compare $\frac{9}{10}$ and $\frac{3}{2}$.

a. Label $\frac{9}{10}$ and $\frac{3}{2}$ on the number line below.

b. Which fraction is greater than 1? _____

c. Which fraction is less than 1? _____

d. Fill in the blank. Explain how you found your answer. $\frac{9}{10}$ ___ $\frac{3}{2}$

_____

_____

_____

Solve.

2 Compare $\frac{5}{6}$ and $\frac{1}{3}$ using the benchmark fraction $\frac{1}{2}$.

a. Label $\frac{5}{6}$ and $\frac{1}{3}$ on the number line below.

0                                 $\frac{1}{2}$ 1

b. Which fraction is greater than $\frac{1}{2}$? _____

c. Which fraction is less than $\frac{1}{2}$? _____

d. Fill in the blank. Explain how you found your answer.

$$\frac{5}{6} \underline{\quad\quad} \frac{1}{3}$$

_____

_____

_____

3 Use a benchmark fraction to compare the fractions $\frac{7}{10}$ and $\frac{5}{12}$. Explain how you found your answer.

_____

_____

_____

4 Tell whether each number sentence is *True* or *False*.

Then write the benchmark you could use to compare the fractions.

                                           Benchmark

a. $\frac{9}{8} > \frac{11}{12}$ ☐ True   ☐ False   _____

b. $\frac{2}{5} < \frac{5}{6}$ ☐ True   ☐ False   _____

c. $\frac{7}{10} < \frac{2}{4}$ ☐ True   ☐ False   _____

d. $\frac{4}{5} > \frac{2}{2}$ ☐ True   ☐ False   _____

e. $\frac{3}{2} < \frac{9}{10}$ ☐ True   ☐ False   _____

Name: _____

Compare Fractions

Solve the problems.

1. Which of the following is greater than $\frac{2}{3}$?

   Circle all that apply.

   A $\frac{3}{4}$ **C** $\frac{8}{12}$

   B $\frac{5}{6}$ **D** $\frac{3}{2}$

   > Find a common denominator for each pair of fractions.

2. Harry ate $\frac{5}{8}$ of a sandwich. Sven ate $\frac{2}{5}$ of a sandwich. Micah ate $\frac{3}{4}$ of a sandwich. Gabe ate $\frac{6}{12}$ of a sandwich. Who ate the most of his sandwich?

   A Harry   **C** Micah

   B Sven   **D** Gabe

   > Compare each fraction to the benchmarks $\frac{1}{2}$ and 1.

3. Erica and Matt earn the same amount of money each month. Erica saves $\frac{3}{10}$ of her earnings. Matt saves $\frac{3}{6}$ of his earnings. Which explanation correctly tells who saves more?

   A Erica saves more because tenths are greater than sixths.

   B Matt saves less because sixths are less than tenths.

   C Erica saves more because $\frac{3}{10} < \frac{3}{6}$.

   D Matt saves more because $\frac{3}{6} > \frac{3}{10}$.

   Fran chose **C** as the correct answer. How did she get that answer?

   _____

   _____

   _____

   > Can using a benchmark fraction help solve this problem?

Solve.

4 Melanie read 45 pages of a 100-page book. Her younger sister read $\frac{1}{2}$ of a 10-page book. Who read a greater fraction of her book, Melanie or her sister?

Show your work.

> One fraction has a denominator of 100; the other fraction has a denominator of 10.

Solution: _____

5 Compare $\frac{5}{4}$ and $\frac{9}{10}$. Describe two methods you could use to compare the fractions.

$$\frac{5}{4} \underline{\hspace{1cm}} \frac{9}{10}$$

Method A _____

_____

_____

_____

Method B _____

_____

_____

_____

_____

> Some ways to compare fractions are finding a common denominator, finding a common numerator, and using a benchmark.

Dear Family,

This week your child is exploring fraction addition and subtraction.

Adding fractions means joining or putting together parts of the same whole. When you add $\frac{2}{4} + \frac{3}{4}$, you are putting one-fourths together.

You can use a number line to show $\frac{2}{4} + \frac{3}{4}$.

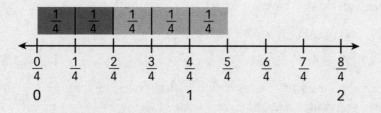

Subtracting fractions means separating or taking away. You can use a number line to show fraction subtraction, too.

The number line below shows a segment of length $\frac{5}{4}$. Take away a segment of length $\frac{2}{4}$ to show $\frac{5}{4} - \frac{2}{4}$.

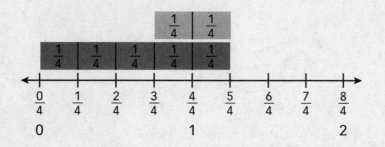

Adding and subtracting fractions is just like adding and subtracting whole numbers. When the denominators of the fractions are the same, you can just add or subtract the numerators.

Invite your child to share what he or she knows about fraction addition and subtraction by doing the following activity together.

NEXT

Lesson 15 Understand Fraction Addition and Subtraction

Fraction Addition and Subtraction Activity

Do an activity with your child to explore adding and subtracting fractions.

Materials: one piece of fruit (or a picture of one piece of fruit)

- Cut the fruit (or the picture of the fruit) into sixths.

- Have your child take some of the pieces. You take some of the pieces.

- Now talk about putting your pieces of fruit together. How much of the whole fruit do you have together?

    Example: Your child takes $\frac{2}{6}$. You take $\frac{3}{6}$.
    Together you have $\frac{5}{6}$ of the fruit.

- Put your and your child's pieces of fruit together and look at the total. Have your child take (and eat!) some of the pieces. How much of the whole fruit is left?

    Example: Your child takes 3 pieces.
    Start with $\frac{5}{6}$. Take away $\frac{3}{6}$.
    That means $\frac{2}{6}$ of the fruit is left.

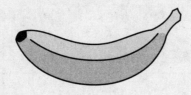

Look for other real-life opportunities to practice exploring adding and subtracting fractions with your child.

Understand
Fraction Addition and Subtraction

Name: _____

Prerequisite: **How do you show fractions with number lines and area models?**

Study the example problem showing fractions with number lines and area models. Then solve problems 1–7.

Example

How can you draw two different models to show $\frac{3}{4}$?

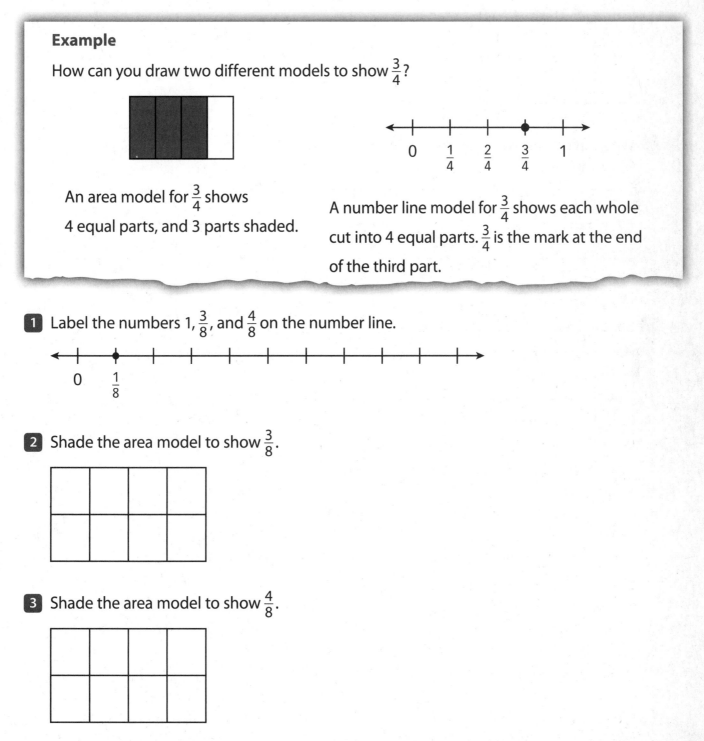

An area model for $\frac{3}{4}$ shows
4 equal parts, and 3 parts shaded.

A number line model for $\frac{3}{4}$ shows each whole cut into 4 equal parts. $\frac{3}{4}$ is the mark at the end of the third part.

1 Label the numbers 1, $\frac{3}{8}$, and $\frac{4}{8}$ on the number line.

2 Shade the area model to show $\frac{3}{8}$.

3 Shade the area model to show $\frac{4}{8}$.

Solve.

4 Show the numbers $\frac{8}{8}$ and $\frac{10}{8}$ on the number line.

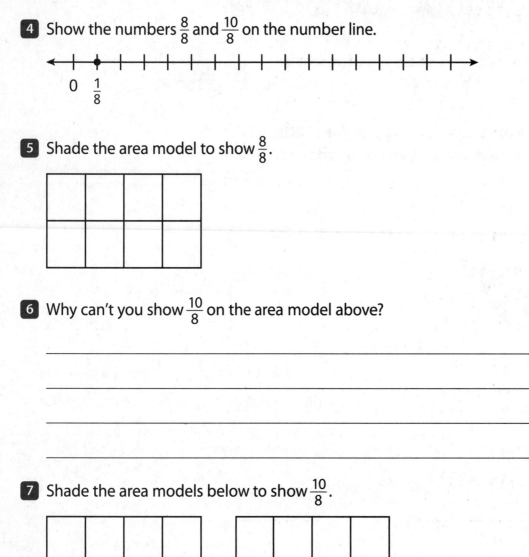

0   $\frac{1}{8}$

5 Shade the area model to show $\frac{8}{8}$.

6 Why can't you show $\frac{10}{8}$ on the area model above?

_____

_____

_____

_____

7 Shade the area models below to show $\frac{10}{8}$.

Name: _____

Show Adding and Subtracting Fractions

Study how the example shows adding fractions.
Then solve problems 1–12.

Example

You can count on or count back to add or subtract whole numbers.
You can do the same to add or subtract fractions.

To add fourths, use a number line that shows fourths.

Add $\frac{3}{4} + \frac{2}{4}$.

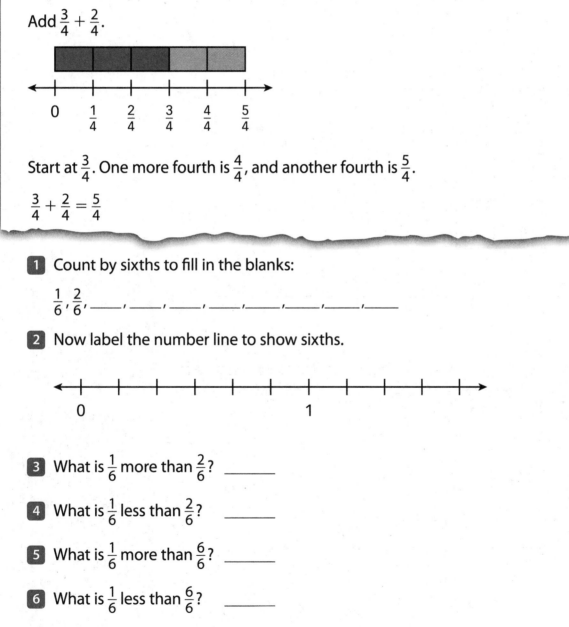

Start at $\frac{3}{4}$. One more fourth is $\frac{4}{4}$, and another fourth is $\frac{5}{4}$.

$$\frac{3}{4} + \frac{2}{4} = \frac{5}{4}$$

1 Count by sixths to fill in the blanks:

$\frac{1}{6}, \frac{2}{6},$ _____, _____, _____, _____, _____, _____, _____, _____

2 Now label the number line to show sixths.

0   1

3 What is $\frac{1}{6}$ more than $\frac{2}{6}$? _____

4 What is $\frac{1}{6}$ less than $\frac{2}{6}$? _____

5 What is $\frac{1}{6}$ more than $\frac{6}{6}$? _____

6 What is $\frac{1}{6}$ less than $\frac{6}{6}$? _____

Solve.

7 Label the number line to show fourths.

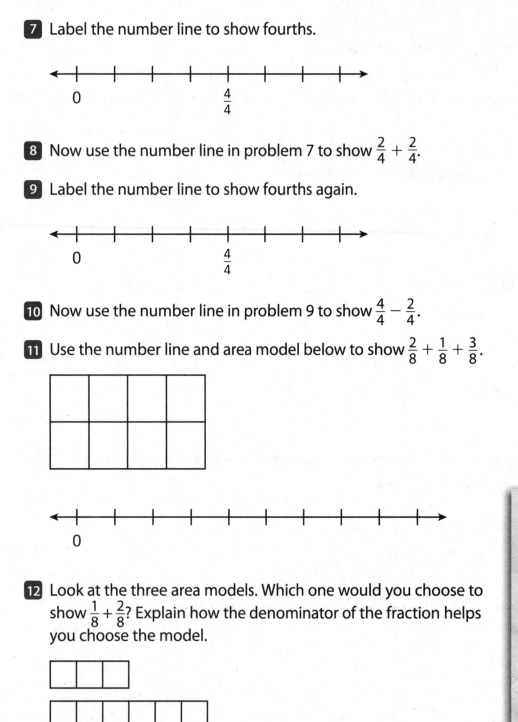

$\frac{4}{4}$

0

8 Now use the number line in problem 7 to show $\frac{2}{4} + \frac{2}{4}$.

9 Label the number line to show fourths again.

0 $\frac{4}{4}$

10 Now use the number line in problem 9 to show $\frac{4}{4} - \frac{2}{4}$.

11 Use the number line and area model below to show $\frac{2}{8} + \frac{1}{8} + \frac{3}{8}$.

0

12 Look at the three area models. Which one would you choose to show $\frac{1}{8} + \frac{2}{8}$? Explain how the denominator of the fraction helps you choose the model.

Name: _____

Reason and Write

Study the example. Underline two parts that you think make it a particularly good answer and a helpful example.

Example

Rob drew this diagram to show $\frac{1}{10} + \frac{3}{10} + \frac{4}{10}$

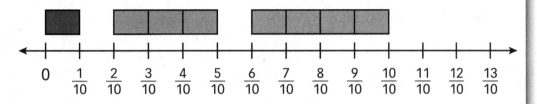

Rob says that his picture shows that

$\frac{1}{10} + \frac{3}{10} + \frac{4}{10} = \frac{10}{10}$ or 1 whole.

What did Rob do right? What did he do wrong?

Show your work. Use pictures, words, or numbers to explain your answer.

Rob drew the number line the right way. He marked it to show tenths because the fractions in the problem are in tenths. He also showed that $\frac{10}{10}$ is one whole.

He shaded 1 tenth and 3 tenths and 4 tenths because the numbers in the problem are $\frac{1}{10}$ and $\frac{3}{10}$ and $\frac{4}{10}$.

His mistake was leaving spaces between the shaded parts. When you count up on a number line, you can't skip numbers. He should have drawn this.

Where does the example . . .

• answer both parts of the question?

• use a picture to explain?

• use numbers to explain?

• use words to explain?

• give details?

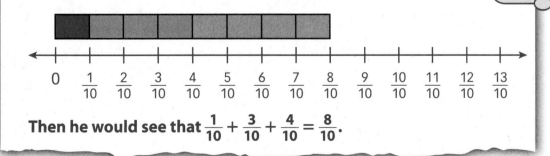

Then he would see that $\frac{1}{10} + \frac{3}{10} + \frac{4}{10} = \frac{8}{10}$.

Lesson 15 Understand Fraction Addition and Subtraction **171**

Solve the problem. Use what you learned from the example.

Paul drew this diagram to show $\frac{12}{10} - \frac{3}{10}$.

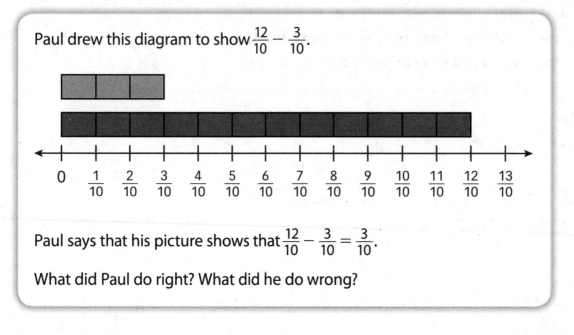

Paul says that his picture shows that $\frac{12}{10} - \frac{3}{10} = \frac{3}{10}$.

What did Paul do right? What did he do wrong?

Show your work. Use pictures, words, or numbers to explain your answer.

Did you . . .

• answer both parts of the question?

• use a picture to explain?

• use numbers to explain?

• use words to explain?

• give details?

Dear Family,

This week your child is learning how to add and subtract like fractions.

Like fractions have denominators that are the same.

like fractions: $\frac{1}{4}$ and $\frac{3}{4}$ **unlike fractions:** $\frac{1}{2}$ and $\frac{3}{4}$

To find the sum of like fractions, understand that you are just adding like units. Just as 3 apples plus 2 apples is 5 apples, 3 eighths plus 2 eighths is 5 eighths. Similarly, when you take away, or subtract, 2 eighths from 5 eighths, you have 3 eighths left.

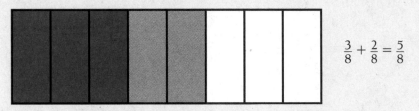

$$\frac{3}{8} + \frac{2}{8} = \frac{5}{8}$$

You can also use a number line to understand adding and subtracting like fractions.

$$\frac{0}{8} \quad \frac{1}{8} \quad \frac{2}{8} \quad \frac{3}{8} \quad \frac{4}{8} \quad \frac{5}{8} \quad \frac{6}{8} \quad \frac{7}{8} \quad \frac{8}{8}$$

Remember that the denominator just names the units in the same way as "apples" names units. So,

• to add two fractions with the same denominator, the sum of the numerators tells how many of those units you have.

• to subtract two fractions with like denominators, the difference of the numerators tells how many of those units you have.

Invite your child to share what he or she knows about adding and subtracting fractions by doing the following activity together.

NEXT

Add and Subtract Fractions Activity

Do an activity with your child to add and subtract fractions.

Materials: a bowl, a measuring cup, and the ingredients shown in the recipe

Follow the recipe below to make a creamy cracker spread or veggie dip. Then add and subtract fractions with these next steps.

- What fraction of a cup is the total amount of spread? $\left(\frac{7}{8}\right)$
- Spread $\frac{1}{8}$ cup on crackers or veggies. How much spread is left? $\left(\frac{6}{8}\right)$
- Make up a simple recipe using fractions for someone else in the family to make.

Recipe for Creamy Spread

Ingredients:

$\frac{5}{8}$ cup peanut butter

$\frac{2}{8}$ cup cream cheese

Crackers or veggies

Directions:

Mix the peanut butter and cream cheese together in a medium size bowl. Serve immediately with crackers or sliced fresh veggies. Enjoy!

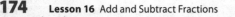

Add and Subtract Fractions

Name: _____

Study the example problem showing fraction addition with number line and area models. Then solve problems 1–8.

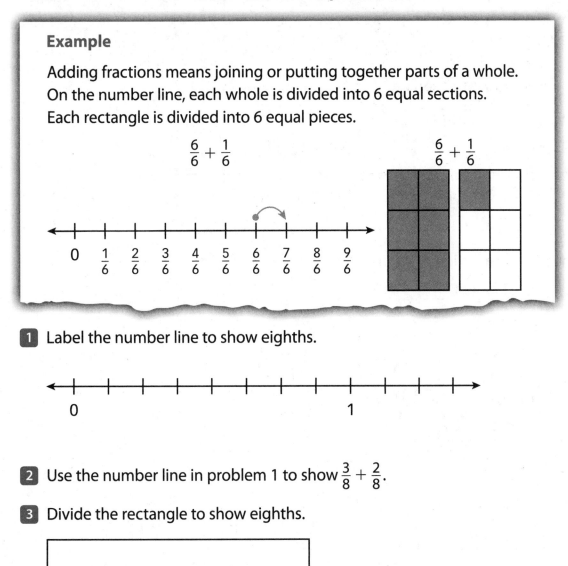

Example

Adding fractions means joining or putting together parts of a whole. On the number line, each whole is divided into 6 equal sections. Each rectangle is divided into 6 equal pieces.

$$\frac{6}{6} + \frac{1}{6}$$

1 **Label the number line to show eighths.**

2 Use the number line in problem 1 to show $\frac{3}{8} + \frac{2}{8}$.

3 Divide the rectangle to show eighths.

4 Use the rectangle in problem 3 to show $\frac{3}{8} + \frac{2}{8}$.

Solve.

5 What is the fraction addition problem shown on this number line? _____

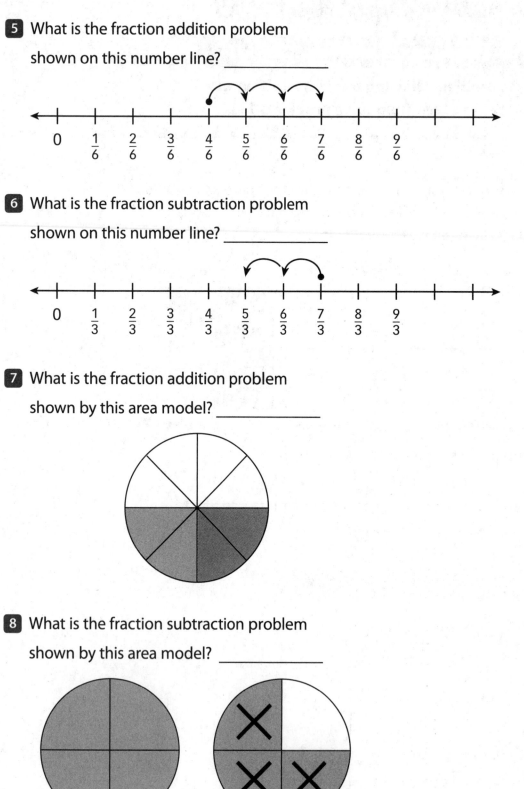

6 What is the fraction subtraction problem shown on this number line? _____

7 What is the fraction addition problem shown by this area model? _____

8 What is the fraction subtraction problem shown by this area model? _____

Name: _____

Add Fractions

Study the example problem showing one way to add fractions. Then solve problems 1–13.

Example

Shrina has a muffin tray that holds 12 muffins. She fills $\frac{3}{12}$ of the tray with apple muffin batter. Then she fills $\frac{6}{12}$ with pumpkin muffin batter. What fraction of the tray is filled?

$$\frac{3}{12} + \frac{6}{12} = \frac{9}{12}$$

So, $\frac{9}{12}$ of the muffin tray is filled.

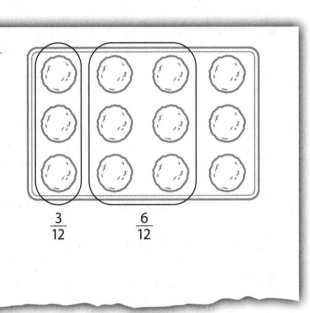

$\frac{3}{12}$ $\frac{6}{12}$

1 Shade $\frac{2}{12}$ of the muffin tray.

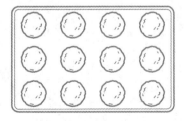

2 Sam fills $\frac{2}{12}$ of the tray with banana muffin batter. Then she fills $\frac{6}{12}$ with lemon muffin batter. Shade the diagram to show this.

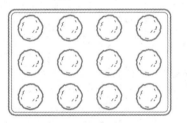

3 In problem 2, what fraction of the tray is filled? _____

Write an equation for this problem that includes your answer. _____

Solve.

Kay ran $\frac{6}{8}$ mile and rested. Then she ran another $\frac{6}{8}$ mile.

4 Divide the number line below to show eighths.

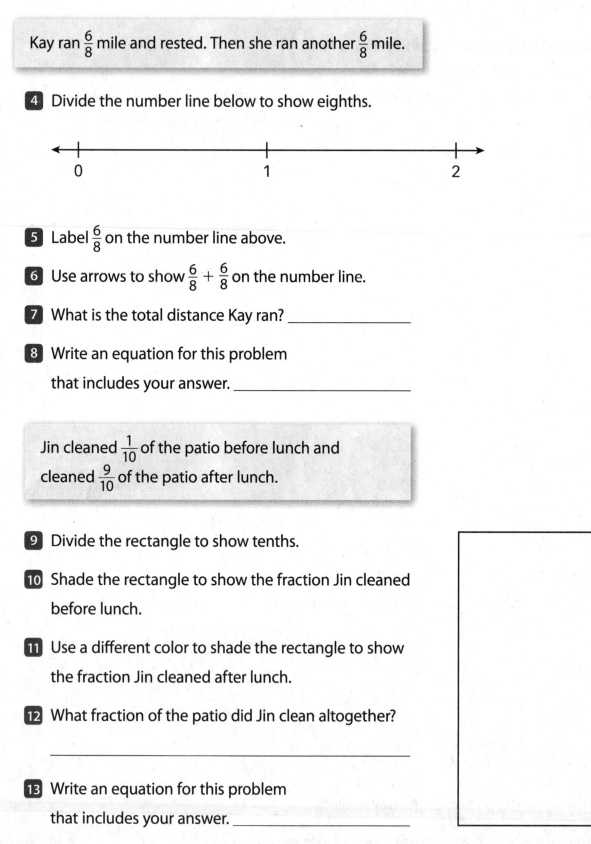

0   1   2

5 Label $\frac{6}{8}$ on the number line above.

6 Use arrows to show $\frac{6}{8} + \frac{6}{8}$ on the number line.

7 What is the total distance Kay ran? _____

8 Write an equation for this problem
that includes your answer. _____

Jin cleaned $\frac{1}{10}$ of the patio before lunch and
cleaned $\frac{9}{10}$ of the patio after lunch.

9 Divide the rectangle to show tenths.

10 Shade the rectangle to show the fraction Jin cleaned
before lunch.

11 Use a different color to shade the rectangle to show
the fraction Jin cleaned after lunch.

12 What fraction of the patio did Jin clean altogether?

_____

13 Write an equation for this problem
that includes your answer. _____

Name: _____

Subtract Fractions

Study the example showing one way to subtract fractions. Then solve problems 1–7.

Example

Ali bought a carton of eggs. He used $\frac{3}{12}$ of the eggs to cook breakfast. He used another $\frac{2}{12}$ to make a dessert for dinner. What fraction of the carton is left?

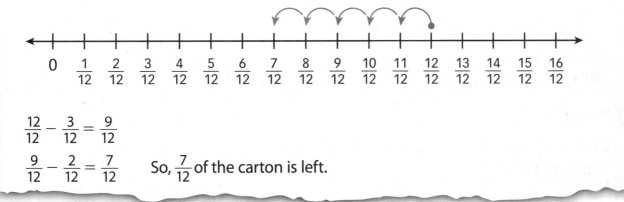

$$\frac{12}{12} - \frac{3}{12} = \frac{9}{12}$$

$$\frac{9}{12} - \frac{2}{12} = \frac{7}{12} \qquad \text{So, } \frac{7}{12} \text{ of the carton is left.}$$

Keisha is going to her friend's house $\frac{8}{10}$ mile from home. Her mother drives her partway, then she walks the last $\frac{3}{10}$ mile.

1 Divide the number line below to show tenths. Then label each tick mark.

```
←——+——————————————————+——→
   0                   1
```

2 Use arrows to show the problem on the number line you drew in problem 1.

3 How far did Keisha's mother drive her? _____

4 Write an equation for this problem that includes your answer. _____

Solve.

5 Anna made a quilt by sewing together green, white, and yellow fabric. When she was done, $\frac{2}{6}$ of the quilt was green and $\frac{3}{6}$ was yellow. The rest was white. What fraction of the quilt was white?

Show your work.

Solution: _____

6 What is $\frac{9}{8} - \frac{8}{8}$?

Use a number line or an area model to show your thinking.

Solution: _____

7 Shanice had 1 whole pizza. After eating some of it, she had $\frac{4}{6}$ of the pizza left. What fraction of the pizza did she eat?

Show your work.

Solution: _____

Name: _____

Add and Subtract Fractions

Solve the problems.

1 Lin bought $\frac{3}{4}$ pound of cheddar cheese and some Swiss cheese. Altogether she bought $\frac{7}{4}$ pounds of cheese. How much Swiss cheese did Lin buy?

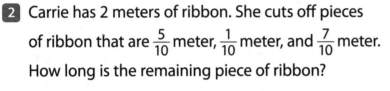

Does it make sense to add or subtract here?

A $\frac{4}{8}$ of a pound   **C** $\frac{10}{8}$ pounds

B $\frac{4}{4}$ of a pound   **D** $\frac{10}{4}$ pounds

2 Carrie has 2 meters of ribbon. She cuts off pieces of ribbon that are $\frac{5}{10}$ meter, $\frac{1}{10}$ meter, and $\frac{7}{10}$ meter. How long is the remaining piece of ribbon?

This problem seems to have more than one step.

A $\frac{1}{10}$ meter   **C** $\frac{7}{10}$ meter

B $\frac{3}{10}$ meter   **D** $\frac{13}{10}$ meters

Lee chose **D** as the correct answer. How did she get that answer?

_____

_____

_____

3 Ms. Atkins had a basket of tomatoes. She used $\frac{5}{12}$ of the tomatoes to make soup. She used $\frac{2}{12}$ in a salad. What fraction of the tomatoes are left?

Show your work.

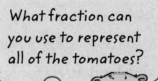

What fraction can you use to represent all of the tomatoes?

Solution: _____

Solve.

4 Jo and Kira are raking leaves in the yard. They divide the yard into 8 equal sections. Jo rakes 4 sections. Kira rakes 2 sections. Which model can be used to find the total fraction of the yard they rake? Circle the letter of all that apply.

Two different models could show the same problem.

A

B

C

0   $\frac{1}{8}$ $\frac{2}{8}$ $\frac{3}{8}$ $\frac{4}{8}$ $\frac{5}{8}$ $\frac{6}{8}$ $\frac{7}{8}$ $\frac{8}{8}$

D

0   $\frac{1}{8}$ $\frac{2}{8}$ $\frac{3}{8}$ $\frac{4}{8}$ $\frac{5}{8}$ $\frac{6}{8}$ $\frac{7}{8}$ $\frac{8}{8}$

5 A pizza is cut into 6 equal pieces. After Eli and Dan eat some, $\frac{1}{6}$ of the pizza is left. What fraction could each boy eat? Give one possible answer.

Show your work.

To find the fraction that was eaten, should you add or subtract?

Solution: _____

6 Milo has 2 hours of free time. He spends $\frac{2}{4}$ of an hour with his dog. He spends $\frac{3}{4}$ of an hour drawing. What fraction of an hour does he have left?

Show your work.

How can you write 2 wholes as a fraction?

Solution: _____

Dear Family,

This week your child is learning to add and subtract mixed numbers.

> **mixed number:** a number with a whole number part and a fractional part.

Using models can help your child add mixed numbers, such as $1\frac{5}{8} + 1\frac{6}{8}$.

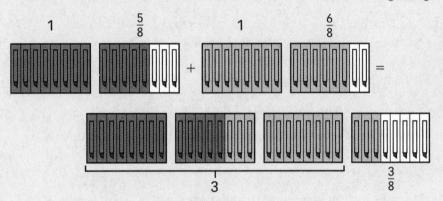

The model shows that you can add the wholes, $1 + 1 = 2$.

Then you can add the parts, $\frac{5}{8} + \frac{6}{8} = \frac{11}{8}$.

$\frac{11}{8}$ is another whole, $\frac{8}{8}$ or 1, and $\frac{3}{8}$.

The model shows the sum is 3 wholes and $\frac{3}{8}$ of a whole.

$1\frac{5}{8} + 1\frac{6}{8} = 3\frac{3}{8}$

Invite your child to share what he or she knows about adding and subtracting mixed numbers by doing the following activity together.

Add and Subtract Mixed Numbers Activity

Do an activity with your child to add and subtract mixed numbers.

Materials: construction paper ($8\frac{1}{2} \times 11$ inches, or 9×12 inches), magazine or newspaper with pictures (or a picture of your own), scissors, ruler, glue or tape

- Use a sheet of construction paper to make a paper frame for a fun photo. Choose a picture from a newspaper or a magazine, or use a photo of your own. Choose a picture that is less than 5 by 8 inches.

- Measure the length and width of your picture to the nearest $\frac{1}{8}$ inch.

- Add 2 inches to the length and 2 inches to the width of your picture. That will be the size of the construction paper you need.

  Example: Your picture is $5\frac{7}{8}$ wide. $5\frac{7}{8} + 2 = 7\frac{7}{8}$

  Your picture is $3\frac{3}{8}$ tall. $3\frac{3}{8} + 2 = 5\frac{3}{8}$

- Subtract your totals from the construction paper's width and length. That is how many inches to cut off the length and width of the construction paper.

- Measure and cut your construction paper to size. Then center the photo and attach it so that there is a 2-inch frame all around the photo.

Look for other real-life opportunities to practice adding and subtracting mixed numbers with your child.

Add and Subtract Mixed Numbers

Name: _____

Study the example problem showing a way to add fractions. Then solve problems 1–5.

Example

Darcy used $\frac{5}{8}$ of a carton of strawberries to make a cake. She used another $\frac{2}{8}$ of a carton of strawberries to decorate the cake. What fraction of a carton of strawberries did Darcy use in all?

$$\frac{5}{8} + \frac{2}{8} = \frac{7}{8}$$

Darcy used $\frac{7}{8}$ of a carton of strawberries.

Jeremy biked $\frac{3}{10}$ of a mile to a friend's house. Then he biked $\frac{5}{10}$ of a mile to school.

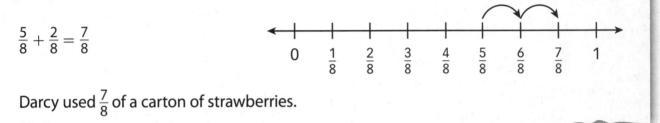

1 Draw jumps on the number line to show $\frac{3}{10} + \frac{5}{10}$.

2 Fill in the boxes to write an equation that shows how far Jeremy biked.

$$\frac{\boxed{}}{10} + \frac{\boxed{}}{10} = \frac{\boxed{}}{10}$$

Solve.

3 George used $\frac{4}{6}$ of a box of raisins to make granola. His sister used $\frac{1}{6}$ of the box of raisins for her cereal. How much more of the box of raisins did George use than his sister?

Show your work.

Solution: George used _____ more of the box of raisins.

4 Sam and his friends shared a pizza. They ate $\frac{5}{8}$ of the pizza. What fraction of the pizza is left?

Show your work.

Solution: _____

5 Sophie read $\frac{1}{5}$ of a book each day from Monday to Friday. What fraction of her book had she read after she finished reading on Tuesday?

Show your work.

Solution: _____

6 Use the numbers below to write true equations. There is more than one correct answer and each number can be used more than once.

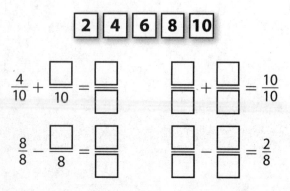

Name: _____

Add Mixed Numbers

Study the example problem showing a way to add mixed numbers. Then solve problems 1–6.

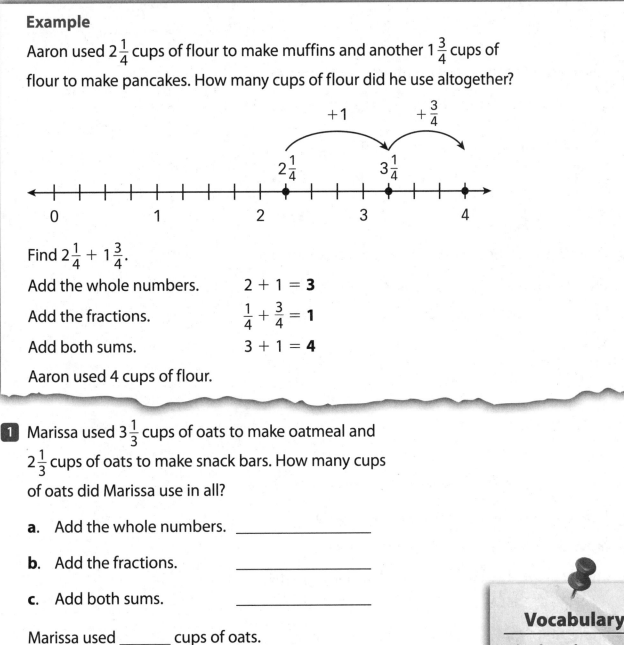

Example

Aaron used $2\frac{1}{4}$ cups of flour to make muffins and another $1\frac{3}{4}$ cups of flour to make pancakes. How many cups of flour did he use altogether?

Find $2\frac{1}{4} + 1\frac{3}{4}$.

Add the whole numbers. $2 + 1 = \textbf{3}$

Add the fractions. $\frac{1}{4} + \frac{3}{4} = \textbf{1}$

Add both sums. $3 + 1 = \textbf{4}$

Aaron used 4 cups of flour.

---

1 Marissa used $3\frac{1}{3}$ cups of oats to make oatmeal and $2\frac{1}{3}$ cups of oats to make snack bars. How many cups of oats did Marissa use in all?

   a. Add the whole numbers. _____

   b. Add the fractions. _____

   c. Add both sums. _____

   Marissa used _____ cups of oats.

2 Draw and label a number line to show $1\frac{1}{4} + 2\frac{2}{4}$.

Vocabulary

mixed number a number with a whole number part and a fractional part.

$2\frac{1}{4}$ and $1\frac{3}{4}$ are mixed numbers.

Lesson 17 Add and Subtract Mixed Numbers **187**

Solve.

3 Which of the following is equal to $7\frac{5}{6} + 2\frac{3}{6}$?
Circle all that apply.

A $9\frac{8}{12}$ C $7 + 2 + \frac{5}{6} + \frac{3}{6}$

B $9 + 1\frac{2}{6}$ D $5\frac{2}{6}$

4 Tell whether each number sentence is *True* or *False*.

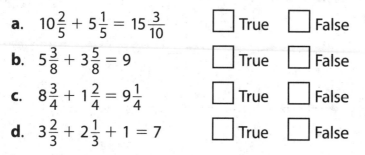

a. $10\frac{2}{5} + 5\frac{1}{5} = 15\frac{3}{10}$ ☐ True ☐ False

b. $5\frac{3}{8} + 3\frac{5}{8} = 9$ ☐ True ☐ False

c. $8\frac{3}{4} + 1\frac{2}{4} = 9\frac{1}{4}$ ☐ True ☐ False

d. $3\frac{2}{3} + 2\frac{1}{3} + 1 = 7$ ☐ True ☐ False

5 Tim used $4\frac{1}{2}$ cups of oranges, $3\frac{1}{2}$ cups of apples, and $5\frac{1}{2}$ cups of pears in a fruit salad. How many cups of fruit did Tim use altogether?

Show your work.

Solution: _____

6 Jerry and two friends took a trip together. Jerry drove $80\frac{7}{10}$ miles. Arthur drove $60\frac{5}{10}$ miles. Charlie drove $40\frac{8}{10}$ miles. How many miles did they drive in all?

Show your work.

Solution: _____

Name: _____

Subtract Mixed Numbers

Study the example problem showing a way to subtract mixed numbers. Then solve problems 1–5.

Example

On a holiday, Sara's family drove $3\frac{1}{4}$ hours to her cousin's house. The drive usually takes $2\frac{2}{4}$ hours. How much longer did the drive take on the holiday?

Find $3\frac{1}{4} - 2\frac{2}{4}$.

$3\frac{1}{4} - 2\frac{2}{4} = \frac{3}{4}$

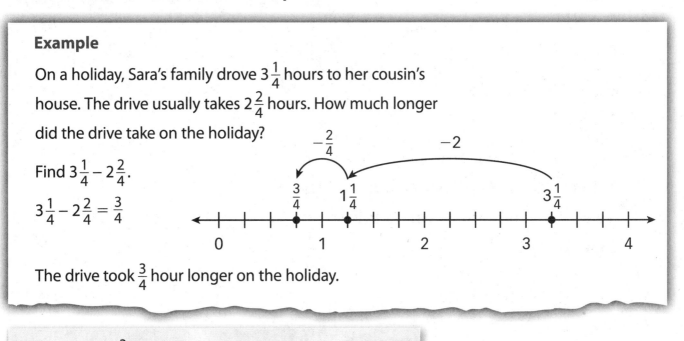

The drive took $\frac{3}{4}$ hour longer on the holiday.

Steve made $9\frac{3}{6}$ cups of pancake batter on a weekend camping trip. He used $3\frac{4}{6}$ cups of batter for breakfast on Saturday.

1 Write each mixed number as a fraction greater than one.

$9\frac{3}{6} = \frac{\Box}{6} + \frac{3}{6} = \frac{\Box}{6}$ $3\frac{4}{6} = \frac{\Box}{6} + \frac{4}{6} = \frac{\Box}{6}$

2 Subtract the fractions to find how many cups of batter were left for breakfast on Sunday.

$\frac{\Box}{6} - \frac{\Box}{6} = \frac{\Box}{6}$

3 Write the difference as a mixed number.

$\frac{\Box}{6} = \Box\frac{\Box}{\Box}$

4 Use addition to check the answer.

$3\frac{4}{6} + \Box\frac{\Box}{\Box} = $ _____

Lesson 17 Add and Subtract Mixed Numbers   **189**

Solve.

5 Which of the following has the same value as $7\frac{5}{6} - 2\frac{3}{6}$?
Circle all that apply.

A $10\frac{2}{6}$

B $\frac{47}{6} - \frac{15}{6}$

C $(7 - 2) + \left(\frac{5}{6} - \frac{3}{6}\right)$

D $5\frac{2}{6}$

6 Helen bought 5 pounds of oranges. She sliced $2\frac{3}{10}$ pounds of oranges to bring to a party. How many pounds of oranges does Helen have left?

Show your work.

Solution: _____

7 Kira reasoned that $6\frac{1}{4} - 2\frac{3}{4} = 4\frac{2}{4}$ because the difference between 6 and 2 is 4 and the difference between $\frac{1}{4}$ and $\frac{3}{4}$ is $\frac{2}{4}$. Is Kira's reasoning correct? Explain why or why not.

_____

_____

_____

_____

_____

_____

Name: _____

Add and Subtract Mixed Numbers

Solve the problems.

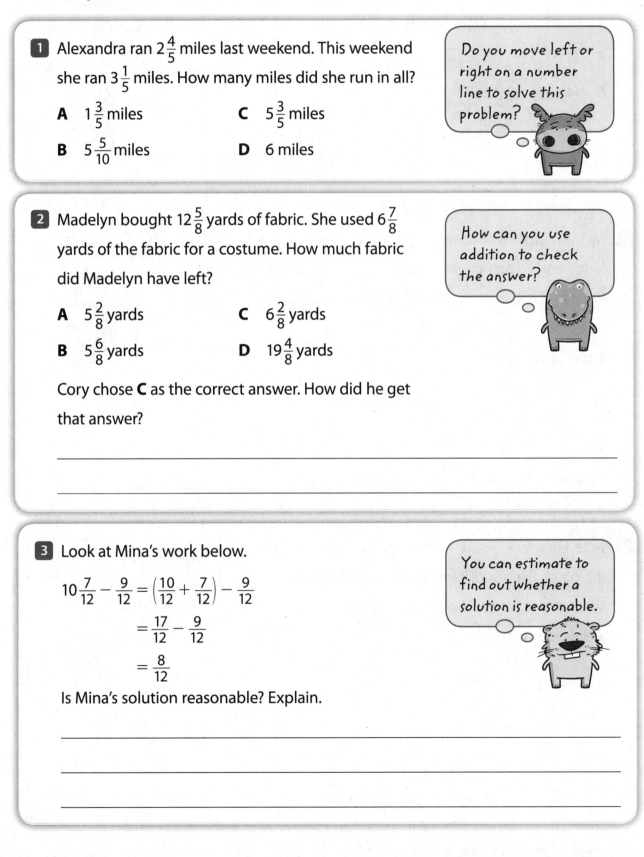

1 Alexandra ran $2\frac{4}{5}$ miles last weekend. This weekend she ran $3\frac{1}{5}$ miles. How many miles did she run in all?

Do you move left or right on a number line to solve this problem?

A $1\frac{3}{5}$ miles   **C** $5\frac{3}{5}$ miles

B $5\frac{5}{10}$ miles   **D** 6 miles

2 Madelyn bought $12\frac{5}{8}$ yards of fabric. She used $6\frac{7}{8}$ yards of the fabric for a costume. How much fabric did Madelyn have left?

How can you use addition to check the answer?

A $5\frac{2}{8}$ yards   **C** $6\frac{2}{8}$ yards

B $5\frac{6}{8}$ yards   **D** $19\frac{4}{8}$ yards

Cory chose **C** as the correct answer. How did he get that answer?

_____

_____

3 Look at Mina's work below.

You can estimate to find out whether a solution is reasonable.

$$10\frac{7}{12} - \frac{9}{12} = \left(\frac{10}{12} + \frac{7}{12}\right) - \frac{9}{12}$$
$$= \frac{17}{12} - \frac{9}{12}$$
$$= \frac{8}{12}$$

Is Mina's solution reasonable? Explain.

_____

_____

_____

Lesson 17 Add and Subtract Mixed Numbers **191**

Solve.

4 Which statement(s) below have the same value as $4\frac{3}{5} - 2\frac{1}{5}$? Circle all that apply.

A $(4 - 2) + \left(\frac{3}{5} - \frac{1}{5}\right)$

B $(4 - 2) - \left(\frac{3}{5} - \frac{1}{5}\right)$

C $\left(\frac{20}{5} + \frac{3}{5}\right) - \left(\frac{10}{5} + \frac{1}{5}\right)$

D $\frac{7}{5} - \frac{3}{5}$

Can writing a mixed number as a fraction help you solve this problem?

5 Jackson ordered 4 submarine sandwiches for a lunch party. Each sandwich was cut into thirds. At the party, 8 people each ate $\frac{1}{3}$ of a sandwich. How much of the sandwiches were left?

Show your work.

Drawing a picture can help you visualize this problem.

Solution: _____

6 Julie, Ellen, and Jenny shared a pizza. Julie ate $\frac{1}{8}$ of the pizza. Ellen and Jenny each ate $\frac{3}{8}$ of the pizza. Did the girls eat the whole pizza? Explain.

Show your work.

What fraction can you write to represent the whole pizza?

Solution: _____

Dear Family,

This week your child is exploring fraction multiplication.

Multiplying fractions is finding the total number of equal-size parts in equal groups.

Your child can use a model to understand fraction multiplication.

This model shows $5 \times \frac{3}{8}$.

You can see that there are 5 groups of $\frac{3}{8}$.

There are $\frac{15}{8}$ in all.

The denominator tells the number of equal-size parts in the whole.

There are 8 equal-size parts in each whole.

Your child can also think about repeated addition to understand fraction multiplication.

Adding $\frac{3}{8}$ five times is the same as multiplying $5 \times \frac{3}{8}$.

$$\frac{3}{8} + \frac{3}{8} + \frac{3}{8} + \frac{3}{8} + \frac{3}{8} = \frac{15}{8}$$

Invite your child to share what he or she knows about fraction multiplication by doing the following activity together.

NEXT

Fraction Multiplication

Do an activity with your child to explore fraction multiplication.

Materials: a bowl and the ingredients shown in the recipe

- Look at the recipe below for snack mix.

- Rewrite the recipe so that you can make four times as much snack mix. Multiply the amount of each ingredient by 4.

- Make the recipe and enjoy!

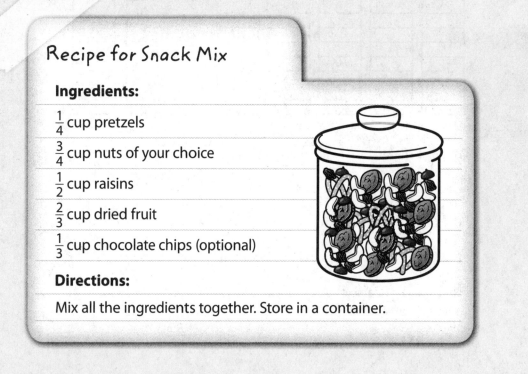

Recipe for Snack Mix

Ingredients:

$\frac{1}{4}$ cup pretzels

$\frac{3}{4}$ cup nuts of your choice

$\frac{1}{2}$ cup raisins

$\frac{2}{3}$ cup dried fruit

$\frac{1}{3}$ cup chocolate chips (optional)

Directions:

Mix all the ingredients together. Store in a container.

Name: _____

> **Prerequisite: What does it mean to multiply numbers?**

Study the example shows ways to describe multiplication. Then solve problems 1–8.

Example

Use words and models to show $5 \times 3 = 15$.

5 groups of 3 is 15.

15 is 5 times as many as 3.

3

3	3	3	3	3

⊢————————— 15 —————————⊣

---

1 Complete the sentences to describe the multiplication that the picture shows.

Words: _____ groups of _____ is _____ .

Equation: _____ × _____ = _____

2 Use the bar model at the right to complete the sentences.

Words: _____ is _____ times as many as _____ .

Equation: _____ × _____ = _____

6

6	6	6	6

⊢————————— 24 —————————⊣

3 How is 6×4 related to 4×6? _____

Solve.

4 Complete the sentences to describe the multiplication that the array shows.

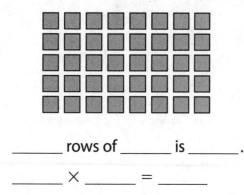

_____ rows of _____ is _____ .

_____ × _____ = _____

5 Draw and label a bar model to show 5 × 9.

6 Nick read 7 books last month. He read twice as many books this month. Draw a bar model that represents the number of books Nick read this month.

7 Look at problem 6. Write the multiplication equation that the bar model describes.

_____

8 Write a word problem that could be modeled by the equation 3 × 6 = 18.

_____

_____

_____

Name: _____

Show Multiplying Fractions

Study how the example shows how to multiply fractions. Then solve problems 1–9.

Example

Find $5 \times \frac{3}{4}$.

You can use repeated addition. $\frac{3}{4} + \frac{3}{4} + \frac{3}{4} + \frac{3}{4} + \frac{3}{4} = \frac{15}{4}$ $\frac{15}{4} = 3\frac{3}{4}$

You can draw a model.

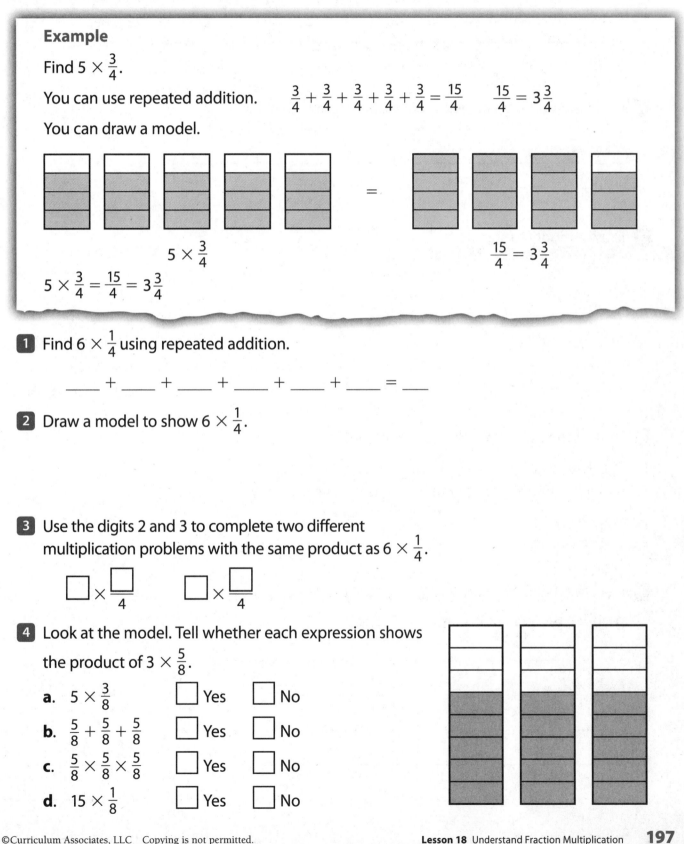

$5 \times \frac{3}{4}$ $=$ $\frac{15}{4} = 3\frac{3}{4}$

$5 \times \frac{3}{4} = \frac{15}{4} = 3\frac{3}{4}$

1 Find $6 \times \frac{1}{4}$ using repeated addition.

_____ + _____ + _____ + _____ + _____ + _____ = _____

2 Draw a model to show $6 \times \frac{1}{4}$.

3 Use the digits 2 and 3 to complete two different multiplication problems with the same product as $6 \times \frac{1}{4}$.

$\square \times \dfrac{\square}{4}$ $\square \times \dfrac{\square}{4}$

4 Look at the model. Tell whether each expression shows the product of $3 \times \frac{5}{8}$.

a. $5 \times \frac{3}{8}$ ☐ Yes   ☐ No

b. $\frac{5}{8} + \frac{5}{8} + \frac{5}{8}$ ☐ Yes   ☐ No

c. $\frac{5}{8} \times \frac{5}{8} \times \frac{5}{8}$ ☐ Yes   ☐ No

d. $15 \times \frac{1}{8}$ ☐ Yes   ☐ No

Solve.

5 The number line below shows _____ × $\dfrac{\square}{\square}$.

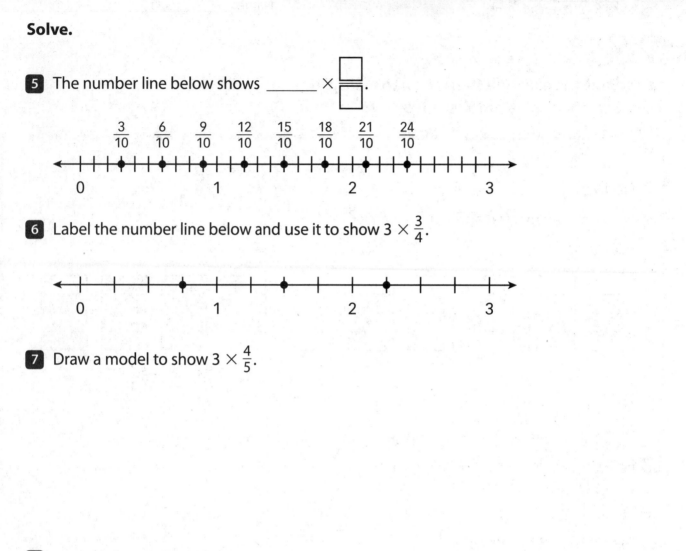

$\dfrac{3}{10}$ $\dfrac{6}{10}$ $\dfrac{9}{10}$ $\dfrac{12}{10}$ $\dfrac{15}{10}$ $\dfrac{18}{10}$ $\dfrac{21}{10}$ $\dfrac{24}{10}$

6 Label the number line below and use it to show $3 \times \dfrac{3}{4}$.

7 Draw a model to show $3 \times \dfrac{4}{5}$.

8 Look at the model you drew in problem 7.

Use the digits 2, 3, 4, 5, and 6 to write two different multiplication problems with the same product as $3 \times \dfrac{4}{5}$.

$\square \times \dfrac{\square}{\square}$ $\square \times \dfrac{\square}{\square}$

9 Lisa says that $3 \times \dfrac{1}{6}$ and $\dfrac{1}{6} \times \dfrac{1}{6} \times \dfrac{1}{6}$ have the same product. Is Lisa's reasoning correct? Explain.

_____

_____

_____

_____

_____

Name: _____

Reason and Write

Study the example. Underline two parts that you think make it a particularly good answer and a helpful example.

Example

Describe how you can use the same methods to find the product 4×2 and the product $4 \times \frac{2}{3}$.

Show your work. Use models, words, and numbers to explain your answer.

I can think of 4×2 as 4 groups of 2.
$4 \times 2 = 8$. 8 is 4 times as many as 2.

I can think of $4 \times \frac{2}{3}$ as 4 groups of 2 thirds. $4 \times \frac{2}{3} = \frac{8}{3}$.
$\frac{8}{3}$ is 4 times as many as $\frac{2}{3}$.

I can find both products using repeated addition.
$2 + 2 + 2 + 2 = 8$

$\frac{2}{3} + \frac{2}{3} + \frac{2}{3} + \frac{2}{3} = \frac{8}{3}$

I can use a model to show
$4 \times 2 = 8$.

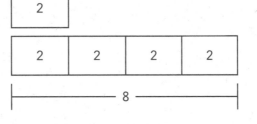

I can use a model to show $4 \times \frac{2}{3} = \frac{8}{3}$.

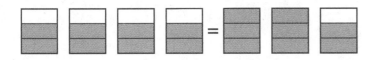

> Where does the example . . .
> • use words to explain?
> • use numbers to explain?
> • use models to show how the products are alike?

Solve the problem. Use what you learned from the example.

Describe how you can use the same methods to find the product 2×3 and the product $2 \times \frac{3}{4}$.

Show your work. Use words, models, and numbers to explain your answer.

Did you . . .

- use words to explain?

- use numbers to explain?

- use models to show how the products are alike?

Dear Family,

This week your child is learning to multiply fractions to solve word problems.

Your child might see a problem like this:

> Randy practiced guitar for $\frac{2}{3}$ of an hour on 4 days this week. How long did Randy practice this week?

Using fraction strips can help your child solve this word problem.

Each fraction strip below is divided into thirds and shows $\frac{2}{3}$, the length of time that Randy practiced each day.

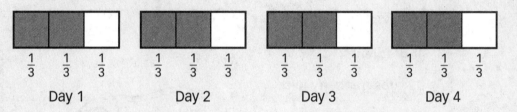

| $\frac{1}{3}$ $\frac{1}{3}$ $\frac{1}{3}$ | $\frac{1}{3}$ $\frac{1}{3}$ $\frac{1}{3}$ | $\frac{1}{3}$ $\frac{1}{3}$ $\frac{1}{3}$ | $\frac{1}{3}$ $\frac{1}{3}$ $\frac{1}{3}$ |
| Day 1 | Day 2 | Day 3 | Day 4 |

The fraction strips show $4 \times \frac{2}{3}$. The fraction strips show $\frac{8}{3}$.

Your child can also write an equation to find how long Randy practiced.

$$4 \times \frac{2}{3} = \frac{8}{3}$$

Then your child can check his or her answer by using repeated addition.

$$\frac{2}{3} + \frac{2}{3} + \frac{2}{3} + \frac{2}{3} = \frac{8}{3} \text{ hours}$$

The answer is that Randy practiced $\frac{8}{3}$, or $2\frac{2}{3}$, hours this week.

Invite your child to share what he or she knows about multiplying fractions by doing the following activity together.

NEXT

Multiplying Fractions Activity

Do an activity with your child to multiply fractions.

Materials: a large pitcher, a measuring cup, and the ingredients shown in the recipe

- Look at the recipe below for party punch. It makes a large amount of punch.

- Rewrite the recipe so that it will be more suitable for your family. Just multiply the amount of each ingredient by $\frac{1}{4}$.

- Make the recipe and enjoy!

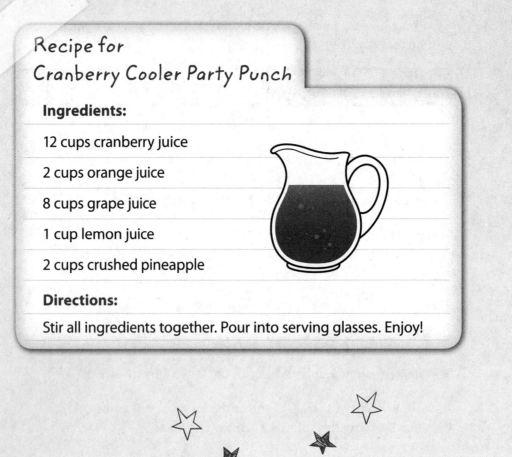

Recipe for Cranberry Cooler Party Punch

Ingredients:

12 cups cranberry juice

2 cups orange juice

8 cups grape juice

1 cup lemon juice

2 cups crushed pineapple

Directions:

Stir all ingredients together. Pour into serving glasses. Enjoy!

Multiply Fractions

Name: _____

Study the example showing fraction multiplication with models. Then solve problems 1–10.

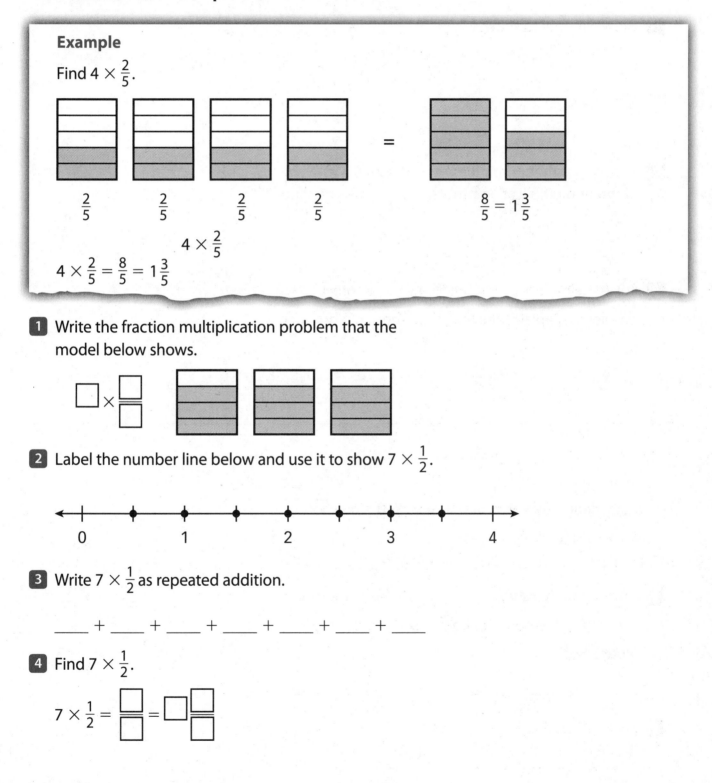

Example

Find $4 \times \frac{2}{5}$.

$\frac{2}{5}$ $\frac{2}{5}$ $\frac{2}{5}$ $\frac{2}{5}$ $\frac{8}{5} = 1\frac{3}{5}$

$4 \times \frac{2}{5}$

$4 \times \frac{2}{5} = \frac{8}{5} = 1\frac{3}{5}$

1 Write the fraction multiplication problem that the model below shows.

$\square \times \dfrac{\square}{\square}$

2 Label the number line below and use it to show $7 \times \frac{1}{2}$.

0   1   2   3   4

3 Write $7 \times \frac{1}{2}$ as repeated addition.

____ + ____ + ____ + ____ + ____ + ____ + ____

4 Find $7 \times \frac{1}{2}$.

$7 \times \dfrac{1}{2} = \dfrac{\square}{\square} = \square\dfrac{\square}{\square}$

Solve.

5 Fill in the blanks to show different ways to write problems with the same product as $4 \times \frac{3}{8}$.

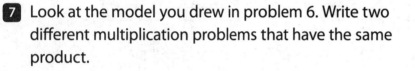

_____ $\times \frac{1}{8}$ $3 \times \dfrac{\square}{8}$

6 Draw a model to show $3 \times \frac{2}{6}$.

7 Look at the model you drew in problem 6. Write two different multiplication problems that have the same product.

_____   _____

8 Solve the multiplication problems you wrote in problem 7. Explain why they have the same product as $3 \times \frac{2}{6}$.

_____

_____

_____

Nadia made 4 loaves of bread. She used $\frac{3}{8}$ teaspoon of baking soda for each loaf.

9 Write a multiplication problem you could use to find how many teaspoons of baking soda Nadia used altogether.

_____

10 Solve the multiplication problem.

_____

Name: _____

Solve Problems with Fraction Multiplication

Study the example problem that shows how to solve a word problem with fraction multiplication. Then solve problems 1–7.

Example

Henry doubled a cookie recipe to make two batches of cookies. The recipe calls for $\frac{7}{8}$ cup of flour for each batch. How much flour did Henry use for both batches of cookies?

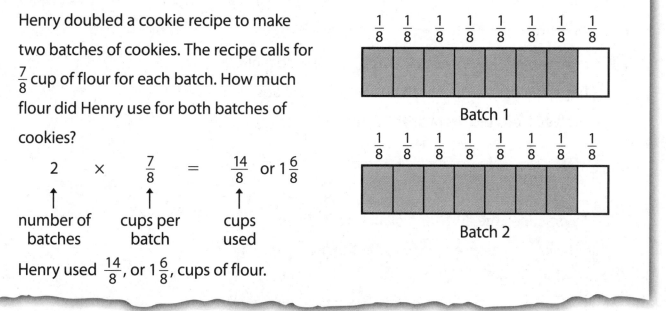

$$2 \quad \times \quad \frac{7}{8} \quad = \quad \frac{14}{8} \text{ or } 1\frac{6}{8}$$

↑   ↑   ↑

number of   cups per   cups
batches   batch   used

Henry used $\frac{14}{8}$, or $1\frac{6}{8}$, cups of flour.

---

1 Benson spent $\frac{5}{6}$ of an hour reading on each of 3 days this week. How long did Benson spend reading this week?

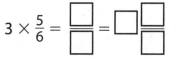

Benson spent _____ hours reading.

2 Show how to use repeated addition to check your answer in problem 1.

_____

3 Sabrina rode her bike $\frac{3}{4}$ of a mile. Katrin rode her bike 4 times as far as Sabrina. How far did Katrin ride her bike?

_____

Solve.

4 On Saturdays, Jorge coaches soccer for $\frac{1}{12}$ of the day. He also coaches tennis and swimming, each for the same amount of time as soccer. What fraction of the day does Jorge spend coaching on Saturdays?

_____

5 Greta planted flower seeds in 12 pots. She used $\frac{2}{6}$ of a bag of flower seeds in each pot. How many bags of flower seeds did Greta use?

_____

Leslie practiced the flute for $\frac{2}{6}$ of an hour 3 times this week. She practiced piano for $\frac{2}{3}$ of an hour 2 times this week.

6 Which expressions below can be used to show how much time Leslie spent practicing both the flute and piano this week? Circle the letter of all that apply.

A $\left(3 \times \frac{2}{6}\right) + \left(2 \times \frac{2}{3}\right)$

B $5 \times \left(\frac{2}{6} + \frac{2}{3}\right)$

C $\frac{2}{6} + \frac{2}{6} + \frac{2}{6} + \frac{2}{3} + \frac{2}{3}$

D $\frac{(3 \times 2)}{6} + \frac{(2 \times 2)}{3}$

7 Which did Leslie practice for a longer amount of time, the flute or the piano?

Show your work.

Solution: _____

Name: _____

Multiply Fractions

Solve the problems.

1 Rick cut a sheet of paper into 4 strips. Each strip was $\frac{3}{4}$ of an inch wide. How wide was the paper Rick cut?

A $\frac{3}{16}$ inch   **C** $\frac{7}{4}$ inches

B $\frac{12}{16}$ inch   **D** $\frac{12}{4}$ inches

Is the answer going to be greater than or less than $\frac{3}{4}$?

2 Diane walked her dog $\frac{4}{10}$ of a mile on 5 days this week. How far did Diane walk her dog this week?

A $\frac{20}{50}$ mile   **C** $\frac{20}{10}$ miles

B $\frac{9}{15}$ mile   **D** $\frac{40}{5}$ miles

Zoe chose **A**. How did she get that answer?

_____

_____

_____

_____

When you multiply a whole number by a fraction, do you multiply the whole number by the numerator or denominator?

3 Leo feeds his cat $\frac{2}{3}$ of a can of food 2 times a day. Leo is going out of town for 3 days. How many cans of food does Leo need to give a neighbor to feed his cat?

Show your work.

What two numbers can you multiply to find how many times the neighbor needs to feed Leo's cat?

Solution: _____

Solve.

4 Luke and Matt went fishing. Luke caught 4 fish, each weighing $\frac{7}{8}$ of a pound. Matt caught 6 fish, each weighing $\frac{3}{4}$ of a pound. Who caught more pounds of fish?

Show your work.

How do you figure out how many pounds each person caught?

Solution: _____

5 Penny is training for a race. First she ran $\frac{1}{10}$ of a mile 4 times. Next she ran $\frac{1}{5}$ of a mile 3 times. Then she ran $\frac{3}{10}$ of a mile two times. How far did Penny run during her training?

Show your work.

Drawing a picture can help you decide which numbers to multiply and which numbers to add.

Solution: _____

Dear Family,

This week your child is learning about fractions as tenths and hundredths.

Your child might see a problem such as $\frac{4}{10} + \frac{50}{100}$. One fraction in the problem has a denominator of 10. The other fraction has a denominator of 100.

Your child is learning how to write tenths fractions as equivalent hundredths fractions. $\frac{1}{10} = \frac{10}{100}$

This model shows $\frac{4}{10}$.   This model shows $\frac{40}{100}$.

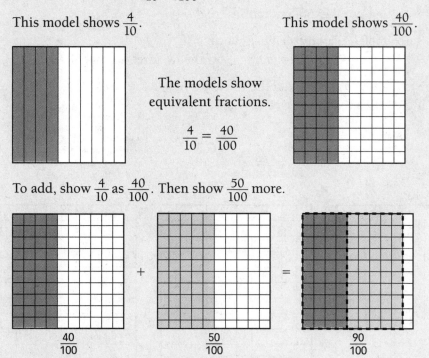

The models show equivalent fractions.

$$\frac{4}{10} = \frac{40}{100}$$

To add, show $\frac{4}{10}$ as $\frac{40}{100}$. Then show $\frac{50}{100}$ more.

$$\frac{40}{100} + \frac{50}{100} = \frac{90}{100} \text{ and } \frac{4}{10} + \frac{50}{100} = \frac{90}{100}$$

Invite your child to share what he or she knows about fractions as tenths and hundredths by doing the following activity together.

NEXT

Lesson 20 Fractions as Tenths and Hundredths

Fractions as Tenths and Hundredths Activity

Do an activity with your child to explore tenths and hundredths fractions.

- Use the tenths and hundredths models below or create your own models using lined paper and grid paper.

- Have your child choose a number between 1 and 5. Shade the tenths model to show that number of tenths.

  Example: Your child chooses 4.
  Your child shades 4 tenths $\left(\frac{4}{10}\right)$ of the tenths model.

- Then have another family member choose a 2-digit number between 10 and 50. Your child shades the hundredths model to show that number of hundredths.

  Example: A family member chooses 28.
  Your child shades $\frac{28}{100}$ of the hundredths model.

- Next, have your child add the fractions. Shade the other hundredths model to show the sum.

  Example: $\frac{4}{10} + \frac{28}{100}$

  $\frac{40}{100} + \frac{28}{100} = \frac{68}{100}$

 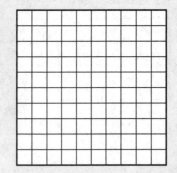

Fractions as Tenths and Hundredths

Name: _____

Study the example showing how to use a number line to find equivalent fractions. Then solve problems 1–8.

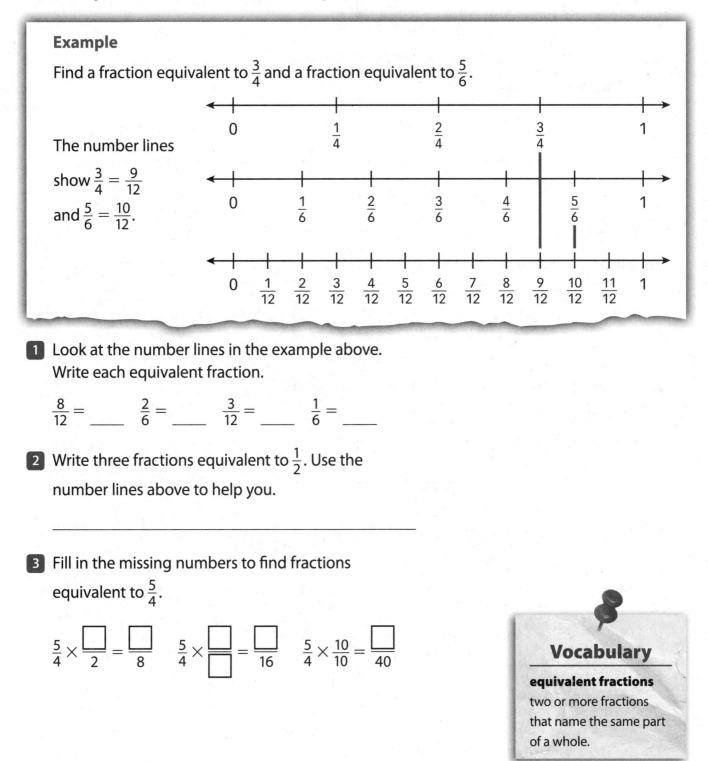

Example

Find a fraction equivalent to $\frac{3}{4}$ and a fraction equivalent to $\frac{5}{6}$.

The number lines

show $\frac{3}{4} = \frac{9}{12}$

and $\frac{5}{6} = \frac{10}{12}$.

1 Look at the number lines in the example above. Write each equivalent fraction.

$\frac{8}{12} =$ _____ $\frac{2}{6} =$ _____ $\frac{3}{12} =$ _____ $\frac{1}{6} =$ _____

2 Write three fractions equivalent to $\frac{1}{2}$. Use the number lines above to help you.

_____

3 Fill in the missing numbers to find fractions equivalent to $\frac{5}{4}$.

$\frac{5}{4} \times \frac{\square}{2} = \frac{\square}{8}$ $\frac{5}{4} \times \frac{\square}{\square} = \frac{\square}{16}$ $\frac{5}{4} \times \frac{10}{10} = \frac{\square}{40}$

Vocabulary

equivalent fractions
two or more fractions that name the same part of a whole.

Lesson 20 Fractions as Tenths and Hundredths   **211**

Solve.

4 Shade the model below to show $\frac{2}{3}$. Then divide the model to show $\frac{2}{3} = \frac{4}{6}$.

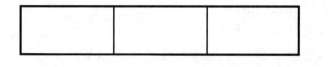

5 Look at problem 4. Explain how dividing the model shows the equivalent fractions $\frac{2}{3} = \frac{4}{6}$.

_____

_____

_____

_____

6 Fill in the missing numbers to write equivalent fractions.

$\dfrac{\square}{\square} \times \dfrac{2}{2} = \dfrac{2}{4}$ $\qquad$ $\dfrac{\square}{3} \times \dfrac{\square}{\square} = \dfrac{8}{12}$ $\qquad$ $\dfrac{\square}{\square} \times \dfrac{\square}{2} = \dfrac{10}{16}$

7 Shade the model to show $\frac{1}{2}$. Then divide the model to show $\frac{1}{2} = \frac{5}{10}$.

8 Fill in the missing numbers to show that $\frac{1}{2} = \frac{5}{10}$.

$\dfrac{1}{2} \times \dfrac{\square}{\square} = \dfrac{5}{10}$

Name: _____

Add Tenths and Hundredths Fractions

Study the example problem showing how to add tenths and hundredths fractions. Then solve problems 1–8.

Example

Jaden found $\frac{8}{10}$ of a dollar in change in his backpack.

He found $\frac{15}{100}$ of a dollar in change in his lunch bag.

What fraction of a dollar in change did he find altogether?

Multiply to find the hundredths fraction equivalent to $\frac{8}{10}$.

$$\frac{8}{10} = \left(\frac{8 \times 10}{10 \times 10}\right) = \frac{80}{100}$$

Add the hundredths fractions.

$$\frac{80}{100} + \frac{15}{100} = \frac{95}{100}$$

Jaden found $\frac{95}{100}$ of a dollar in change.

1 Write $\frac{2}{10}$ as an equivalent fraction with a denominator of 100.

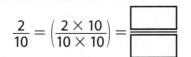

2 Fill in the blanks to show how to find the sum of $\frac{2}{10}$ and $\frac{10}{100}$.

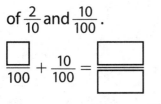

3 Look at problem 2. $\frac{10}{100} = \frac{1}{10}$. What is another way that you could show the sum of $\frac{2}{10}$ and $\frac{10}{100}$?

_____

4 Look at problems 2 and 3. Are the sums equivalent? Explain.

_____

_____

Lesson 20 Fractions as Tenths and Hundredths   **213**

Solve.

Mila has 100 math problems to finish this week.
She solved $\frac{2}{10}$ of the problems on Monday and $\frac{25}{100}$
of the problems on Tuesday.

5 Did Mila solve more problems on Monday or on
Tuesday? Explain.

Show your work.

Solution: _____

_____

6 What fraction of the math problems for the week did
Mila solve on Monday and Tuesday?

Show your work.

Solution: _____

7 Look at problem 6. Is the sum you found greater or less than $\frac{1}{2}$? Explain.

_____

_____

8 Has Mila completed more than half of her math problems
for the week? Explain.

_____

_____

Name: _____

Fractions as Tenths and Hundredths

Solve the problems.

1 $\frac{3}{10} + \frac{3}{100}$ is equal to which of the following?
Circle the letter for all that apply.

A $\frac{33}{100}$

B $\frac{6}{100}$

C $\frac{60}{100}$

D $\frac{30}{100} + \frac{3}{100}$

E $\frac{3}{10} + \frac{3}{10}$

> How many hundredths are in 3 tenths?

2 Sylvia has \$100. She spent $\frac{4}{10}$ of her money on a jacket and $\frac{20}{100}$ of her money on jeans. What fraction of her money did Sylvia spend?

A $\frac{60}{200}$

B $\frac{24}{100}$

C $\frac{6}{10}$

D $\frac{6}{20}$

Josh chose **B** as the correct answer. How did he get that answer?

_____

_____

_____

_____

> There is more than one way to solve this problem.

3 Which is greater, $\frac{6}{10}$ or $\frac{6}{100}$? Explain.

_____

_____

_____

_____

> You can compare the numerators or draw a model to solve this problem.

Solve.

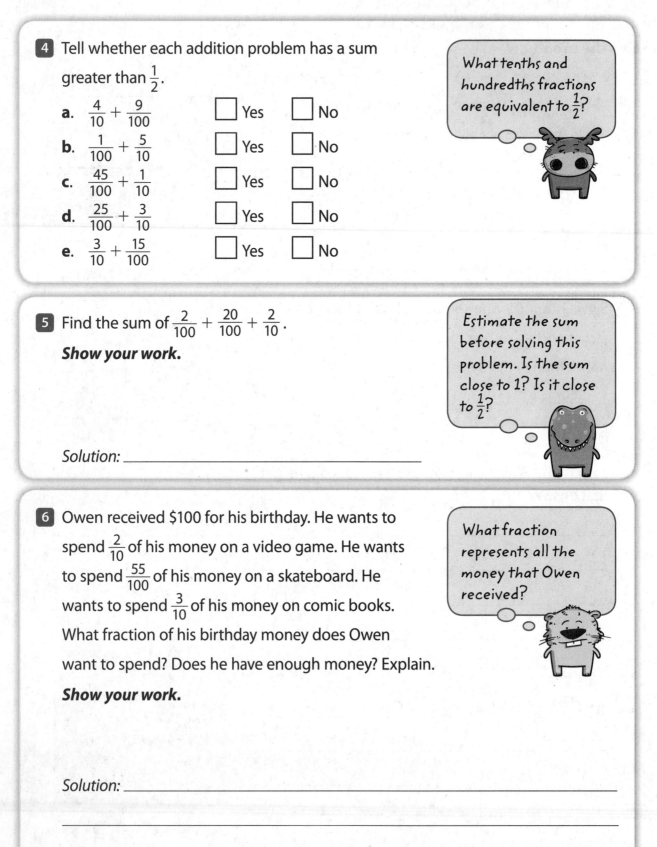

4 Tell whether each addition problem has a sum greater than $\frac{1}{2}$.

a. $\frac{4}{10} + \frac{9}{100}$ ☐ Yes ☐ No

b. $\frac{1}{100} + \frac{5}{10}$ ☐ Yes ☐ No

c. $\frac{45}{100} + \frac{1}{10}$ ☐ Yes ☐ No

d. $\frac{25}{100} + \frac{3}{10}$ ☐ Yes ☐ No

e. $\frac{3}{10} + \frac{15}{100}$ ☐ Yes ☐ No

> What tenths and hundredths fractions are equivalent to $\frac{1}{2}$?

5 Find the sum of $\frac{2}{100} + \frac{20}{100} + \frac{2}{10}$.

Show your work.

> Estimate the sum before solving this problem. Is the sum close to 1? Is it close to $\frac{1}{2}$?

Solution: _____

6 Owen received $100 for his birthday. He wants to spend $\frac{2}{10}$ of his money on a video game. He wants to spend $\frac{55}{100}$ of his money on a skateboard. He wants to spend $\frac{3}{10}$ of his money on comic books. What fraction of his birthday money does Owen want to spend? Does he have enough money? Explain.

Show your work.

> What fraction represents all the money that Owen received?

Solution: _____

_____

_____

Dear Family,

> **This week your child is learning about relating decimals and fractions.**

Tenths and hundredths can be written as decimal fractions.

You can use models to show the fraction $\frac{48}{100}$ as the decimal 0.48.

four tenths or 0.4

 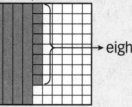 → eight hundredths or 0.08

48 hundredths (0.48) is 4 tenths (0.4) and 8 hundredths (0.08).

To write the mixed number $2\frac{48}{100}$ as a decimal, use a place-value chart.

decimal point
↓

Ones	.	Tenths	Hundredths
2	.	4	8

whole number   number less than 1

Your child is learning to read the decimal 2.48:
1. Say the whole number part, if there is one.   *two*
2. Say *and* for the decimal point.   *and*
3. Read the rest of the digits as a whole number.   *forty-eight*
4. Say the place-value name of the last digit.   *hundredths*

Say: *two and forty-eight hundredths.*

Invite your child to share what he or she knows about relating decimals and fractions by doing the following activity together.

NEXT

Relate Decimals and Fractions Activity

Do an activity with your child to relate decimals and fractions. You can use money to relate decimals and fractions because money is counted in tenths and hundredths. There are 100 pennies in 1 dollar, so one penny is 0.01, or $\frac{1}{100}$ of a dollar. There are 10 dimes in 1 dollar, so one dime is 0.1 (or 0.10), or $\frac{1}{10}$ of a dollar.

- With your child, collect pennies from around the house. Have your child write the amount as a decimal and as a fraction.

    Example: You have 23 pennies.

    Write the decimal 0.23 and the fraction $\frac{23}{100}$.

    Example: You have 30 pennies. Write the decimal 0.30 and the

    fraction $\frac{30}{100}$. Challenge your child to write the

    equivalent tenths decimal and fraction: 0.3 and $\frac{3}{10}$.

- Next, collect dimes from around the house and have your child write the amount as a decimal and as a fraction.

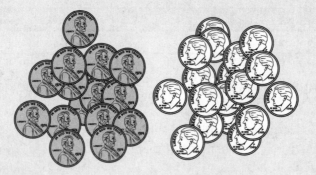

Look for other real-life opportunities to relate decimals and fractions with your child.

Relate Decimals and Fractions

Name: _____

Prerequisite: Find Equivalent Fractions

Study the example showing how to identify equivalent fractions with denominators of 10 and 100. Then solve problems 1–5.

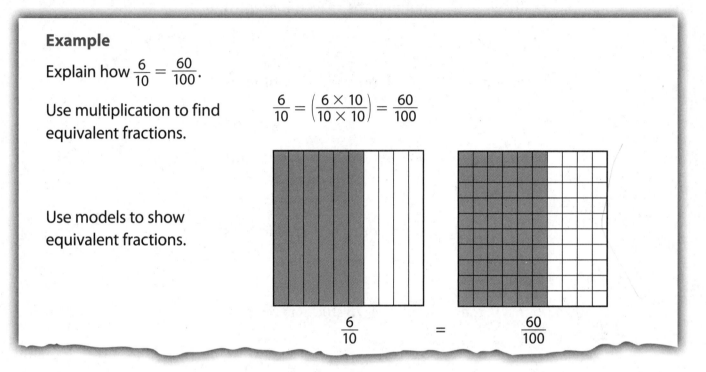

Example

Explain how $\frac{6}{10} = \frac{60}{100}$.

Use multiplication to find equivalent fractions.

$$\frac{6}{10} = \left(\frac{6 \times 10}{10 \times 10}\right) = \frac{60}{100}$$

Use models to show equivalent fractions.

$$\frac{6}{10} \qquad = \qquad \frac{60}{100}$$

1 Write the fractions that the models below show.

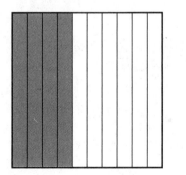

_____   _____

2 Look at problem 1. Use multiplication to find the equivalent fractions.

_____

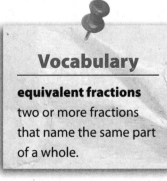

Vocabulary

equivalent fractions
two or more fractions that name the same part of a whole.

Solve.

3 Fill in the blanks with numbers and fractions to make true sentences.

a. _____ $+ \dfrac{15}{100} = \dfrac{55}{100}$

_____ tenths + _____ hundredths = 55 hundredths.

b. _____ $+ \dfrac{4}{10} = \dfrac{55}{100}$

_____ hundredths + _____ tenths = 55 hundredths.

c. _____ $+ \dfrac{5}{100} = \dfrac{55}{100}$

_____ tenths + _____ hundredths = 55 hundredths.

d. _____ $+ \dfrac{25}{100} = \dfrac{55}{100}$

_____ tenths + _____ hundredths = 55 hundredths.

> Of the 100 students in the fourth grade, 70 students are girls.

4 Write a fraction in tenths and a fraction in hundredths to tell what fraction of the fourth-grade students are girls.

_____

5 Write a fraction in tenths and a fraction in hundredths to tell what fraction of the fourth-grade students are boys.

_____

Name: _____

Name the Same Amount

Study the example showing ways to name the same amount as a fraction and a decimal. Then solve problems 1–7.

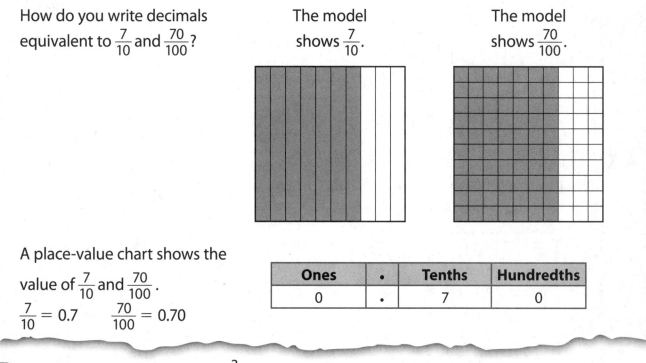

Example

How do you write decimals equivalent to $\frac{7}{10}$ and $\frac{70}{100}$?

The model shows $\frac{7}{10}$.

The model shows $\frac{70}{100}$.

A place-value chart shows the value of $\frac{7}{10}$ and $\frac{70}{100}$.

$\frac{7}{10} = 0.7$ $\frac{70}{100} = 0.70$

Ones	.	Tenths	Hundredths
0	.	7	0

---

1. What decimal is equivalent to $\frac{3}{10}$?

   Fill in the place-value chart to show the decimal.

Ones	.	Tenths
	.	

2. What decimal is equivalent to $\frac{55}{100}$?

   Fill in the place-value chart to show the decimal.

Ones	.	Tenths	Hundredths
	.		

3. Write a decimal equivalent to $\frac{75}{100}$. _____

Vocabulary

decimal fraction (or decimal) a number containing a decimal point that separates a whole from fractional place values, such as tenths and hundredths.

0.7 and 0.70 are decimals.

Solve.

4 What decimal is equivalent to $\frac{80}{100}$? Shade the model below to show the fraction and the decimal. Then write the decimal.

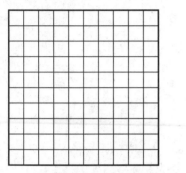

$$\frac{80}{100} = \underline{\hspace{1.5cm}}$$

5 Look at problem 4. Shade the model below to show an equivalent tenths fraction and decimal. Then write the fraction and decimal.

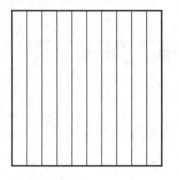

$$\underline{\hspace{1.5cm}} = \underline{\hspace{1.5cm}}$$

6 Use what you know about equivalent fractions to explain why 0.8 and 0.80 are equivalent.

_____

_____

7 Find the sum of $\frac{80}{100}$ and $\frac{20}{100}$. Then use what you know about equivalent fractions to explain why $0.8 + 0.2 = 1$.

_____

_____

_____

Name: _____

Write a Decimal as an Equivalent Fraction

Study the example problem showing how to write a decimal as an equivalent fraction. Then solve problems 1–8.

Example

Alanna has an assortment of books in her bookcase. 0.09 of her books are comic books. What fraction of the books are comic books?

Decimal: 0.09

Words: 9 hundredths

Fraction: $\frac{9}{100}$

$\frac{9}{100}$ of the books are comic books.

Ones	.	Tenths	Hundredths
0	.	0	9

1 Shade the model below to show 0.34.

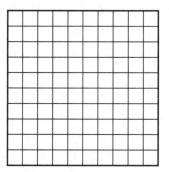

2 Show 0.34 in a place-value chart.

Ones	.	Tenths	Hundredths
	.		

3 Write 0.34 in words. _____

4 Write 0.34 as a fraction. _____

Solve.

5 Tell whether each number sentence is *True* or *False*.

a. $0.3 = \frac{3}{100}$ ☐ True ☐ False

b. $0.03 = \frac{3}{100}$ ☐ True ☐ False

c. $0.3 = \frac{30}{100}$ ☐ True ☐ False

d. $0.3 = \frac{3}{10}$ ☐ True ☐ False

6 Write two equivalent fractions to 0.3.

_____

7 Which of the following names the same number as 0.62? Circle the letter for all that apply.

A sixty-two hundredths

B six tenths and 2 hundredths

C $\frac{62}{10}$

D $\frac{62}{100}$

8 The number line below shows 1 whole divided into tenths. Write numbers in the boxes to label the missing fractions and decimal. Explain how you know what numbers to write.

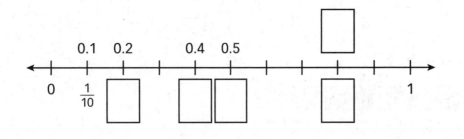

_____

_____

_____

_____

Name: _____

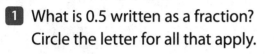

Relate Decimals and Fractions

Solve the problems.

1 What is 0.5 written as a fraction?
Circle the letter for all that apply.

How can you say the decimal in words?

A $\frac{5}{100}$

B $\frac{5}{10}$

C $\frac{50}{100}$

D $\frac{50}{10}$

2 Rita correctly answered 9 questions out of 10 on a test. What fraction of the test questions did Rita answer incorrectly?

What fraction represents all the questions?

A $\frac{9}{10}$

B $\frac{9}{100}$

C $\frac{1}{10}$

D $\frac{1}{100}$

Patrick chose **A** as the correct answer. How did he get that answer?

_____

_____

_____

_____

_____

Solve.

3 Austin bought an eraser for 65 cents and a pencil for 20 cents. What fraction of a dollar did he spend? Write the fraction as a decimal.

What fraction of a dollar is 1 cent?

Show your work.

Solution: _____

4 Tell whether each number below is equivalent to $\frac{15}{100}$.

How do you write this fraction in words and as a decimal?

a. fifteen hundredths ☐ Yes ☐ No

b. 1.5 ☐ Yes ☐ No

c. $\frac{15}{10}$ ☐ Yes ☐ No

d. 0.15 ☐ Yes ☐ No

5 Mackenzie has 1 dollar, 2 dimes, and 3 pennies. Jorge has only dimes and pennies but has the same amount of money as Mackenzie. How many dimes and pennies could Jorge have?

Can you represent the value of a dollar, a dime, and a penny as fractions or decimals to help you solve this problem?

Show your work.

Solution: _____

_____

Dear Family,

This week your child is learning to compare decimals.

A model can help your child compare decimals when one decimal is in tenths and the other decimal is in hundredths.

The models show 0.75 and 0.8.

0.75
seventy-five hundredths

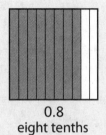

0.8
eight tenths

A greater area is shaded for 0.8 than for 0.75, so 0.8 is greater than 0.75.

Your child can also use a place-value chart to compare decimals in tenths and hundredths.

8 tenths equals 80 hundredths. $\frac{8}{10} = \frac{80}{100}$

Ones	.	Tenths	Hundredths
0	.	7	5
0	.	8	0

The place-value chart shows that eighty hundredths, or eight tenths, is greater than seventy-five hundredths. Compare the digits in the tenths place: 8 > 7.

0.80 > 0.75 and 0.8 > 0.75

Invite your child to share what he or she knows about comparing decimals by doing the following activity together.

NEXT

Compare Decimals Activity

Do an activity with your child to compare decimals.

Materials: fliers for grocery, drug, or hardware stores (optional)

- Look for items around the house or look through the fliers to find at least 6 decimal numbers. Make a list of the numbers as you find them; do not include the units.

    Example: You have a box of crackers that is 6.75 ounces.

- Take turns. One person marks two decimal numbers for the other person to compare. Make and use place-value charts if needed.

- Challenge! Of all the decimal numbers you have compared, can you tell which is the greatest of all? Talk about how you know.

Look for other real-life opportunities to compare decimals with your child.

Compare Decimals

Name: _____

Prerequisite: Compare Fractions

Study the example showing ways to compare fractions. Then solve problems 1–6.

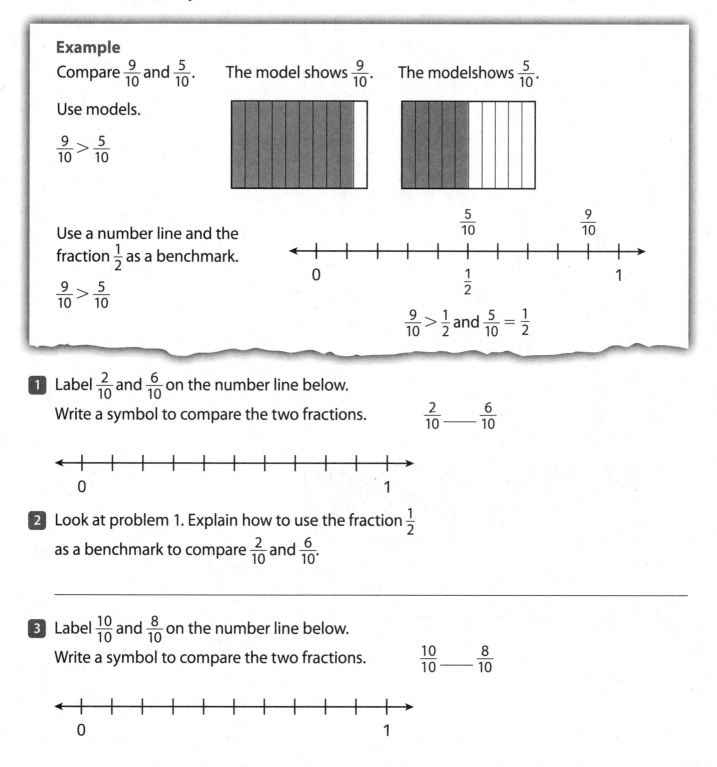

Example

Compare $\frac{9}{10}$ and $\frac{5}{10}$.   The model shows $\frac{9}{10}$.   The modelshows $\frac{5}{10}$.

Use models.

$\frac{9}{10} > \frac{5}{10}$

Use a number line and the fraction $\frac{1}{2}$ as a benchmark.

$\frac{9}{10} > \frac{5}{10}$

$\frac{9}{10} > \frac{1}{2}$ and $\frac{5}{10} = \frac{1}{2}$

1. Label $\frac{2}{10}$ and $\frac{6}{10}$ on the number line below.
Write a symbol to compare the two fractions. $\frac{2}{10}$ ——— $\frac{6}{10}$

2. Look at problem 1. Explain how to use the fraction $\frac{1}{2}$ as a benchmark to compare $\frac{2}{10}$ and $\frac{6}{10}$.

_____

3. Label $\frac{10}{10}$ and $\frac{8}{10}$ on the number line below.
Write a symbol to compare the two fractions. $\frac{10}{10}$ ——— $\frac{8}{10}$

Solve.

4 Shade and label the models below to show $\frac{3}{10}$ and $\frac{3}{100}$.
Write a symbol to compare the fractions. $\frac{3}{10}$ _____ $\frac{3}{100}$

_____   _____

5 Use the symbols $<$, $>$, and $=$ to compare the fractions.

a. $\frac{5}{10}$ _____ $\frac{50}{100}$

b. $\frac{4}{10}$ _____ $\frac{4}{100}$

c. $\frac{11}{10}$ _____ $\frac{12}{10}$

d. $\frac{62}{100}$ _____ $\frac{6}{10}$

e. $\frac{9}{100}$ _____ $\frac{9}{10}$

6 Write the fraction that each model shows. Explain
which fraction is greater.

_____   _____

_____

_____

Name: _____

Compare Hundredths Decimals

Study the example problem showing how to compare hundredths decimals to solve a problem. Then solve problems 1–7.

Example

Jacob bought an apple and a pear. The apple weighed 0.33 of a pound. The pear weighed 0.35 of a pound. Which piece of fruit weighed less?

Write equivalent fractions.
The denominators are the same.
Compare numerators. 33 < 35.

$0.33 = \frac{33}{100}$ $0.35 = \frac{35}{100}$

same denominator

0.33 < 0.35
The apple weighed less than the pear.

1 Shade and label the models below to show 0.33 and 0.35.

_____   _____

2 Explain how the models show which decimal is less. _____

_____

3 Complete the place-value chart to show 0.33 and 0.35.

Ones	•	Tenths	Hundredths
	•		
	•		

4 Explain how the place-value chart shows which decimal is less. _____

_____

Solve.

5 Use the digits in the tiles below to create decimals
that make each inequality true.

a. $0.21 > 0.2\square$

b. $0.46 < 0.\square6$

c. $0.99 < \square.00$

d. $0.7\square > 0.7\square$

6 Write the symbol ($>$, $<$, $=$) that makes each
statement below true.

a. 0.85 _____ 0.82

b. 0.09 _____ 0.10

c. 0.45 _____ 0.54

d. 1.10 _____ 1.01

e. 0.30 _____ 0.3

7 Ryder bought 0.75 pound of turkey and 0.57 pound
of cheese. Did he buy more turkey or cheese?

Show your work.

Solution: _____

Name: _____

Compare Tenths and Hundredths Decimals

Study the example problem showing how to compare tenths and hundredths decimals. Then solve problems 1–6.

Example

Colin lives 0.6 mile from school and 0.65 mile from the park. Which place is closer to his home?

Write each decimal as an equivalent fraction. $0.6 = \frac{6}{10}$ $0.65 = \frac{65}{100}$

Write the tenths fraction as a hundredths fraction. $\frac{6}{10} = \frac{60}{100}$

Compare hundredths fractions. $\frac{60}{100} < \frac{65}{100}$

$0.6 < 0.65$

The school is closer to his home.

Lucas bought 0.6 pound of fish and 0.85 pound of shrimp to make a stew.

1 Shade the models below to compare 0.6 and 0.85.

2 Write a symbol to compare the decimals. 0.6 _____ 0.85

3 Did Lucas buy more fish or shrimp?
Use equivalent fractions to explain your answer.

_____

_____

Lesson 22 Compare Decimals   **233**

Solve.

4 Compare 0.2 and 0.25 using $>$, $=$, or $<$. Use equivalent fractions to explain your answer.

_____

_____

_____

_____

5 Compare 0.09 and 0.1 using $>$, $=$, or $<$. Use a place-value chart to explain your answer.

Ones	•	Tenths	Hundredths
	•		
	•		

_____

_____

_____

_____

6 Write the decimals 1.00, 0.20, and 0.03 in the place-value chart below. Which number is the greatest? Which number is the least? Use equivalent fractions to explain.

Ones	•	Tenths	Hundredths
	•		
	•		
	•		

_____

_____

_____

_____

Name: _____

Compare Decimals

Solve the problems.

1 Which decimal is less than 0.35?

A 0.5   **C** 0.36

B 0.29   **D** 0.53

Do you compare the tenths or hundredths place?

2 Which is the greatest—0.19, 1.00, 0.91, or 0.02?

A 0.02   **C** 0.91

B 0.19   **D** 1.00

Sadie chose **B** as the correct answer. How did she get that answer?

_____

_____

_____

_____

A place-value chart can help you compare decimals.

3 Classify each decimal below as less than half, equal to half, or greater than half, by writing each decimal in the correct column of the chart.

0.05   0.52   0.25   0.48   0.9   0.50   0.6   1.05

Less than Half	Equal to Half	Greater than Half

You can think about half as the benchmark fraction $\frac{1}{2}$ to help solve this problem.

Solve.

4 Milk costs $0.50 and juice costs $0.55. Which costs less, milk or juice?

Show your work.

Which place value do you compare first?

Solution: _____

5 Julie has 2 dollars to spend on lunch. A slice of pizza is $2.25. A sandwich is $2. A bowl of soup is $1.95. What can Julie buy for lunch? Explain your answer.

Show your work.

Think of each price as a decimal. Then compare each price to the amount of money Julie has.

Solution: _____

_____

Unit 4 Game

Fraction Sums

What you need: Recording Sheet, two 1–6 number cubes

Directions

- Players each choose a denominator from the list on the Recording Sheet. Players write their numbers in the Denominator Choice column of the Recording Sheet.

- Player A rolls the number cubes and makes two fractions using the numbers rolled as the numerators along with the chosen denominator.

- Player A writes and solves an addition problem with the two fractions on the Recording Sheet.

- Player B takes a turn following the same steps as Player A.

- Players compare the two fraction sums. The player with the greater sum wins the round.

- In each round, players choose a denominator that they have not used yet. The player with more wins after 5 rounds wins the game.

Fraction Sums Recording Sheet

Name: _Maya_

Denominators
2 3 4̸ 6 8

Denominators
2 3 4 6 8̸

_____Maya_____
Player A Name

Denominator Choice	Equation
1. ___4___	$\frac{3}{4} + \frac{4}{4} = \frac{7}{4}$
2. _____	_____

_____Isaac_____
Player B Name

Denominator Choice	Equation
1. ___8___	$\frac{4}{8} + \frac{6}{8} = \frac{10}{8}$
2. _____	_____

I chose fourths.
$\frac{3}{4} + \frac{4}{4} = \frac{7}{4}$.
That's the same as $\frac{14}{8}$. I win this round because $\frac{14}{8}$ is more than your sum of $\frac{10}{8}$.

Fraction Sums Recording Sheet

| Denominators |
| 2 3 4 6 8 |

| Denominators |
| 2 3 4 6 8 |

_____
Player A Name

Denominator Choice	Equation
1. _____	_____
2. _____	_____
3. _____	_____
4. _____	_____
5. _____	_____

Final Score Player A [ ]

_____
Player B Name

Denominator Choice	Equation
1. _____	_____
2. _____	_____
3. _____	_____
4. _____	_____
5. _____	_____

Final Score Player B [ ]

Name: _____

Number and Operations—Fractions

In this unit you learned to:	Lesson
find equivalent fractions, for example: $\frac{2}{3} = \frac{4}{6}$.	13
compare fractions with unlike denominators, for example: $\frac{2}{5} > \frac{3}{10}$.	14
add and subtract fractions with like denominators; add and subtract mixed numbers, for example: $\frac{2}{6} + \frac{3}{6} = \frac{5}{6}$.	15, 16, 17
multiply a fraction by a whole number, for example, $3 \times \frac{1}{2} = \frac{3}{2}$.	18, 19
write a decimal as a fraction, for example: $0.4 = \frac{4}{10}$.	20, 21
compare decimals, for example: $0.65 < 0.7$.	22

Use these skills to solve problems 1–5.

1 Use $<$, $>$, or $=$ to complete each number sentence.

a. $\frac{2}{4}$ ☐ $\frac{1}{3}$

b. $\frac{3}{4}$ ☐ $3 \times \frac{4}{4} \times 3$

c. $\frac{2}{10}$ ☐ 0.20

d. $\frac{3}{4}$ ☐ $\frac{15}{20}$

e. 0.5 ☐ 0.09

2 Write each of the following numbers in one box below to show where on the number line it belongs.

1.03

1.4

1.34

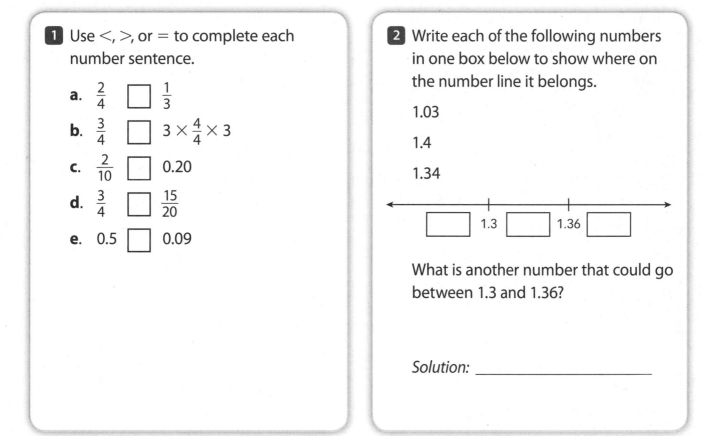

What is another number that could go between 1.3 and 1.36?

Solution: _____

Solve.

3 Diego wants to ride a bike path that is 10 miles long. He bikes $3\frac{3}{10}$ miles and stops for a rest. Then he goes another $3\frac{5}{10}$ miles and stops for lunch. How many more miles does Diego have to ride? Write your answer as a decimal.

Show your work.

Solution: _____

4 Alicia and Gwen need to find 12 different leaves for a science project. Alicia has found $\frac{2}{3}$ of her leaves. Gwen has found $\frac{3}{4}$ of her leaves.

Who has collected more leaves? How do you know?

_____

_____

_____

_____

_____

_____

_____

5 Cleo and Li both made a dozen cupcakes.

• Cleo made 3 of her cupcakes without nuts.

• Li made 4 of her cupcakes without nuts.

In the space below, draw pictures of the two batches of cupcakes.
Use numbers to show the fraction of cupcakes without nuts in each batch.

Name: _____

Answer the questions and show all your work on separate paper.

A grocery store sells fruit salad made with pineapples, strawberries, raspberries, blueberries, blackberries, and grapes. The store sells three different kinds of salad:

The Hawaiian: More than $\frac{1}{2}$ of the salad is made of pineapple. The rest is made of grapes and blueberries.

The Red Rose: Less than $\frac{1}{2}$ of the salad is made of red grapes. The rest is made of strawberries and raspberries.

The Berry Basket: The salad has equal parts of strawberries, blueberries, raspberries, and blackberries.

Make an ingredient list for each of the salads. Write a fraction for the fruits that are included in each salad. Explain why your lists fit the description of each salad.

Checklist

Did you . . .

- ☐ meet the given conditions?
- ☐ check your work?
- ☐ reread your explanation to see if it makes sense?

The Hawaiian	The Red Rose	The Berry Basket
$\frac{}{8}$ _____	$\frac{}{8}$ _____	$\frac{}{8}$ _____
$\frac{}{8}$ _____	$\frac{}{8}$ _____	$\frac{}{8}$ _____
$\frac{}{8}$ _____	$\frac{}{8}$ _____	$\frac{}{8}$ _____
		$\frac{}{8}$ _____

Reflect on Mathematical Practices

After you complete the task, choose one of the following questions to answer.

1 Make Sense of Problems How did you know which fraction to find first for The Hawaiian and The Red Rose salads?

2 Use Structure How did you decide which fractions to use after you found the first fraction?

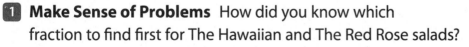

Performance Task Tips

Word Bank Here are some words that you might use in your answer.

more	fraction	add
greater than	whole	equal
less	part	equivalent
less than	sum	

Models Here are some models that you might use to find the solution.

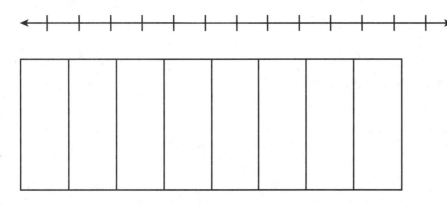

Sentence Starters Here are some sentence starters that might help you write an explanation.

The fractions _____

An equivalent fraction _____

_____ is greater than _____

_____ is less than _____

Unit 4 Vocabulary

Name: _____

My Examples

fraction

a number that names part of a whole

numerator

the number above the line in a fraction; it tells how many equal parts are described

denominator

the number below the line in a fraction; it tells how many equal parts are in a whole

equivalent fractions

two or more fractions that name the same part of a whole

mixed number

a number with a whole number part
and a fractional part

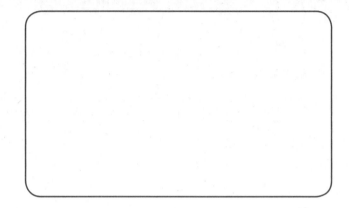

decimal fraction (or decimal)

a number containing a decimal point
that separates a whole from fractional
place values, such as tenths and
hundredths

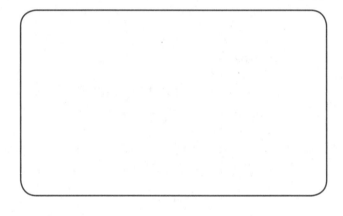

compare

to decide if one number is greater than,
less than, or equal to another number

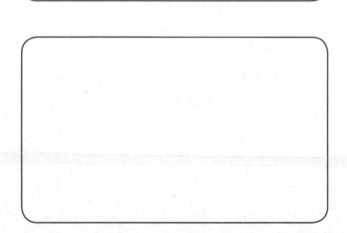

greater than (>)

a comparison that says one number has
greater value than another number

My Examples

less than (<)

a comparison that says one number has less value than another number

multiplication

an operation used to find the total number of items in equal-sized groups

product

the result of multiplication

divide

to separate an amount into equal groups and find the number in each group or the number of groups

My Words

_____

_____

_____

_____

_____

_____

_____

_____

_____

_____

_____

_____

My Examples

Dear Family,

This week your child is learning to convert measurements.

When you convert from a larger unit, such as a pound, to a smaller unit, such as an ounce, you use multiplication.

Knowing that there are 16 ounces in one pound, you multiply by 16 to find the number of ounces in any number of pounds. For example, to find how many ounces are in 12 pounds, you multiply 12 by 16.

When your child is converting larger units to smaller units, he or she is not only becoming more familiar with the relative sizes of units, but is also getting good practice with multiplication!

Sometimes it's convenient to use a table to convert measurements. The diagram below shows that each pound is the same as 16 ounces.

12 pounds (lb)

1 lb	1 lb	1 lb	1 lb	1 lb	1 lb	1 lb	1 lb	1 lb	1 lb	1 lb	1 lb
16 oz	16 oz	16 oz	16 oz	16 oz	16 oz	16 oz	16 oz	16 oz	16 oz	16 oz	16 oz

192 ounces (oz)

The table below shows exactly how many ounces are in any number of pounds.

Pounds (lb)	1	2	3	4	5	6	7	8	9	10	11	12
Ounces (oz)	16	32	48	64	80	96	112	128	144	160	176	192

When your child writes $p \times 16$ to tell how many ounces are in p pounds, he or she is applying the skill of writing an expression. The expression gives the formula for converting any number of pounds to ounces.

Invite your child to share what he or she knows about converting measurements by doing the following activity together.

NEXT

Converting Measurements Activity

Do an activity with your child to convert measurements.

Materials: ruler or yardstick

Measure the stride of your child. Put a mark at your child's toe to create a "starting point."

- Ask your child to take a long step and put another mark at the heel of the foot taking the step.

- Measure the distance *in feet* between the marks.

- Now, find the measure of your child's stride in inches by converting feet to inches. There are 12 inches in one foot.

- Talk with your child about different ways you could convert the measurement, such as using a bar model or a table, drawing a picture, or writing an expression. How could you use a different way to convert the measurement?

- Next, measure the stride of another family member. First find the measure in feet and then convert it to inches. Compare the length of this stride to the length of your child's stride. Who has a longer stride? Who has a shorter stride?

Convert Measurements

Prerequisite: Multiply with Measurements

Study the example showing how to use multiplication to solve a measurement problem. Then solve problems 1–5.

Example

Kian filled 5 pitchers with water. Each pitcher holds 2 liters. How many liters of water did Kian use to fill the pitchers?

1 pitcher | 2

5 pitchers | 2 | 2 | 2 | 2 | 2

|———————— 10 ————————|

The picture shows that
2 + 2 + 2 + 2 + 2 = 10.

Kian used 10 liters of water.

The bar model shows multiplication as a comparison, 5 × 2 = 10.

1 Yvonne's house has 4 bedrooms. It takes 1 gallon of paint to paint each bedroom. How many gallons of paint are needed to paint all 4 bedrooms? Show how to add or multiply to find the answer.

_____

2 One granola bar has 5 grams of protein. A package has 6 granola bars. How many grams of protein are in a package? Draw a bar model to show how to find the answer.

Solution: _____

Solve.

3 Miranda's family brought 3 large coolers full of lemonade to the family picnic. Each cooler contains 8 liters of lemonade. How much lemonade did the family bring to the picnic?

Show your work.

Solution: The family brought _____ of lemonade.

4 The table below shows the number of grams of sugar in a 1-cup serving of each kind of fruit.

Fruit	Strawberries	Apples	Bananas
Grams of sugar in a 1-cup serving	7 g	13 g	18 g

  a. How many grams of sugar are in 3 cups of strawberries?

    _____

  b. How many grams of sugar are in 2 cups of apples?

    _____

  c. Are there more grams of sugar in 3 cups of strawberries or 2 cups of apples? Explain.

    _____

    _____

5 Look at the table in problem 4. Madeleine made a strawberry-banana smoothie to share with her friends. She put 4 cups of strawberries and 2 cups of bananas in a blender. How many total grams of sugar are in the smoothie?

Show your work.

Solution: _____

Name: _____

Convert Units of Weight and Mass

Study the example showing how to convert from a larger unit to a smaller unit of weight and mass. Then solve problems 1–7.

Example

Eleanor bought a 3-pound watermelon and 32 ounces of strawberries. How much more does the watermelon weigh than the strawberries?

1 pound (lb) = 16 ounces (oz)

Write an expression to convert pounds to ounces. Let p stand for the number of pounds.

$p \times 16$

Find the weight of the watermelon in ounces. The watermelon weighs 48 ounces.

Substitute 3 for p.
$3 \times 16 = 48$

$48 - 32 = 16$

The watermelon weighs 16 ounces more than the strawberries.

---

1 John has a watermelon with a mass of 3 kilograms. Complete the bar model. Then write the mass of the watermelon in grams.

3 kilograms (kg)

1 kg	1 kg	
1,000 g	1,000 g	

_____ grams (g)

2 Write an expression that shows how to convert kilograms to grams. Use K to stand for the number of kilograms.

_____

3 Convert the units of mass.

2 kg = _____ g   4 kg = _____ g

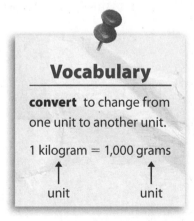

Vocabulary

convert to change from one unit to another unit.

1 kilogram = 1,000 grams
↑   ↑
unit   unit

Solve.

4 Complete the table to convert from a larger unit to a smaller unit of weight.

Pounds (lb)	1	2	3	4	5	6	7
Ounces (oz)	16		48				112

5 Neil brought 2 pounds of grapes for fruit salad at the class picnic. There are 8 ounces of grapes left. How many ounces of grapes were used? Look at the table in problem 4 to help you answer the question.

Show your work.

Solution: _____

6 Choose *Yes* or *No* to tell whether the given weight is equal to 6 pounds.

a. 22 ounces   ☐ Yes   ☐ No

b. 96 ounces   ☐ Yes   ☐ No

c. 4 pounds, 32 ounces   ☐ Yes   ☐ No

d. 5 pounds, 16 ounces   ☐ Yes   ☐ No

7 An adult bottlenose dolphin has a mass of 200 kilograms. What is the mass of an adult bottlenose dolphin in grams?

1 kilogram = 1,000 grams

Show your work.

Solution: _____

Name: _____

Convert Units of Liquid Volume

Study the example showing how to convert from a larger unit to a smaller unit of liquid volume. Then solve problems 1–7.

Example

Josie made 4 quarts of iced tea for a family picnic. Her sister made 14 cups of punch for the picnic. Who made a greater amount of beverages?

Use a table to convert quarts to cups.

Quarts	1	2	3	4	5
Cups	4	8	12	16	20

1 quart = 4 cups

Josie made 4 quarts, or 16 cups of iced tea.
16 > 14

Josie made a greater amount of beverages.

1 The soccer coach has a container that holds 5 liters of water. How many milliliters of water does the container hold?

Fill in the table to answer the question.

Liters (L)	1	2	3	4	5
Milliliters (mL)	1,000		3,000		

The container holds _____ of water.

2 Write an expression that shows how to convert liters to milliliters. Use L to stand for the number of liters.

_____

3 Convert the units of liquid volume.

6 L = _____ mL $\frac{1}{2}$ L = _____ mL

Vocabulary

convert to change from one unit to another unit.

1 liter = 1,000 milliliters
↑   ↑
unit   unit

Solve.

4 Carla had 2 liters of juice to share. She and her 3 friends each drank an equal amount of the juice. How many milliliters of juice did each friend have?

1 liter = 1,000 milliliters

Show your work.

Solution: _____

5 Theo filled up a 3-liter watering can to water the garden. He has 750 milliliters of water left in the watering can. How many milliliters of water did Theo use?

Show your work.

Solution: _____

6 A small bottle contains 2 cups of juice. Do 5 small bottles of juice have a greater amount of juice than a 1-quart bottle of juice? Explain.

1 quart = 4 cups

_____

_____

_____

_____

7 Rachel has a 4-liter jug of water. She fills 3 small vases each with 900 mL of water. How much water did she use? How much water is left in the jug?

Show your work.

Solution: _____

©Curriculum Associates, LLC   Copying is not permitted.

Name: _____

Convert Measurements

Solve the problems.

1 How many weeks are in 2 years?

A 26 weeks   **C** 54 weeks

B 52 weeks   **D** 104 weeks

> There are 52 weeks in a year.

2 How many cups of milk are in 8 quarts?

A 2 cups

B 12 cups

| 1 quart = 4 cups |

C 16 cups

D 32 cups

Jeff chose **A** as the correct answer. How did he get that answer?

_____

_____

_____

> Which is the larger unit, quarts or cups?

3 Stacia buys 6 yards of ribbon to make a costume. She has 2 feet of ribbon left over. How many feet of ribbon did Stacia use to make the costume?

Show your work.

| 1 yard = 3 feet |

> You can write an equation to show the relationship between yards and feet.

Solution: _____

Solve.

4 Which of the following is equal to 2 days, 12 hours?
Circle the letter for all that apply.

1 day = 24 hours

A   48 hours

B   60 hours

C   1 day, 36 hours

D   1 day, 24 hours

5 Jason is 5 foot 11 inches tall. Amy is 63 inches tall.
Who is taller and by how much?

Do you compare the heights in inches or feet?

1 foot = 12 inches

Show your work.

Solution: _____

6 How many 250 mL glasses can be filled with
2 L of water?

A picture or a table can help you understand and solve this problem.

1 liter = 1,000 milliliters

Show your work.

Solution: _____

Dear Family,

This week your child is learning about converting units of time and money.

Your child is learning different ways to solve multi-step problems converting larger units to smaller units for time and money. Here's a time problem your child might see.

> Penny has 2 hours to complete her chores. She spends 15 minutes putting away her clean clothes. She spends 45 minutes cleaning her closet. It takes her 40 minutes to clean the bathroom. How much time does Penny have left to give her dog a bath?

Since the problem has information in both minutes and hours, the first step is to convert the hours to minutes. There are 60 minutes in one hour, so multiply by 2 to convert 2 hours to minutes: $2 \times 60 = 120$.

Then, one way to solve the problem is to show the information on a number line.

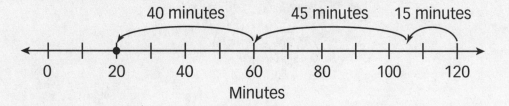

Only 20 minutes are left for the dog bath!

Other ways to solve a problem like this include writing an equation, such as $d = 120 - 15 - 45 - 40$, where d is the time left for the dog bath. Ask your child to compare the equation and the number line diagram to see how they are similar.

Invite your child to share what he or she knows about converting units to solve multi-step problems about time and money by doing the following activity together.

NEXT

Converting Time and Money Activity

Do an activity with your child to convert units of time and money.

Make up multi-step problems about time and money that might occur in everyday life. Here are some examples you might use:

- Pete bought 4 rolls of tape and 2 packages of markers for his project. The tape cost $0.75 a roll, and the markers cost $1.25 for each package. Pete gave the clerk a $10 bill. How much change did Pete receive? ($4.50)

- Marta wanted to spend one hour gardening. She spent 30 minutes planting flowers. Then she spent 10 minutes watering the flowers and 15 minutes pruning roses. Did Marta spend more or less time than she wanted to spend gardening? (She spent less time. There are 60 minutes in an hour and she spent 55 minutes in all.)

- Talk with your child about how to solve the problem.

- Ask your child if he or she could solve the problem another way. (Ways to solve the problem include using a bar model, a number line, a picture, or an equation.)

Look for other real-life opportunities to practice converting units of time and money with your child.

Time and Money

Name: _____

Prerequisite: Solve Problems About Money and Time

Study the example showing how to solve a word problem about money. Then solve problems 1–5.

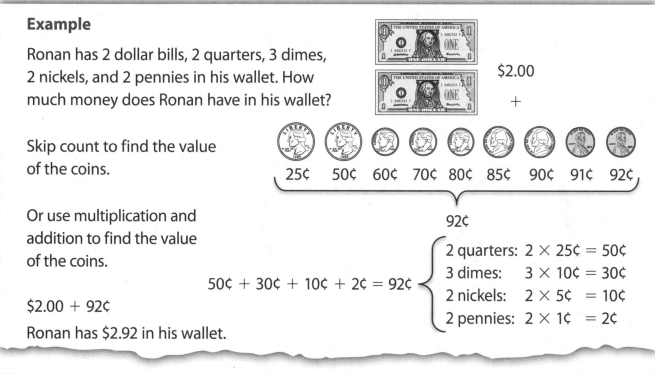

Example

Ronan has 2 dollar bills, 2 quarters, 3 dimes, 2 nickels, and 2 pennies in his wallet. How much money does Ronan have in his wallet?

$2.00
+

Skip count to find the value of the coins.

25¢ 50¢ 60¢ 70¢ 80¢ 85¢ 90¢ 91¢ 92¢

92¢

Or use multiplication and addition to find the value of the coins.

50¢ + 30¢ + 10¢ + 2¢ = 92¢

2 quarters: 2 × 25¢ = 50¢
3 dimes: 3 × 10¢ = 30¢
2 nickels: 2 × 5¢ = 10¢
2 pennies: 2 × 1¢ = 2¢

$2.00 + 92¢

Ronan has $2.92 in his wallet.

1 Fill in the blanks below with numbers to show different ways to make 50 cents with quarters, dimes, and nickels.

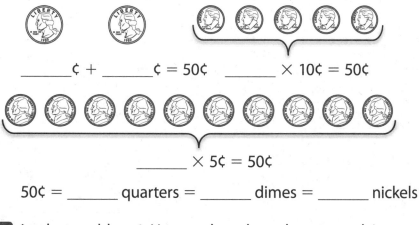

_____¢ + _____¢ = 50¢   _____ × 10¢ = 50¢

_____ × 5¢ = 50¢

50¢ = _____ quarters = _____ dimes = _____ nickels

2 Look at problem 1. Use words and numbers to explain a different way to make 50 cents with a quarter, dimes, and nickels.

_____

_____

Solve.

3 Daphne woke up at 7:15. It took her 15 minutes to dress and brush her teeth. She ate breakfast for 20 minutes. Then it took 5 minutes for her to walk to the bus stop and wait for the bus to arrive. What time did the bus arrive?

The clock below shows the start time at 7:15 when Daphne woke up. Draw and label arrows on the clock to show how to find the end time when the bus arrived.

Draw hands on the clock below to show the end time when the bus arrived.

4 Evan got to the practice field at 8:00. He stretched for 15 minutes. He did sprints for 30 minutes. Then he did practice drills for 25 minutes. What time did Evan finish practice drills? Complete and label the jumps on the number line to find the end time.

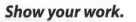

| 8:00 | 8:15 | 8:30 | 8:45 | 9:00 | 9:15 |

Evan finished practice drills at _____.

5 Kurt got home at 4:00. He did homework for 25 minutes and played outside for 20 minutes. Then he read a book for 15 minutes before dinner. What time was dinner?

Show your work.

There are 60 minutes in 1 hour.

Solution: _____

©Curriculum Associates, LLC   Copying is not permitted.

Name: _____

Solve Problems About Time

Study the example showing how to solve a problem about time. Then solve problems 1–6.

Example

Amy had 1 hour to do activities. She talked on the phone for 5 minutes. She rode her bike for 15 minutes. She played a game with her brother for 25 minutes. How much time did Amy have left to spend painting a picture?

Amy had 60 minutes to do activities.   1 hour = 60 minutes

Add the minutes for the known activities. $5 + 15 + 25 = 45$ minutes

Write an equation to find how much time $45 + P = 60$ or $P = 60 - 45$
Amy had left to paint a picture. $P = 15$ $P = 15$

Amy had 15 minutes left to paint a picture.

1 Complete the labels on the number line to represent the example problem.

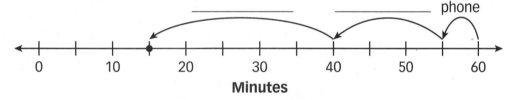

2 Look at the number line in problem 1. What does the dot at 15 represent?

_____

3 Milo visited an amusement park for 3 hours. He rode rides for 50 minutes, played carnival games for 40 minutes, and ate food for 30 minutes. He spent the rest of the time waiting in lines. How much time did Milo spend waiting in lines? Write and solve an equation to find the answer.

3 hours = _____ minutes

Known activities = _____ + _____ + _____ = _____ minutes

Equation: _____

Milo spent _____ minutes waiting in lines.

Solve.

4 Tell whether each amount of time is equivalent to 2 hours and 10 minutes.

    a. 210 minutes   ☐ Yes   ☐ No

    b. 130 minutes   ☐ Yes   ☐ No

    c. 1 hour, 70 minutes   ☐ Yes   ☐ No

5 One of the fastest times for a 1,500-meter race is 3 minutes and 34 seconds. How many seconds is this time?

Show your work.

Solution: _____

6 Bennett spent 4 hours at school today. He attended three 70-minute classes. There is a 5-minute break between classes. Then he ate lunch before going home. How long did Bennett spend eating lunch?

Show your work.

Solution: _____

Name: _____

Solve Problems About Money

Study the example showing how to solve a problem about money. Then solve problems 1–7.

> **Example**
>
> Rita bought milk for $0.50, a sandwich for $2.50, and a fruit salad for $1.25. She paid for her lunch with a $5.00 bill. How much change did Rita get?
>
> | $1.00 = 100 cents |
> | $5.00 = 500 cents |
>
> Rita spent: 50 + 250 + 125 = 425 cents
>
> 500 cents − 425 cents = 75 cents
>
> Rita got 75 cents, or $0.75, in change.

1 The picture below shows that $5.00 is the same as $3.00 in bills plus 8 quarters. Cross out the bills and coins to show the amount that Rita spent on lunch in the example above.

| 1 dollar = 4 quarters |
| 1 quarter = 25 cents |

2 How can you find the change Rita gets by looking at the picture above? Explain. _____

_____

_____

3 Josh bought 4 movie tickets and 2 large popcorns. Each movie ticket is $8. Each popcorn is $5. How much money did Josh spend?

Tickets: _____   Popcorn: _____

Tickets and popcorn: _____

Josh spent _____ .

Solve.

4 Mandy has a total of $2.00 in change in her purse. Complete each set of coins below to show amounts equivalent to $2.00.

    a. 4 quarters, 5 dimes, _____ nickels

    b. 10 pennies, _____ dimes, 3 quarters, 5 nickels

    c. 2 quarters, 12 dimes, 3 nickels, _____ pennies

    d. _____ quarters, 4 dimes, 6 nickels, 5 pennies

5 A pound of apples costs $1.30. Sawyer bought $2\frac{1}{2}$ pounds of apples. How much did Sawyer pay?

Show your work.

Solution: _____

6 Brie earns $3,000 a month. Every month, she spends $1,400 on rent and bills, $700 on groceries, $200 on a car payment, and $100 on gas. She saves the rest. How much money does Brie save?

Show your work.

Solution: _____

7 Regular bananas cost $0.20 each at the supermarket. Organic bananas cost $0.30 each. If you have $3.00, how many more regular bananas than organic bananas can you buy?

Show your work.

Solution: _____

Name: _____

Time and Money

Solve the problems.

1 How many days are in 1 year and 5 weeks?

   A 372 days

   B 378 days

   C 400 days

   D 1,825 days

There are 365 days in a year. There are 7 days in a week.

2 Rowan bought 2 comic books for $2.50 each, a fiction book for $7, and a poster for $1.25 at the book fair. Rowan paid with a $20.00 bill. How much change did he get?

   A $6.75   **C** $13.25

   B $12.75   **D** $17.75

What operation do you use to represent the cost of the 2 comic books?

Courtney chose **C** as the correct answer. How did she get that answer?

_____

_____

_____

3 How many minutes are there in one day?

Show your work.

There are 24 hours in one day.

Solution: _____

Solve.

4 A private music lesson at Parker Music costs $40 for 1 hour. A private music lesson at Joelle Music costs $25 for 30 minutes. How much more does a 1-hour private lesson cost at Joelle Music than at Parker Music?

What is the cost for 60 minutes of lessons at each store?

Show your work.

Solution: _____

5 Susan bought 4 boxes of granola bars and 2 cartons of milk. Each box of granola bars cost $2.50 and each carton of milk cost $2.75, including tax. Susan gave the clerk a $20.00 bill. What did she get in change? List two different ways Susan could have received change.

What coins are equal in value to 1 dollar?

Show your work.

Solution: bills: _____ coins: _____

bills: _____ coins: _____

Dear Family,

This week your child is learning to convert units of length, liquid volume, and mass.

Your child is learning different ways to solve multi-step problems converting larger units to smaller units for measurements of length, liquid volume, and mass. Here's a liquid volume problem your child might see.

Ethan, Dave, and Robert are making punch for a party. They combine 1 liter of lemonade, a 2-liter bottle of sparkling water, and 450 milliliters of fruit juice. How many milliliters of punch do the boys make for the party?

One way to help solve the problem is to use a picture to think about the size of the measurements.

1 liter   2 liters   450 milliliters

Since the problem is in liters and milliliters, the first step is to convert the liters to milliliters. Then combine the milliliters to find the total. You can show the measurements with a bar model like the one below.

1 liter	2 liters	450 milliliters
1,000 milliliters	2,000 milliliters	450 milliliters

1 liter is the same as 1,000 milliliters.

Multiply 2 by 1,000 to convert 2 liters to milliliters: $1,000 \times 2 = 2,000$. Add all the milliliter measurements to find the total:
$1,000 + 2,000 + 450 = 3,450$ milliliters.

Invite your child to share what he or she knows about converting units to solve multi-step problems by doing the following activity together.

NEXT

Converting Units of Length Activity

Do an activity with your child to convert units of length.

Materials: ruler

- Each person uses a ruler to measure the lengths of three household items. Measure the length of each item in feet and inches, to the nearest whole inch.

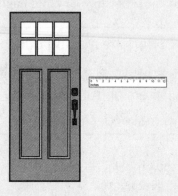

- List the three items along with their measurements on a sheet of paper.

    Examples: Picture frame: 9 inches

    Table top: $1\frac{1}{2}$ feet

    Door: 2 feet 8 inches

- Exchange papers and find the total length, in inches, of the three items on the other person's list. Remember, there are 12 inches in 1 foot.

    Example: Picture frame: 9 inches

    Table top: $1\frac{1}{2}$ feet = 18 inches

    Door: 2 feet 8 inches = 32 inches

    Total: 9 + 18 + 32 = 59 inches

- The person whose measured items add up to a total length closest to 100 inches wins.

Look for other real-life opportunities to practice converting units of length, as well as units of liquid volume and mass, with your child.

Length, Liquid Volume, and Mass

Name: _____

Prerequisite: Convert Measurements

Study the example problem showing how to convert from a larger to a smaller unit of length. Then solve problems 1–7.

Example

Tess needs 75 inches of ribbon for a project. She has 6 feet of ribbon. Does she have enough ribbon? How much extra ribbon does she have or how much more ribbon does she need?

Use a table to convert from the larger unit, feet, to the smaller unit, inches.

| 1 foot = 12 inches |

Feet (ft)	1	2	3	4	5	6
Inches (in)	12	24	36	48	60	72

The table shows that 6 feet = 72 inches.
Since 72 < 75, Tess does not have enough ribbon.

75 − 72 = 3, so Tess needs 3 more inches of ribbon.

---

1 A concrete walkway is 6 meters long. How many centimeters long is the walkway?

| 1 meter = 100 centimeters |

Fill in the missing numbers in the table. Circle the numbers that show how many centimeters are equal to 6 meters.

Meters (m)	1	2				
Centimeters (cm)	100					

The walkway is _____ centimeters long.

2 Explain how to use multiplication to solve problem 1.

_____

_____

_____

_____

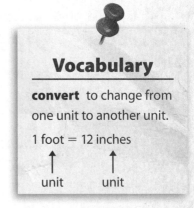

Vocabulary

convert to change from one unit to another unit.

1 foot = 12 inches

   ↑   ↑

  unit   unit

Solve.

3 The cooler at a softball game holds 5 quarts of sports drink. How many cups of sports drink does the cooler hold?

1 quart = 4 cups

Show your work.

Solution: _____

4 Mark brought 2 1-liter bottles of water to basketball practice. He drank 1,500 milliliters of water during practice. How many milliliters of water does he have left?

1 liter = 1,000 milliliters

Show your work.

Solution: _____

5 Write an expression to convert kilograms to grams. Let *K* stand for kilograms.

1 kilogram = 1,000 grams

Expression: _____

6 Write an expression to convert pounds to ounces. Let *p* stand for pounds.

1 pound = 16 ounces

Expression: _____

7 Look at problems 5 and 6 to answer the questions below.

a. How many grams are in 4 kilograms?

_____

b. How many ounces are in 7 pounds?

_____

Name: _____

Solve Length Problems

Study the example problem showing how to solve a multi-step problem about length. Then solve problems 1–5.

Example

Wendy has a fence that is 10 feet long. Vines cover a section of fence that is $\frac{5}{6}$ foot long. Wendy and 4 friends will each paint an equal length of the rest of the fence. How long is the section of fence that each friend will paint?

Length of fence

Length with vines   Each length to paint

1 foot = 12 inches

Length of fence: 10 feet = 120 inches

Length covered with vines: $\frac{5}{6} \times 12$ inches = 10 inches

Length to paint: 120 − 10 = 110 inches

Length of each section: 110 ÷ 5 = 22 inches

The section of fence each friend will paint is 22 inches.

1 Nestor needs 750 centimeters of rope. Rope comes in lengths of $4\frac{1}{2}$ meters and 9 meters at the hardware store. Which length of rope should Nestor buy?

1 meter = 100 centimeters

$4\frac{1}{2}$ meters = _____ centimeters

9 meters = _____ centimeters

a. Which length is greater than 750 centimeters? _____ centimeters

b. Nestor should buy rope with a length of _____ .

2 Which length is greater, $\frac{1}{2}$ meter or 240 centimeters? Explain.

_____

_____

_____

        Lesson 25 Length, Liquid Volume, and Mass   **271**

Solve.

3 Jorge is playing football. He carries the ball forward $5\frac{2}{3}$ yards and then moves backward 1 foot. How far forward is the ball, in feet, from where Jorge started carrying the ball?

Show your work.

$$1 \text{ yard} = 3 \text{ feet}$$

Solution: _____

4 Last summer, Marion was $3\frac{1}{2}$ feet tall. She was 4 inches taller than her brother Elijah. She was $1\frac{1}{4}$ feet shorter than her sister Lorie. How tall were Elijah and Lorie last summer?

Show your work.

$$1 \text{ foot} = 12 \text{ inches}$$

Solution: Elijah: _____ Lorie: _____

5 Paula has $4\frac{2}{3}$ yards of ribbon. She cuts 4 inches off each end of the ribbon to remove the frayed ends. She divides the remaining ribbon into 16 equal pieces to make bows. What is the length of ribbon, in inches, used to make each bow?

Show your work.

Solution: _____

Name: _____

Solve Liquid Volume Problems

Study the example showing how to solve a liquid volume problem. Then solve problems 1–5.

Example

Naomi has a container of water. She uses 4 liters to water her vegetable garden. She uses $3\frac{1}{2}$ liters to water flowers. She uses the remaining 500 milliliters in the container to fill up a bird bath. How many milliliters of water did Naomi have in the container?

| 1 liter (L) = 1,000 milliliters (mL) |

Write an equation to find the total amount of water.

$W = 4\,L + 3\frac{1}{2}\,L + 500\,mL$

Convert liters to milliliters.

$4 \times 1,000\,mL = 4,000\,mL$
$3 \times 1,000\,mL = 3,000\,mL$ and $\frac{1}{2} \times 1,000\,mL = 500\,mL$

Write the equation using milliliters and solve.

$W = 4,000\,mL + 3,500\,mL + 500\,mL$
$W = 8,000\,mL$

Naomi had 8,000 milliliters of water in the container.

Benny has two small fish tanks with one fish in each tank. One tank has $3\frac{1}{2}$ quarts of water. The other tank has 12 cups of water. Benny combines the water into one large fish tank with both fish in the large tank.

| 1 quart = 4 cups |

1 How many cups of water are in the large tank?

$3\frac{1}{2}$ quarts: 3×4 cups = _____ cups and $\frac{1}{2} \times 4$ cups = _____ cups

$3\frac{1}{2}$ quarts = _____ cups; _____ cups + _____ cups = _____ cups

There are _____ of water in the large tank.

2 At least 5 cups of water are needed for each fish in a tank. How many more fish would Benny be able to put in the large tank? Explain.

_____

_____

Lesson 25 Length, Liquid Volume, and Mass

Solve.

3 Tamara prepared fruit punch for a party. She used $\frac{3}{4}$ gallon of pineapple juice, 2 quarts of lemonade, and $1\frac{1}{4}$ gallons of orange juice. How many quarts of punch did Tamara prepare?

Show your work.

1 gallon = 4 quarts

Solution: _____

4 Sharon and her cousin are making milkshakes at a family reunion. Sharon brought $2\frac{1}{2}$ gallons of milk. Her cousin brought 2 quarts of milk. The girls used 8 quarts of milk for the milkshakes. How much milk is left? There may be more than one correct answer. Circle the letter for all that apply.

A 4 quarts   **D** 1 gallon

B 6 quarts   **E** $1\frac{1}{2}$ gallons

C $\frac{1}{2}$ gallon

5 Rob has 6 quarts of apple cider for the fall fair. He pours the cider into glasses to set on picnic tables. He pours 6 ounces of cider into each glass. How many glasses of cider does Rob set on the tables?

Show your work.

1 quart = 4 cups
1 cup = 8 ounces

Solution: _____

Name: _____

Solve Mass and Weight Problems

Study the example problem showing how to solve a mass and weight problem. Then solve problems 1–5.

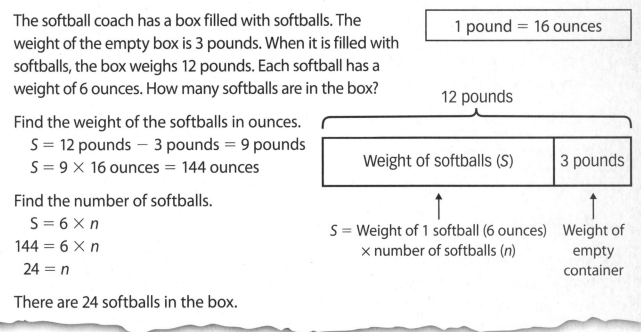

Example

The softball coach has a box filled with softballs. The weight of the empty box is 3 pounds. When it is filled with softballs, the box weighs 12 pounds. Each softball has a weight of 6 ounces. How many softballs are in the box?

1 pound = 16 ounces

Find the weight of the softballs in ounces.

$S = 12$ pounds $- 3$ pounds $= 9$ pounds
$S = 9 \times 16$ ounces $= 144$ ounces

12 pounds

Weight of softballs (S)	3 pounds

Find the number of softballs.

$S = 6 \times n$
$144 = 6 \times n$
$24 = n$

$S =$ Weight of 1 softball (6 ounces) × number of softballs (n)

Weight of empty container

There are 24 softballs in the box.

1 Look at the example above. Explain why you need to find the weight of the softballs in the box in ounces.

_____

_____

_____

2 Tyson's baby brother weighed 7 pounds, 3 ounces when he was born. The baby lost 9 ounces after a few days, and then gained 1 pound, 6 ounces by the end of the week. How much did the baby weigh at the end of the week?

Show your work.

Solution: _____

Solve.

3 A large truck that moves cars can carry a maximum load of 15,720 pounds. The table below shows the weight of each kind of car that could be loaded onto the truck.

Kind of Car	Compact	Mid-size	Full-size
Weight (in tons)	$1\frac{1}{2}$	$2\frac{1}{4}$	3

$$1 \text{ ton} = 2,000 \text{ pounds}$$

Choose *Yes* or *No* to tell whether the truck is able to carry each load of cars below.

a. 2 full-size cars, 1 compact car ☐ Yes ☐ No

b. 2 compact cars, 2 full-size cars ☐ Yes ☐ No

c. 2 mid-size cars, 2 compact cars ☐ Yes ☐ No

d. 4 mid-size cars ☐ Yes ☐ No

4 Melinda donated fudge for the school bake sale. She wrapped 80 pieces of fudge. Each piece of fudge weighed 1 ounce. How many pounds of fudge did Melinda wrap?

$$1 \text{ pound} = 16 \text{ ounces}$$

Show your work.

Solution: _____

5 A paper clip has a mass of 1 gram. A box of paper clips has 100 paper clips. Which equation below can be used to find the number of boxes of paper clips that will have a mass of 1 kilogram? Let n be the number of boxes. Circle the letter for all that apply.

$$1 \text{ kilogram} = 1,000 \text{ grams}$$

A $100 = 1,000 \div n$

B $n = 1,000 \times 100$

C $n = 1,000 \div 100$

D $1,000 = n \times 100$

Name: _____

Length, Liquid Volume, and Mass

Solve the problems.

1 Miguel and his brother put two 8-foot tables end to end for a graduation party. The tablecloth they plan to use is 5 yards in length. Is the tablecloth long enough to cover both tables?

1 yard = 3 feet. What units should you use to compare the length of the tables and the length of the tablecloth?

A Yes, because 8 feet < 10 yards.

B Yes, because the tables are 8 feet long and the tablecloth is 15 feet long.

C No, because the tables are 16 feet long and the tablecloth is 15 feet long.

D No, because 8 feet > 5 yards.

2 Patel bought a 2-pound bag of trail mix. He poured $\frac{1}{2}$ pound of the mix into a bowl and divided the remaining amount into bags. Each bag had 2 ounces of trail mix. How many bags did Patel use?

1 pound = 16 ounces. How many ounces of trail mix is he dividing into bags?

A 20 bags

B 16 bags

C 12 bags

D 8 bags

Jen chose **A** as the correct answer. How did she get that answer?

_____

_____

_____

_____

Solve.

3 Marcus poured an equal amount of milk into 4 bottles. He started with 1 quart of milk. After pouring, he had $\frac{1}{4}$ of a quart of milk left. How many ounces of milk did Marcus pour into each bottle?

Show your work.

> 1 quart = 4 cups.
> 1 cup = 8 ounces.
> There are two steps in this problem.

Solution: _____

4 Maya cut a length of wood into strips to make 5 small picture frames. She used 14 inches of wood for each frame. For another project, she cut another length of wood into 3 strips of 1 foot each and 4 strips of $\frac{1}{6}$ foot each. How much wood, in inches, did Maya use in all?

Show your work.

> 1 foot = 12 inches. You can use multiplication and addition to solve this problem.

Solution: _____

Dear Family,

This week your child is learning about perimeter and area.

Some real-world situations that involve perimeter and area are installing a fence around a yard and determining how much flooring is needed for a room.

To find perimeter, find the total length of all the sides of a rectangle. One way to do this is by adding together the lengths of all the sides.

For example, to find the length of fencing that is needed to enclose a rectangular yard like the one shown below, add the 4 side lengths.

Perimeter = length + length + width + width
          = 20 feet + 20 feet + 14 feet + 14 feet
          = 68 feet

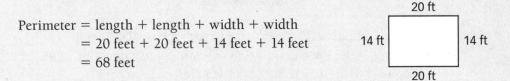

Another way to find the perimeter of a rectangle is to use a formula. P stands for perimeter, l stands for length, and w stands for width.

$$P = 2l + 2w \qquad \text{or} \qquad P = 2(l + w)$$
$$= 2(20) + 2(14) \qquad\qquad = 2(20 + 14)$$
$$= 40 + 28 \qquad\qquad\qquad = 2 \times 34$$

$$P = 68 \text{ feet}$$

You need 68 feet of fencing to enclose the yard.

To find the area of a rectangle, use the area formula.
Area = length × width $A = l \times w$

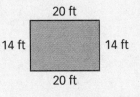

The area of the rectangle at the right is:
14 feet × 20 feet = 280 square feet

If you were covering the rectangular yard with pavers, you would need enough pavers to cover 280 square feet.

Invite your child to share what he or she knows about perimeter and area by doing the following activity together.

NEXT

Perimeter and Area Activity

Do an activity with your child to find perimeter and area.

Materials: ruler or yardstick

- Look around the house for items that are shaped like a rectangle.

    Examples: a TV or computer screen, a table top, a rug, the floor of a room

- Help your child measure each side of the rectangular item. Have your child write the measurements. Be sure to use the same units of measurement, such as inches or feet, for each side.

- Have your child use the measurements to find the perimeter of the item.

- Now measure a different rectangular-shaped item and find its perimeter. Is the perimeter greater or less than the perimeter of the first item you measured?

- Next, find area. Suppose you want to cover a window in your home with a shade. Choose a window and measure each side. Have your child find the area and tell how many square inches or square feet of shade are needed to cover the window.

- Find the area of other items in your home, such as different-size windows or floors.

Look for other real-life opportunities to practice finding perimeter and area with your child.

Perimeter and Area

Name: _____

Prerequisite: Connect Area and Perimeter

Study the example showing how to find the area and perimeter of a rectangle. Then solve problems 1–7.

Example

Find the area and perimeter of the rectangle at right.

Area
Count square units or multiply side lengths.
The rectangle is 4 units by 10 units.
$4 \times 10 = 40$ square units

Area = 40 square units

Perimeter
Add the lengths of all the sides.
$4 + 10 + 4 + 10 = 28$ units

Perimeter = 28 units

---

1 Find the area and perimeter of the rectangle at right.

Area = _____ square units   Perimeter = _____ units

2 Look at the rectangle in problem 1. Draw a rectangle with the same area but a different perimeter.

What is the perimeter of the rectangle you drew?

_____

3 Look at the rectangle in problem 1. Draw a rectangle with the same perimeter but a different area.

What is the area of the rectangle you drew?

_____

Solve.

4 Look at the shape below. Find the area and perimeter of the shape.

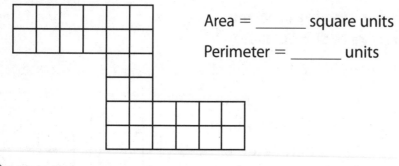

Area = _____ square units

Perimeter = _____ units

5 What is the area and perimeter of a square with side lengths of 4 units? Draw the square below.

Area = _____ square units

Perimeter = _____ units

6 Look at the square you drew in problem 5.

a. Draw a rectangle with the same area as the square and a different perimeter than the square.

b. What is the perimeter of the rectangle you drew? Is it equal to, greater than, or less than the perimeter of the square you drew in problem 5? Explain.

_____

_____

_____

7 The perimeter of each triangle below is 12 centimeters. Write the missing side length on each triangle.

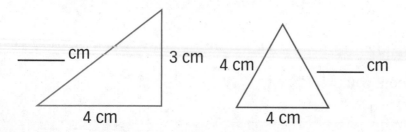

©Curriculum Associates, LLC   Copying is not permitted.

Name: _____

Solve Perimeter Problems

Study the example problem showing how to solve a problem about perimeter. Then solve problems 1–6.

Example

The community center has a rectangular kiddie pool. The length of the pool is 25 feet. The width is 15 feet. What is the perimeter of the kiddie pool?

Use a formula for the perimeter of a rectangle.

$$P = 2l + 2w \qquad\qquad P = 2(l + w)$$
$$= (2 \times 25) + (2 \times 15) \qquad = 2(25 + 15)$$
$$= 50 + 30 \qquad\qquad\qquad = 2(40)$$
$$= 80 \qquad\qquad\qquad\qquad = 80$$

25 ft

15 ft

The perimeter of the pool is 80 feet.

1 A rectangular photograph has a length of 10 inches and a width of 8 inches. Fill in the numbers in the formulas below to show two ways to find the perimeter of the photograph.

$$P = \qquad 2l \qquad + \qquad 2w \qquad\qquad P = 2(l + w)$$

$$P = (2 \times \underline{\hspace{1cm}}) + (2 \times \underline{\hspace{1cm}}) \qquad\qquad P = 2(\underline{\hspace{1cm}} + \underline{\hspace{1cm}})$$

$$= \underline{\hspace{1cm}} + \underline{\hspace{1cm}} \qquad\qquad\qquad\qquad = 2(\underline{\hspace{1cm}})$$

$$= \underline{\hspace{1cm}} \qquad\qquad\qquad\qquad\qquad\qquad = \underline{\hspace{1cm}}$$

The perimeter is _____ inches.

2 Jason's rectangular computer screen is 50 centimeters across and 36 centimeters high. What is the perimeter of Jason's computer screen?

Show your work.

Solution: P = _____ *centimeters*

Solve.

3 A rectangular garden has a width of 90 feet. The perimeter is 500 feet. What is the length of the garden?

$$500 = (2 \times l) + (\underline{\hspace{1cm}} \times \underline{\hspace{1cm}})$$

$$500 = 2l + \underline{\hspace{1cm}}$$

$$\underline{\hspace{1cm}} = 2l$$

$$\underline{\hspace{1cm}} \div 2 = l$$

$$\underline{\hspace{1cm}} = l$$

The length of the garden is _____ feet.

4 What is the perimeter of a square with side lengths of 3 inches?

Show your work.

Solution: _____

5 Amy has a ribbon that is 36 inches long. Choose *Yes* or *No* to tell whether she has enough ribbon to wrap around the perimeter of a picture frame for each frame with the given shape and size.

a. square, side lengths of 9 inches ☐ Yes ☐ No

b. rectangle, 18 inches by 10 inches ☐ Yes ☐ No

c. rectangle, 12 inches by 24 inches ☐ Yes ☐ No

d. square, side lengths of 6 inches ☐ Yes ☐ No

6 The square and the rectangle at the right each have a perimeter of 200 centimeters. What are the side lengths of the square and rectangle?
(Hint: First find the side length of the square.)

Show your work.

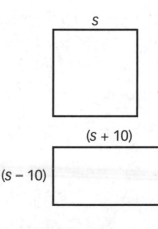

Square: side length _____ cm   Rectangle: length _____ cm width _____ cm

Name: _____

Solve Area Problems

Study the example showing how to solve a problem about area. Then solve problems 1–6.

Example

Michelle wants to use bricks to make a rectangular patio. She has enough bricks to cover an area of 135 square feet. She wants the length of the patio to be 15 feet. How wide should she make the patio?

Write an equation to represent the area of a rectangle: $A = l \times w$

$$A = 15 \times w$$
$$135 = 15 \times w$$
$$135 \div 15 = w$$
$$9 = w$$

Michelle should make the patio 9 feet wide.

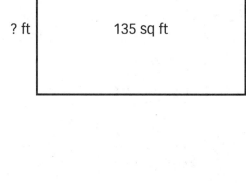

15 ft

? ft   135 sq ft

---

1 Juan is installing new flooring in a large entryway. The picture at the right shows the length and width of the entryway. How many square feet of flooring does Juan need?

$A =$ _____ $\times$ _____

$A =$ _____

Juan needs _____ square feet of flooring.

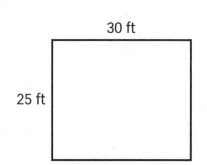

30 ft

25 ft

---

2 Look at the picture at the right. Alyssa wants to tile a room with an area of 480 square feet. The width of the room is 12 feet. What is the length of the room?

_____ $= l \times$ _____

_____ $\div$ _____ $= l$

_____ $= l$

The length of the room is _____ feet.

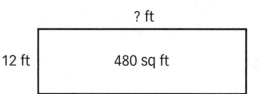

? ft

12 ft   480 sq ft

Solve.

3 Jim is painting the surface of a picnic table. The surface has an area of 2,160 square inches. The width of the table is 30 inches. What is the length of the table?

Show your work.

Solution: _____

4 An Olympic floor exercise mat has an area of 144 square meters. Its length is 12 meters. What is the width of the mat?

Show your work.

Solution: _____

5 Look at problem 4. What is the shape of the floor exercise mat? Explain how you know.

_____

_____

6 Melissa has enough paint to cover an area of 250 square feet. She wants to paint two walls. The rectangular wall is 9 feet high and 20 feet wide. The square wall has a height of 9 feet. Does Melissa have enough paint to cover the area of both walls?

Show your work.

Solution: _____

Name: _____

Solve Perimeter and Area Problems

Solve the problems.

1 The area of a rectangle is 40 square feet. What could be the perimeter of the rectangle? Circle the letter for all that apply.

A 82 ft   **D** 28 ft

B 44 ft   **E** 26 ft

C 40 ft

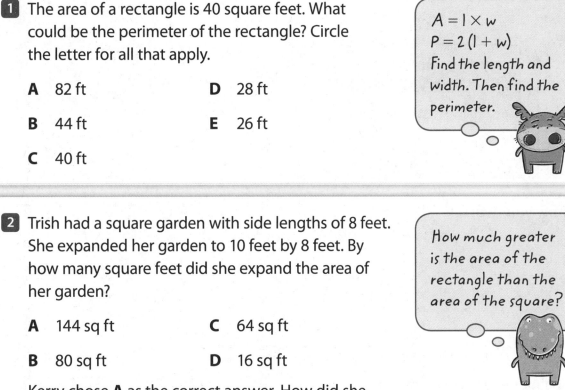

$A = l \times w$
$P = 2(l + w)$
Find the length and width. Then find the perimeter.

2 Trish had a square garden with side lengths of 8 feet. She expanded her garden to 10 feet by 8 feet. By how many square feet did she expand the area of her garden?

A 144 sq ft   **C** 64 sq ft

B 80 sq ft   **D** 16 sq ft

Kerry chose **A** as the correct answer. How did she get that answer?

_____

_____

How much greater is the area of the rectangle than the area of the square?

3 Layla painted the walls of a rectangular room. Two walls are 9 feet by 12 feet. The other two walls are 9 feet by 20 feet. What is the total area of wall that Layla painted?

Show your work.

How do you find the area of all four walls?

Solution: _____

Solve.

4 Olivia is putting decorations around the photo in the picture frame shown below. What is the area of the frame that she can decorate?

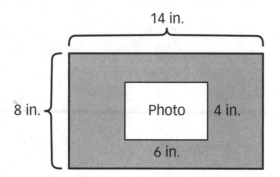

14 in.

8 in.

Photo

4 in.

6 in.

You can find the difference between the area of the larger rectangle and the area of the smaller rectangle.

Show your work.

Solution: _____

5 A painter needs a piece of glass to protect a painting. He is also putting wooden strips around the perimeter to make a frame for the painting. The painting is 85 centimeters by 62 centimeters. How many square centimeters of glass does he need to cover the area of the painting? What is the total length of wooden strips that he needs to frame the perimeter of the painting?

You need to find both the area and the perimeter.

Show your work.

Solution: Glass: _____

Wooden strips: _____

Lesson 26 Perimeter and Area

Dear Family,

This week your child is learning to use line plots to solve problems.

A line plot is a way to organize a group of data, such as a set of measurements. A line plot gives a visual view of the data.

The line plot below shows the lengths of different pieces of yarn. Each X represents a piece of yarn. Since there are 9 Xs, there are 9 pieces of yarn.

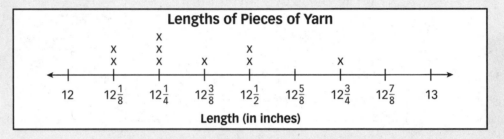

Lengths of Pieces of Yarn

Length (in inches)

Xs that are one above another show pieces of yarn that have the same length. You can see at a glance that:

- 2 pieces of yarn are $12\frac{1}{8}$ inches long.
- the longest piece of yarn is $12\frac{3}{4}$ inches.

To find the total length of all the pieces of yarn, add the individual lengths. For each X on the line plot, write a length. Then add the lengths.

$12\frac{1}{8}$	$12\frac{1}{8}$	$12\frac{1}{4}$	$12\frac{1}{4}$	$12\frac{1}{4}$	$12\frac{3}{8}$	$12\frac{1}{2}$	$12\frac{1}{2}$	$12\frac{3}{4}$

In order to add, all the fractions must have the same denominator. Write the fractions as eighths. For example, write $12\frac{1}{4}$ as $12\frac{2}{8}$.

Add the whole numbers: $12 + 12 + 12 + 12 + 12 + 12 + 12 + 12 + 12 = 108$.

Add the fractions: $\frac{1}{8} + \frac{1}{8} + \frac{2}{8} + \frac{2}{8} + \frac{2}{8} + \frac{3}{8} + \frac{4}{8} + \frac{4}{8} + \frac{6}{8} = \frac{25}{8}$.

$108 + \frac{25}{8} = 108 + 3\frac{1}{8} = 111\frac{1}{8}$

The total length of all the pieces of yarn is $111\frac{1}{8}$ inches.

Invite your child to share what he or she knows about using line plots to solve problems by doing the following activity together.

NEXT

Line Plot Activity

Do an activity with your child to use a line plot to solve the problem below. Then have your child answer the questions below using the line plot you make.

> Steve took 12 nails out of a toolbox.
> He measured the length of each nail.
> This is what he wrote:
>
> • 1 nail measures $\frac{1}{8}$ inch.
>
> • 4 nails measure $\frac{3}{8}$ inch.
>
> • 3 nails measure $\frac{1}{2}$ inch.
>
> • 3 nails measure $\frac{5}{8}$ inch.
>
> • 1 nail measures $\frac{7}{8}$ inch.

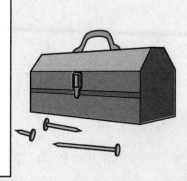

- Make a line plot to show the lengths of the nails. Use a blank number line. Label it with eighths fractions from 0 through 1.

- Write a title for the line plot, such as "Lengths of Nails from the Toolbox." Be sure to write a label below the number line, such as "Lengths (in inches)."

- Mark Xs on the line plot to show the data.

- Ask questions and have your child use the line plot to find the answers.

    Examples:

    Which length of nail is there the greatest number of? $\left(\frac{3}{8}\right)$

    What is the difference between the lengths of the longest nail and the shortest nail? $\left(\frac{6}{8}, \text{ or } \frac{3}{4} \text{ inch}\right)$

    How would the line plot change if there was another nail that measures $1\frac{1}{4}$ inches? $\left(\text{Add eighths labels through } 1\frac{2}{8} \text{ and mark an X above } 1\frac{2}{8}.\right)$

Line Plots

Name: _____

Study the example problem showing how to display data on a line plot. Then solve problems 1–6.

Example

Ginny measured the heights of tomato seedlings in her garden. The heights are shown in the table below. Make a line plot to represent the data.

Seedling Heights							
Seedling	A	B	C	D	E	F	G
Height (in inches)	$1\frac{1}{4}$	$\frac{3}{4}$	$1\frac{1}{4}$	2	$1\frac{3}{4}$	$1\frac{1}{2}$	$\frac{1}{2}$

Use a number line with a scale of $\frac{1}{4}$ inch.

For each seedling, put an X on the line plot above its height.

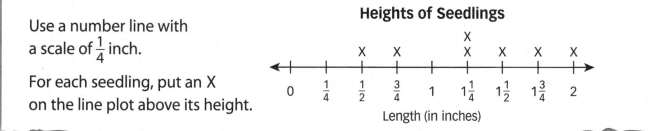

Heights of Seedlings

Length (in inches)

For problems 1–3, use the line plot in the example above.

1 Explain how to use the line plot to find how many seedlings Ginny measured.

_____

_____

2 What are the heights of the shortest seedling and the tallest seedling? Explain how you know.

Shortest seedling: _____ Tallest seedling: _____

_____

_____

3 Two seedlings have the same height. What is the height? Explain how you know. _____

_____

Solve.

4 The lengths of snakes at a zoo are shown in the table below.

Snake Lengths

Snake	A	B	C	D	E	F	G	H
Length (in inches)	9	$7\frac{1}{4}$	$8\frac{1}{4}$	$7\frac{1}{4}$	8	7	$7\frac{3}{4}$	$8\frac{1}{4}$

Complete the line plot below to represent the data in the table.

Lengths of Snakes

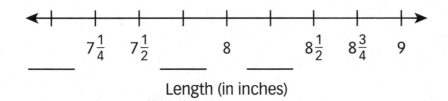

$7\frac{1}{4}$ $7\frac{1}{2}$ 8 $8\frac{1}{2}$ $8\frac{3}{4}$ 9

_____   _____   _____

Length (in inches)

5 Look at the line plot in problem 4. How many snakes are less than 8 inches long? Explain how you know.

_____

_____

_____

6 Sally measured the width of seashells she collected. The table below shows the data.

Seashell Widths

Seashell	A	B	C	D	E	F	G	H
Width (in inches)	2	$\frac{3}{4}$	$1\frac{3}{4}$	$\frac{1}{2}$	$1\frac{1}{4}$	$\frac{1}{4}$	$\frac{3}{4}$	$1\frac{3}{4}$

Draw a line plot to represent the data in the table.

Widths of Seashells

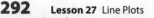

Name: _____

Represent Data on a Line Plot

Study the example problem showing how to make a line plot. Then solve problems 1–5.

Example

Students in science class measured the widths of butterfly wingspans in inches. The widths are shown in the table. Make a line plot to represent the data.

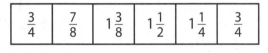

| $\frac{3}{4}$ | $\frac{7}{8}$ | $1\frac{3}{8}$ | $1\frac{1}{2}$ | $1\frac{1}{4}$ | $\frac{3}{4}$ |

Draw and label a number line by eighths. Put an X above each butterfly wingspan width.

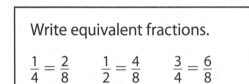

Write equivalent fractions.

$$\frac{1}{4} = \frac{2}{8} \qquad \frac{1}{2} = \frac{4}{8} \qquad \frac{3}{4} = \frac{6}{8}$$

Butterfly Wingspan Widths

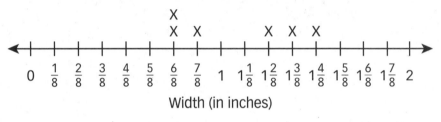

Width (in inches)

The height of fourth graders was measured on the first day of school and on the last day of school. The growth in inches of some students is listed below.

$$3, 1\frac{3}{4}, 2\frac{1}{4}, 1\frac{1}{2}, 2\frac{1}{4}, 2\frac{7}{8}$$

1 Write the data in eighths, by using equivalent fractions.

3, _____, _____, _____, _____, $2\frac{7}{8}$

2 Complete the line plot below to represent the data.

Growth of Students

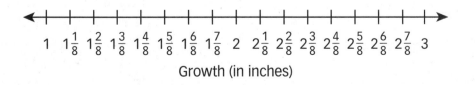

Growth (in inches)

Solve.

3 Look at the measurements in inches listed below. What fractions could be labeled on a number line with a line plot of the data? Circle all that apply.

$$10\frac{1}{4}, 10\frac{1}{2}, 11, 11\frac{3}{4}$$

A Halves **C** Fourths

B Thirds **D** Eighths

Micah's dog has 8 puppies. The length in inches of each puppy is listed below.

$$4, 4\frac{3}{4}, 4\frac{3}{8}, 4\frac{1}{2}, 4\frac{1}{2}, 4\frac{7}{8}, 4\frac{1}{4}, 4$$

---

4 Draw a line plot to represent the data.

5 Use the line plot to answer the questions.

a. How many measurements are recorded? _____

b. What is the longest length of a puppy? _____

c. What is the shortest length of a puppy? _____

d. How many puppies are less than or equal to $4\frac{1}{2}$ inches in length? _____

e. How many puppies are greater than $4\frac{1}{2}$ inches in length? _____

Vocabulary

line plot a graph using marks along a number line to show how many objects are in a set.

Name: _____

Solve Addition Problems with Line Plots

Study the example showing how to solve an addition problem with a line plot. Then solve problems 1–5.

Example

Ashley is decorating a frame with seashells. She wants to know if all the shells will fit along the edge of a 16-inch wide frame. She measures the width of each shell and records the information in a line plot. If Ashley puts all the shells in a row, will the total width of the shells fit on the frame?

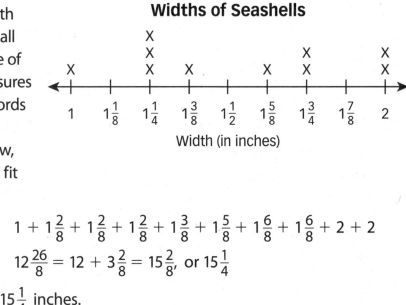

Widths of Seashells

Width (in inches)

Write the fractions in eighths. $1 + 1\frac{2}{8} + 1\frac{2}{8} + 1\frac{2}{8} + 1\frac{3}{8} + 1\frac{5}{8} + 1\frac{6}{8} + 1\frac{6}{8} + 2 + 2$

Then add. $12\frac{26}{8} = 12 + 3\frac{2}{8} = 15\frac{2}{8}$, or $15\frac{1}{4}$

The total width of the shells is $15\frac{1}{4}$ inches.

$15\frac{1}{4} < 16$, so the shells will fit on the frame.

1 Look at the line plot in the example. Ashley decides to glue the five largest shells along the edge of another frame. The shells fit exactly. How wide is the other frame?

Show your work.

Solution: _____

2 Ashley puts the $1\frac{1}{4}$ inch shells onto a string. What is the total width of the shells on the string?

Show your work.

Solution: _____

Vocabulary

line plot a graph using marks along a number line to show how many objects are in a set.

Solve.

A standard-sized brick should be $7\frac{5}{8}$ inches long. The line plot shows the actual lengths of 12 different bricks.

Lengths of Bricks

```
                                X
                                X
                                X
                                X
                                X
                      X         X
            X         X         X         X         X
  <----+----+----+----+----+----+----+----+---->
    7   7 1/8  7 1/4  7 3/8  7 1/2  7 5/8  7 3/4  7 7/8   8
```
Length (in inches)

3 What is the sum of the lengths of all the bricks that are exactly $7\frac{5}{8}$ inches long?

Show your work.

Solution: _____

4 What is the sum of the lengths of all the bricks that are less than $7\frac{5}{8}$ inches long?

Show your work.

Solution: _____

5 What is the sum of the lengths of all the bricks that are greater than $7\frac{5}{8}$ inches long?

Show your work.

Solution: _____

Name: _____

Solve Subtraction Problems with Line Plots

Study the example showing how to solve a subtraction problem with a line plot. Then solve problems 1–5.

Example

The monthly rainfall in inches for one city is shown in the line plot. What is the difference in inches of rain between the month with the greatest amount of rain and the month with the least amount of rain?

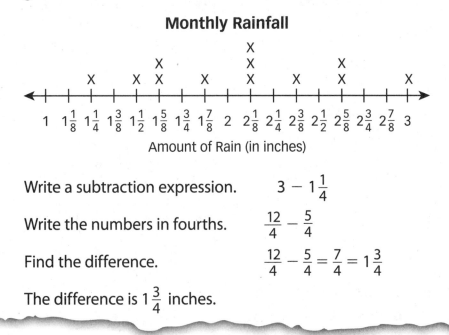

Monthly Rainfall

Amount of Rain (in inches)

Write a subtraction expression. $3 - 1\frac{1}{4}$

Write the numbers in fourths. $\frac{12}{4} - \frac{5}{4}$

Find the difference. $\frac{12}{4} - \frac{5}{4} = \frac{7}{4} = 1\frac{3}{4}$

The difference is $1\frac{3}{4}$ inches.

1 Which questions below can be answered using the line plot in the example above? Circle all that apply.

A In 3 months, it rained the same amount. What is the difference between that amount and the amount in the month when it rained the most?

B What was the total amount of rainfall for the year?

C In how many months did it rain more than 2 inches?

D How much rainfall occurred in January?

2 Look at the choices you circled in problem 1. Which can be solved using subtraction? What is the solution? Explain.

_____

_____

Solve.

Marine biologists caught fish for research. They measured the sea bass they caught and recorded the lengths in the line plot below.

Lengths of Sea Bass

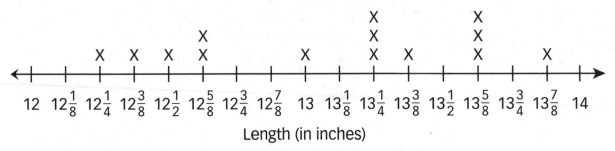

Length (in inches)

3 What is the difference in length between the longest and shortest sea bass that the biologists caught?

Show your work.

Solution: _____

4 Sea bass that are caught and that have a length less than 13 inches must be thrown back into the ocean. How many more inches does the shortest fish need to grow before it can be taken out of the ocean?

Show your work.

Solution: _____

5 Sea bass can grow to a maximum length of 23 inches. How much more would the longest fish caught need to grow in order to reach the maximum length?

Show your work.

Solution: _____

Name: _____

Solve Problems with Line Plots

Solve the problems.

1 The line plot shows the finish times of races run by a relay running team. What is the difference in minutes between the team's two fastest times?

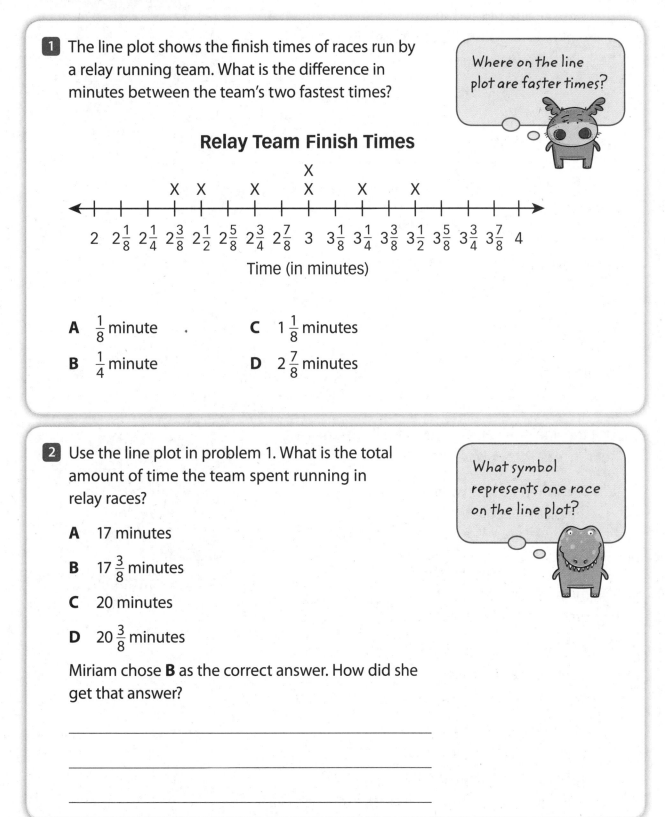

Where on the line plot are faster times?

Relay Team Finish Times

Time (in minutes)

A $\frac{1}{8}$ minute

C $1\frac{1}{8}$ minutes

B $\frac{1}{4}$ minute

D $2\frac{7}{8}$ minutes

2 Use the line plot in problem 1. What is the total amount of time the team spent running in relay races?

What symbol represents one race on the line plot?

A 17 minutes

B $17\frac{3}{8}$ minutes

C 20 minutes

D $20\frac{3}{8}$ minutes

Miriam chose **B** as the correct answer. How did she get that answer?

_____

_____

_____

Solve.

3 Ginny recorded how much her tomato plants grew this season. She plotted the growth of each plant in a line plot. What was the total length in inches that her plants grew this season?

> What operation do you use to find the combined length?

Growth of Plants

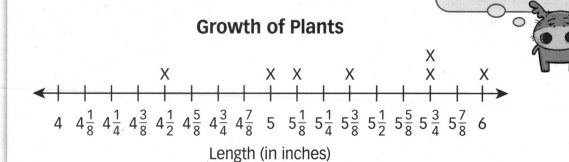

Length (in inches)

Show your work.

Solution: _____

4 Use the line plot in problem 4 to tell whether each sentence is *True* or *False*.

> Plants that grew a greater number of inches are farther to the right on the number line in the line plot.

a. The difference between the plant that grew the most and least is $2\frac{1}{2}$ inches. ☐ True ☐ False

b. Two plants that grew the most have a combined growth of $10\frac{1}{2}$ inches. ☐ True ☐ False

c. Two plants that grew the least have a combined growth of $9\frac{1}{2}$ inches. ☐ True ☐ False

d. Two plants grew the same amount. The combined growth of these two plants is $11\frac{1}{2}$ inches. ☐ True ☐ False

Dear Family,

This week your child is exploring angles.

Your child is learning that an angle is a kind of geometric shape.

> **angle** a geometric shape made by two rays from a common endpoint, called a vertex.

Two pencils with erasers placed end to end can represent an angle.

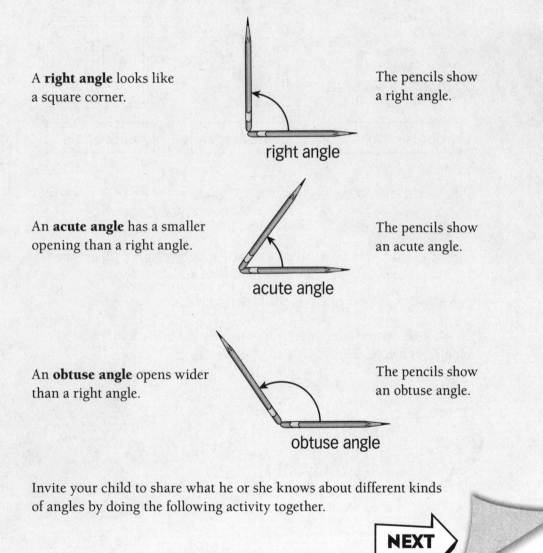

A **right angle** looks like a square corner.

The pencils show a right angle.

right angle

An **acute angle** has a smaller opening than a right angle.

The pencils show an acute angle.

acute angle

An **obtuse angle** opens wider than a right angle.

The pencils show an obtuse angle.

obtuse angle

Invite your child to share what he or she knows about different kinds of angles by doing the following activity together.

NEXT ➡

Identifying Angles Activity

Do an activity with your child to explore angles.

- Look around the house for objects that have different kinds of angles.

  Examples: Patches on a soccer ball have obtuse angles.
  A stair railing and a spindle form an acute angle.
  A corner of a window forms a right angle.

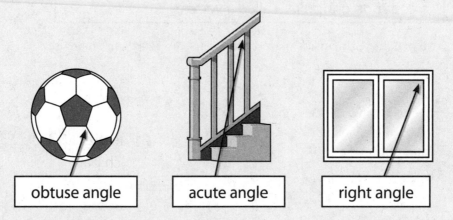

| obtuse angle | acute angle | right angle |

- Give points for each kind of angle you find: an acute angle is worth 3 points, an obtuse angle is worth 2 points, and a right angle is worth 1 point.

- Search for 10 minutes. Then count how many points each person has. The person with the most points wins.

- Challenge! Find an object that has all three kinds of angles.

Look for other real-life opportunities to identify different kinds of angles with your child.

Prerequisite: **What does it mean to multiply with fractions?**

Study the example problem showing multiplication with a fraction. Then solve problems 1–6.

Example

4 friends shared a whole pizza. Each person ate an equal amount.

Draw lines on the circle at the right to show the fraction of the pizza that each person ate.

Use multiplication to show that the four parts together equal the whole.

$4 \times \frac{1}{4} = \frac{4}{1} \times \frac{1}{4} = \frac{4}{4} = 1$ whole

The pizza is divided into 4 parts.
Each part is $\frac{1}{4}$ of the pizza.

1 8 friends shared a pizza. Each person ate an equal amount. Draw lines on the circle at the right to show the fraction of the pizza that each person ate.

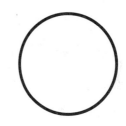

a. What fraction of the pizza did each person eat?

_____

b. Use multiplication to show that all the parts are equal to the whole.

_____

2 A pizza is cut into 8 equal slices.

a. What fraction of the pizza is each slice? _____

b. Mandy eats 2 slices. What fraction of the pizza did Mandy eat? _____

c. Use multiplication to explain how you found the answer to **b.** _____

Solve.

3 Look at the clock at the right. When the minute hand moves from the 12 to the 3, it moves over $\frac{1}{4}$ of a circle.

   a. How many minutes are in 1 hour? _____

   b. When the minute hand moves from the 12 to the 3, how many minutes have passed? Use fraction multiplication to show your answer.

   $\frac{1}{4} \times$ _____ = _____ minutes

4 Look at the clock at the right.

   a. When the minute hand moves from the 12 to the 6, what fraction of a circle does it move over?

   _____ of a circle

   b. How many minutes have passed? Use fraction multiplication to show your answer.

   _____

5 Look at the clock at the right. When the minute hand moves from the 12 to the 4, it moves over $\frac{1}{3}$ of a circle. How many minutes have passed? Use fraction multiplication to show your answer.

_____

6 Look at the clock at the right. When the minute hand moves from the 12 to the 1, how many minutes have passed? Use fraction multiplication to show your answer.

_____

Name: _____

Show Measures of Angles

**Study the example showing the measure of an angle.
Then solve problems 1–6.**

Example

The drawing below shows an angle that turns
through 9 one-degree angles.

1°

How many degrees does the angle measure?

The angle measures 9° because it turns
through 9 one-degree angles.

> The measure of any angle is equal to
> the number of one-degree angles it
> turns through.

1 An angle turns through 60 one-degree angles.
What is the measure of the angle? _____ degrees

2 An angle turns through 160 one-degree angles.
What is the measure of the angle? _____ degrees

3 The circle at the right has 4 equal parts. The angle
shown in the circle is a right angle.

  a. What fraction of the circle does the right angle

    turn through? _____ of the circle

  b. Complete the sentence.

    A circle has 360°. A right angle turns through

    □/□ of a circle, or □/□ of _____ degrees.

  c. Use fraction multiplication to show how you
    can find the measure of a right angle.

    _____

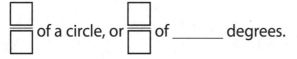

Vocabulary

angle a geometric
shape made by two rays
that meet at a common
endpoint, called a vertex.

right angle an angle
that looks like a square
corner and measures 90°.

Solve.

4 The circle at the right has 6 equal parts. The angle shown in the circle is an acute angle.

   a. What fraction of the circle does the acute angle

      turn through? _____ of the circle

   b. Complete the sentence.
      A circle has 360°. The acute angle turns through

      $\dfrac{\square}{\square}$ of the circle, or $\dfrac{\square}{\square}$ of _____ degrees.

   c. Use fraction multiplication to show how you can find the measure of the acute angle.

   _____

5 The larger part of the circle at the right is twice as big as the smaller part.

   a. What fraction of the circle is the smaller part? $\dfrac{\square}{3}$

   b. What fraction of the circle is the larger part? $\dfrac{\square}{3}$

   c. What fraction of the circle does the angle shown by

      the arrow turn through? $\dfrac{\square}{3}$ of the circle

   d. Complete the sentence.

      A circle has 360°. The angle shown by the arrow turns

      through $\dfrac{\square}{\square}$ of the circle, or $\dfrac{\square}{\square}$ of _____ degrees.

   e. Use fraction multiplication to show how you can find the measure of the angle shown by the arrow.

   _____

6 What is the measure of an angle that turns through $\dfrac{1}{12}$ of a circle?

_____

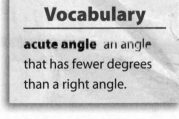

Vocabulary

acute angle an angle that has fewer degrees than a right angle.

Name: _____

Reason and Write

Study the example. Underline two parts that you think make it a particularly good answer and a helpful example.

Example

Describe and compare the angles shown by the hands on the clocks below. What kinds of angle are shown? Which angle has a greater measure?

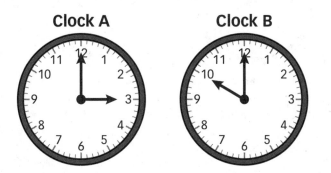

Clock A   Clock B

Show your work. Use numbers and words to explain your answer.

The angle formed by the hands of Clock A turns through 15 minutes out of 60 minutes on the clock.

This is $\frac{15}{60}$, or $\frac{1}{4}$, of the circle on the clock.

$\frac{1}{4}$ of 360 degrees in a circle is the measure of the angle.

$$\frac{1}{4} \times 360 = 90$$

The angle measures 90 degrees, so it is a right angle.

The angle formed by the hands of Clock B turns through 10 minutes out of 60 minutes.

This is $\frac{10}{60}$, or $\frac{1}{6}$, of the circle.

$\frac{1}{6}$ of 360 degrees in a circle is the measure of the angle.

$$\frac{1}{6} \times 360 = 60$$

The angle measures 60 degrees, so it is an acute angle.

The angle in Clock A has a greater measure than the angle in Clock B because 90 degrees > 60 degrees.

> *Where does the example . . .*
> - *describe each angle?*
> - *compare the measures of the angles?*
> - *use numbers to explain?*
> - *use words to explain?*

Solve the problem. Use what you learned from the model.

Describe and compare the angles shown by the hands on the clocks below. What kinds of angle are shown? Which angle has a greater measure?

Clock A

Clock B

Show your work. Use numbers and words to explain your answer.

Did you . . .

- describe each angle?

- compare the measures of the angles?

- use numbers to explain?

- use words to explain?

Dear Family,

This week your child is learning to measure and draw angles.

Your child is learning how to estimate the measure of an angle, as well as how to find an angle's exact measure.

Estimate the measure of an angle by using benchmarks, such as a right angle and a straight angle. For example, to estimate the measure of the purple angle below, compare it to a right angle and to a straight angle.

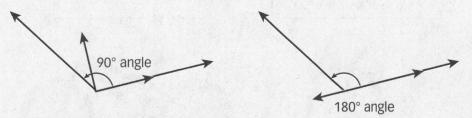

90° angle

180° angle

A right angle has a measure of 90 degrees. A straight angle has a measure of 180 degrees. The measure of the purple angle is between 90 degrees and 180 degrees.

To find the exact measure of the angle, your child is learning to use a tool called a protractor.

- Line up the center point of the protractor with the vertex of the angle.

- Then line up one ray with the 0° mark.

- Read the mark on the protractor that the other ray passes through.

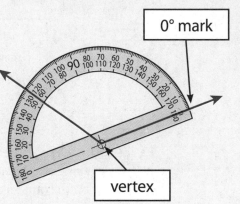

0° mark

vertex

The angle measures 125°. (The ray also passes through the 55° mark, but since the angle is bigger than a 90° angle, the measure is not 55°.)

Invite your child to share what he or she knows about measuring and drawing angles by doing the following activity together.

NEXT

Do an activity with your child to estimate the measure of angles.

- Identify angles in and around the house or outside in the yard or neighborhood. You can also look through magazines or newspapers for pictures that show angles.

  Examples of angles you might find (or make) are:

Angles formed by the hands on a clock or watch

Angles made by a bicycle frame

Angles formed by fingers or by the bend of an elbow

- Estimate the measure of each angle by using right angles and straight angles as benchmarks. You can use the benchmark angles shown on the other side of this page.

Look for other real-life opportunities to estimate angle measures with your child.

Prerequisite: Identify Angles

Study the example problem showing how to identify angles. Then solve problems 1–8.

Example

Logan sketched the front of his townhouse. He labeled the angles in his sketch. Fill in the table below to identify angles *V* through *Z* as acute, right, or obtuse.

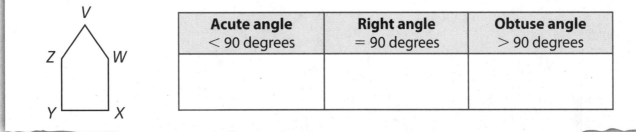

Acute angle < 90 degrees	Right angle = 90 degrees	Obtuse angle > 90 degrees

For problems 1–3, write *A* for an acute angle, *R* for a right angle, and *O* for an obtuse angle.

1 Identify and label the three angles in the sign at the right.

2 Identify and label the four angles in the sign at the right.

3 Identify and label one angle in the sign at the right.

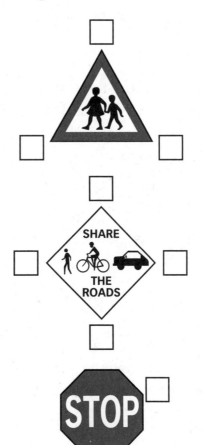

Solve.

4 Identify the angles in the triangles below. Write *A* for acute, *R* for right, and *O* for obtuse.

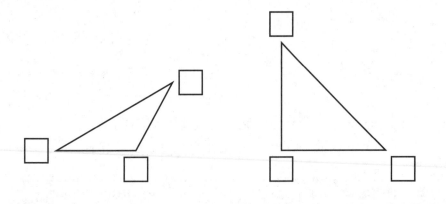

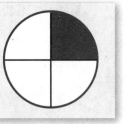

A water sprinkler moves back and forth to water a lawn. The sprinkler turns through 90 degrees of a circle-shaped section in a backyard.

5 What kind of angle is formed in the section of the backyard that the sprinkler turns through?

_____

6 If the sprinkler is adjusted to turn through an additional 90-degree section of the backyard, how many degrees is the new angle formed by the section that the sprinkler turns through? _____

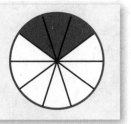

The sprinkler is adjusted again to turn through the shaded section of the circle shown at right. The circle is divided into tenths.

7 What fraction of the circle does the angle turn through? _____

8 Use fraction multiplication to find the measure of the angle. Remember that a circle has 360 degrees.

_____ × 360 = _____ degrees

Name: _____

Use a Protractor to Measure Angles

Study the example showing how to use a protractor to measure an angle. Then solve problems 1–5.

Example

Omar drew the angle at the right. What is the measure of the angle?

Line up the 0° or the 180° mark on a protractor with one ray of the angle.

Line up the center point of the protractor with the vertex of the angle.

Look at the other ray. Read the number of degrees on the protractor. Read the number that is less than 90, since the angle is less than 90°.

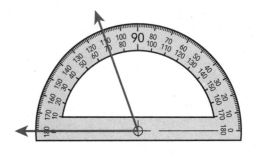

The angle measures 70°.

---

1 Read the number of degrees on the protractor to find the measure of the angle.

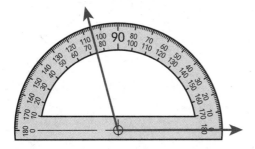

The angle measures _____ degrees.

2 Use a protractor to measure the angle below.

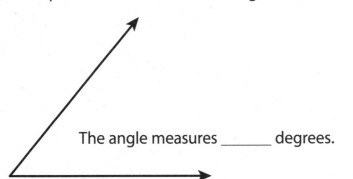

The angle measures _____ degrees.

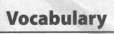

Vocabulary

ray a straight row of points that starts at one point and goes on forever in one direction.

vertex the point where two rays or lines meet to form an angle.

protractor a tool used to measure angles.

Solve.

For problems 3–5, use a protractor to measure the angles. Write each measure.

3 The beam from the flashlight forms an angle.

The angle measures _____ degrees.

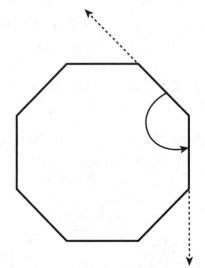

4 Measure one angle of the polygon at the right.

The angle measures _____ degrees.

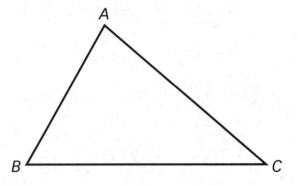

5 Measure the angles of the triangle at the right.

Angle *A* measures _____ degrees.

Angle *B* measures _____ degrees.

Angle *C* measures _____ degrees.

Name: _____

Draw Angles

**Study the example showing how to draw an angle.
Then solve problems 1–6.**

Example

Stephanie wants to draw a 60° angle. She drew a ray and positioned the endpoint of the ray on a protractor's center point. Then she drew a point at 0° on the ray. How does she draw the other ray to form a 60° angle?

Find 60° on the protractor.

Draw a point at the 60°-degree mark.

Draw a ray from the vertex through this point.

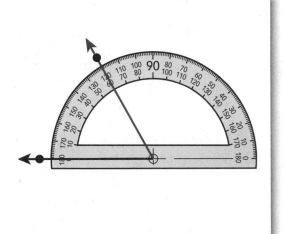

1 Draw a ray to show a 70° angle.

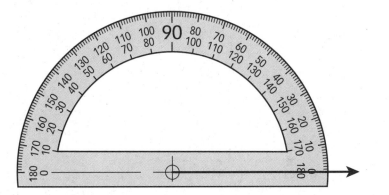

2 Draw a ray to show a 100° angle.

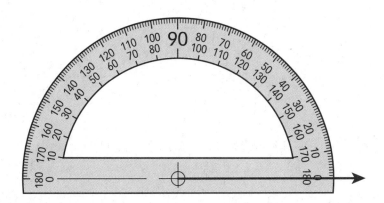

Vocabulary

ray a straight row of points that starts at one point and goes on forever in one direction.

vertex the point where two rays or lines meet to form an angle.

protractor a tool used to measure angles.

Solve.

3 Draw a 160° angle.

4 Draw a 20° angle.

5 Draw a 45° angle.

6 Draw a 135° angle.

Name: _____

Measure and Draw Angles

Solve the problems.

1 Vincent turned his head 30° to the side. Which of the following shows the angle that he turned his head?

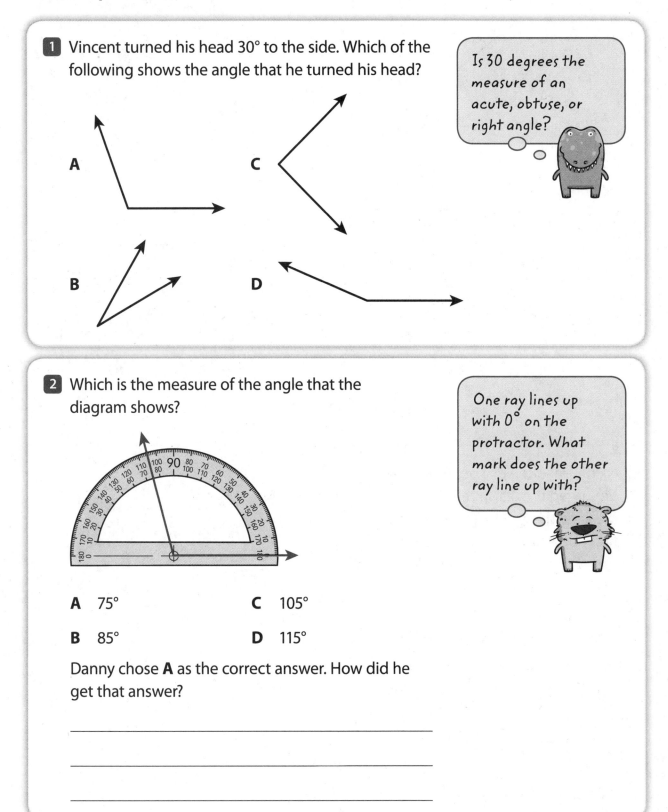

Is 30 degrees the measure of an acute, obtuse, or right angle?

A

B

C

D

2 Which is the measure of the angle that the diagram shows?

One ray lines up with 0° on the protractor. What mark does the other ray line up with?

A 75°   **C** 105°

B 85°   **D** 115°

Danny chose **A** as the correct answer. How did he get that answer?

_____

_____

_____

Solve.

3 What is the measure of the angle below?

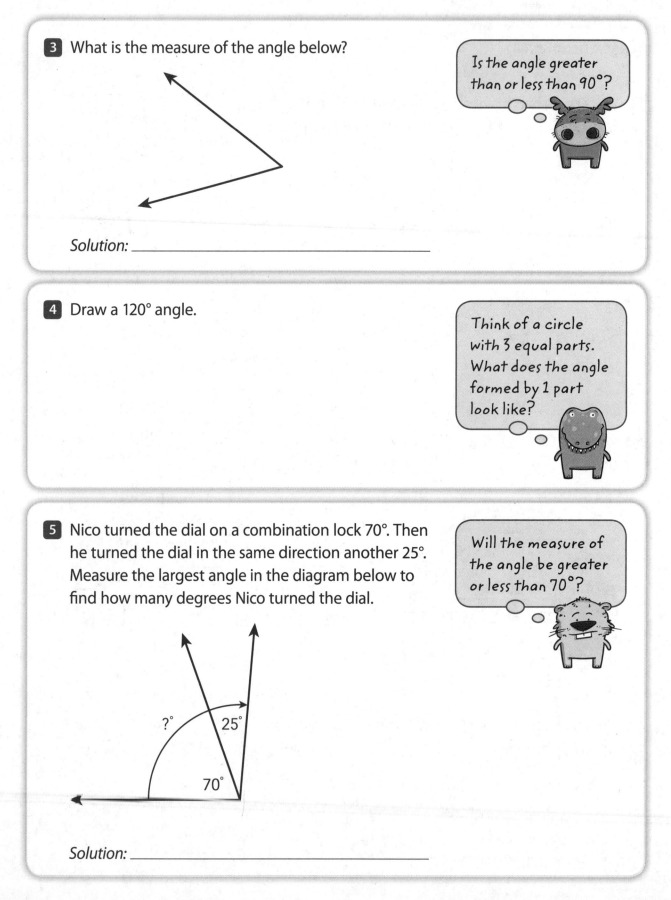

> Is the angle greater than or less than 90°?

Solution: _____

4 Draw a 120° angle.

> Think of a circle with 3 equal parts. What does the angle formed by 1 part look like?

5 Nico turned the dial on a combination lock 70°. Then he turned the dial in the same direction another 25°. Measure the largest angle in the diagram below to find how many degrees Nico turned the dial.

> Will the measure of the angle be greater or less than 70°?

?° 25°

70°

Solution: _____

Dear Family,

This week your child is learning to add and subtract with angles.

The two shapes at the right are placed together as shown. Two angle measures are given: 108° and 53°.

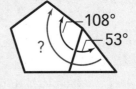

Since there are no gaps and no overlaps between the shapes, you can add the two angle measures together to find the measure of the larger angle formed by the two angles in the shapes.

$108° + 53° = 161°$

The larger combined angle measures 161°.

Your child is also learning to use subtraction to find angle measures. In the example above, if the measure of the larger angle was given and the measure of one of the other angles was unmarked, your child could subtract to find the measure of the unmarked angle.

For example, $161° - 108° = 53°$.

Invite your child to share what he or she knows about adding and subtracting angles by doing the following activity together.

Add and Subtract with Angles Activity

Do an activity with your child to practice adding angle measures.

Materials: sheet of paper, scissors

- Cut out a piece from a rectangular sheet of paper. Cut at an angle.

- Estimate the measure of the angle at the bottom of the piece you cut. For example, estimate that the angle measures about 50 degrees.

- Then estimate the measure of the angle at the bottom corner where you cut the sheet of paper. For example, estimate that the angle measures about 130 degrees.

- Now put the two pieces of paper back together. Add the estimates of the angle measures in order to find the measure of the angle formed by combining both angles. For example, 50° + 130° = 180°.

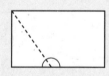

- Ask your child to explain how you know the measure of the combined angle is 180 degrees. (Both angles combine to form a straight angle, which has a measure of 180°.)

320 **Lesson 30** Add and Subtract with Angles

Add and Subtract with Angles

Name: _____

Prerequisite: Measure and Draw Angles

Study the example explaining how to use a protractor to measure angles to solve a word problem. Then solve problems 1–5.

Example

Charlie is designing a roof for a new building. He draws the angles below to show two roof designs. What is the measure of the angle at the top of each roof in the drawings?

Use a protractor to measure each angle.

This angle measures _____.   This angle measures _____.

1 Draw a roof design that has an angle measure between 42° and 68°.

This angle measures _____.

2 Draw a roof design that has an obtuse angle. What does the angle measure?

This angle measures _____.

Solve.

3 Madison drew three rays and realized she had drawn an acute and an obtuse angle.

   a. Label the angles *acute* and *obtuse*.

   b. Use a protractor to measure each angle. Write the angle measure.

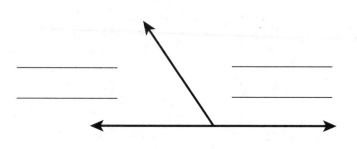

_____

_____

                                _____

                                _____

4 Draw a 152° angle.

5 Measure each angle in the quadrilateral below. Write each angle measure.

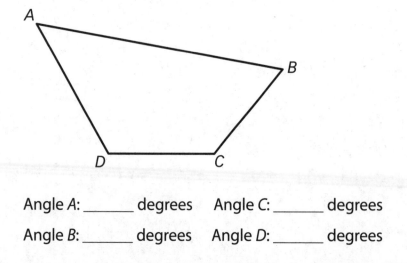

Angle *A*: _____ degrees   Angle *C*: _____ degrees

Angle *B*: _____ degrees   Angle *D*: _____ degrees

Name: _____

Combine Angles

Study the example problem showing how to combine smaller angles to form a larger angle. Then solve problems 1–5.

Example

A spotlight in a theater casts a beam that has an angle measure of 24°.

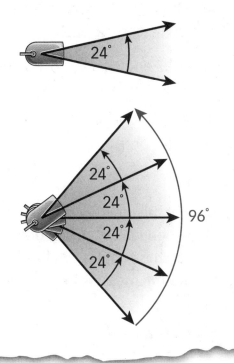

If four spotlights are placed so that they have a common endpoint, what is the measure of the greater angle formed by the beams of all four spotlights?

Four 24° angles compose the greater angle. Use addition to combine the angles.

$$24° + 24° + 24° + 24° = 96°$$

The measure of the greater angle is 96°.

---

1 Look at the example above. Suppose three spotlights are placed to have a common endpoint. What is the measure of the greater angle formed by the beams of the three spotlights? Write an addition equation to find the measure of this angle.

_____

2 Another way to compose a 96° angle is to combine two angles: a 90° angle and a 6° angle. Write an addition equation to show why this is true.

_____

Vocabulary

compose to combine parts.

Lesson 30 Add and Subtract with Angles   **323**

Solve.

3 Tell whether each statement is *True* or *False*.

    a. A 20° angle and a 70° angle can be composed into a 90° angle.   ☐ True   ☐ False

    b. Three 50° angles compose an angle that measures 350°.   ☐ True   ☐ False

    c. A 15° angle and a 60° angle compose an angle that measures 75°.   ☐ True   ☐ False

    d. Four 50° angles can be composed into a 200° angle.   ☐ True   ☐ False

4 Look at the drawing of a hand fan at the right. The angle between each wooden stick on the fan is 12°. If 11 of these angles combine to form the open fan, what is the measure of the purple angle on the open fan?

Show your work.

Solution: _____

5 Sam lifts the front of his skateboard at a 15° angle to the ground as he gets ready to jump. He lifts his skateboard another 27° when he jumps. What is the measure of the angle that Sam lifts his skateboard from the ground?

Show your work.

Solution: _____

Name: _____

Use Addition and Subtraction to Find Unknown Angles

Study the example problem showing how to use subtraction to find an unknown angle measure. Then solve problems 1–6.

Example

Emma turned the knob on a combination lock 117°. How many more degrees does she need to turn the knob to make one full turn?

Write and solve an equation to find the measure of the unknown angle.

$$360° - 117° = x$$
$$243° = x$$

Emma needs to turn the knob another 243°.

A full turn is 360°.

---

1 Alice is pushing her brother in a swing. The swing is hanging straight down. She pulls the swing back 35° and lets go. The swing moves forward 65°. How many degrees forward from the original straight down position of the swing did the swing move?

Show your work.

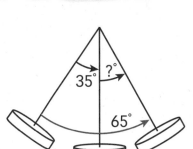

Solution: _____

2 A sprinkler in a backyard turns through 180°. The sprinkler has turned 96° so far. How many more degrees will the sprinkler turn through to reach 180°?

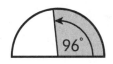

Solution: _____

Solve.

3 A sprinkler turns through 180° every 5 seconds. It turns through 36° every second. Fill in the table below.

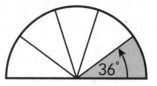

Time (seconds)	Degrees
1	
2	
3	
4	
5	

4 Write the measure of the unknown angle in the box below.

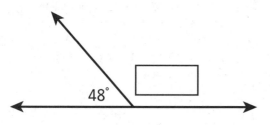

48°

The line makes a straight angle with a measure of 180°.

5 Write the measure of the unknown angle in the box below.

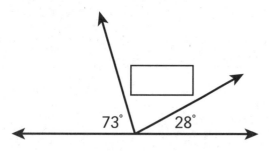

73°   28°

6 Use the angle measures below to fill in the boxes in the diagram with the correct angle measures.

45°   110°   115°   135°

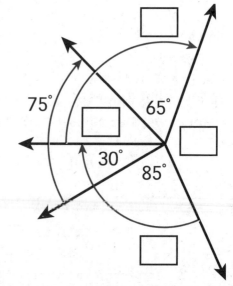

75°   65°   30°   85°

Name: _____

Add and Subtract with Angles

Solve the problems.

1 Alex blew on a pinwheel. The pinwheel turned 240°. How many degrees more does the pinwheel need to turn to make one full turn?

A 60°

B 120°

C 180°

D 360°

240°

There are 360 degrees in a full turn.

2 Vicky turned the knob on her combination lock one full turn and then another 144°. How many degrees did she turn the knob?

A 144°

B 216°

C 360°

D 504°

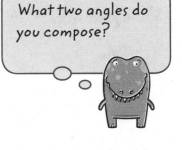

What two angles do you compose?

Jen chose **A** as the correct answer. How did she get that answer?

_____

_____

_____

_____

Solve.

3 An amusement park has a swinging ship ride that goes back and forth. At its highest point, the ship is 170° from its starting position. If it swings 170° in each direction from the starting position, how many degrees does it turn through?

Show your work.

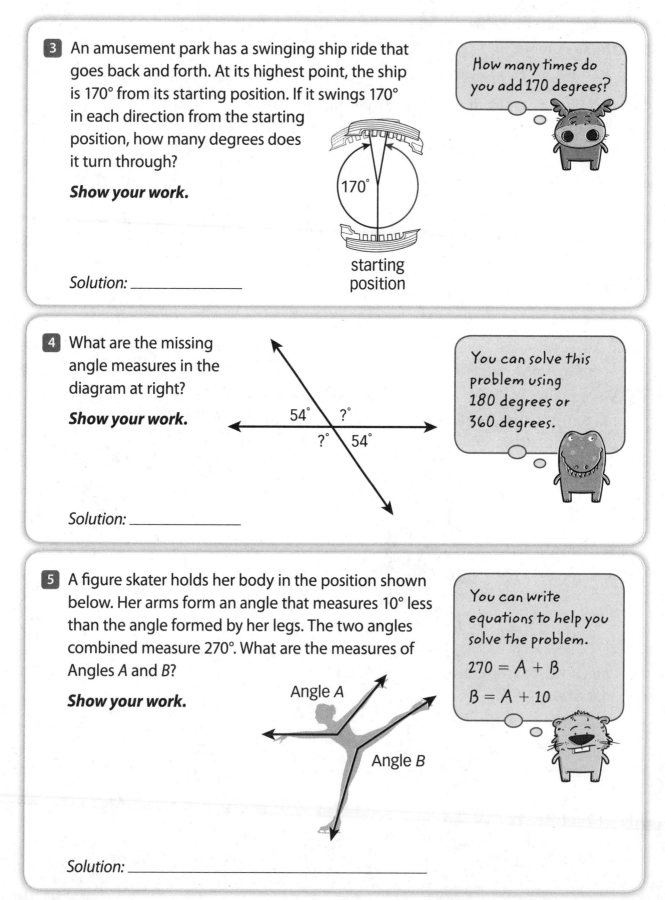

How many times do you add 170 degrees?

170°

starting position

Solution: _____

4 What are the missing angle measures in the diagram at right?

Show your work.

54° ?°
?° 54°

You can solve this problem using 180 degrees or 360 degrees.

Solution: _____

5 A figure skater holds her body in the position shown below. Her arms form an angle that measures 10° less than the angle formed by her legs. The two angles combined measure 270°. What are the measures of Angles *A* and *B*?

Show your work.

Angle *A*

Angle *B*

You can write equations to help you solve the problem.

270 = A + B

B = A + 10

Solution: _____

Unit 5 Game

Angle Sums

What you need: Recording Sheet, 2 sets of Angle Sums Game Cards, 1 protractor for each player

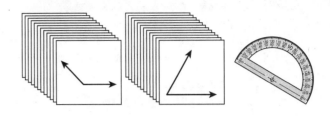

Directions

- Mix both sets of Game Cards. Stack the cards and lay out 6 cards face up.

- Each player will choose a total of 2 cards. Take turns picking each card. Return the 2 unused cards to the stack. Your goal is to choose two angles that will have the greatest angle measure when they are combined.

- Both players use a protractor to measure their angles. Players add their angle measures and write their addition equations on the Recording Sheet. Remember to write the degree symbol (°)!

- Players compare the combined angle measures. The player with the greater combined angle measure wins the round.

- Set aside the cards you used. In each round, choose 2 new cards. The loser of the round picks the first card in the next round. The player with more wins after 5 rounds wins the game.

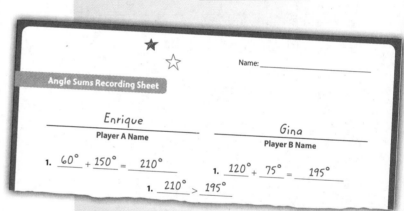

The sum of my two angle measures is 210°. My combined angle measure of 210° is greater than your combined angle measure of 195°, so I win the first round.

Angle Sums Recording Sheet

Player A Name	**Player B Name**

_____   _____

Player A Name   **Player B Name**

1. _____ + _____ = _____   **1.** _____ + _____ = _____

             1. _____ > _____

2. _____ + _____ = _____   **2.** _____ + _____ = _____

             2. _____ > _____

3. _____ + _____ = _____   **3.** _____ + _____ = _____

             3. _____ > _____

4. _____ + _____ = _____   **4.** _____ + _____ = _____

             4. _____ > _____

5. _____ + _____ = _____   **5.** _____ + _____ = _____

             5. _____ > _____

Final Score Player A _____   **Final Score Player B** _____

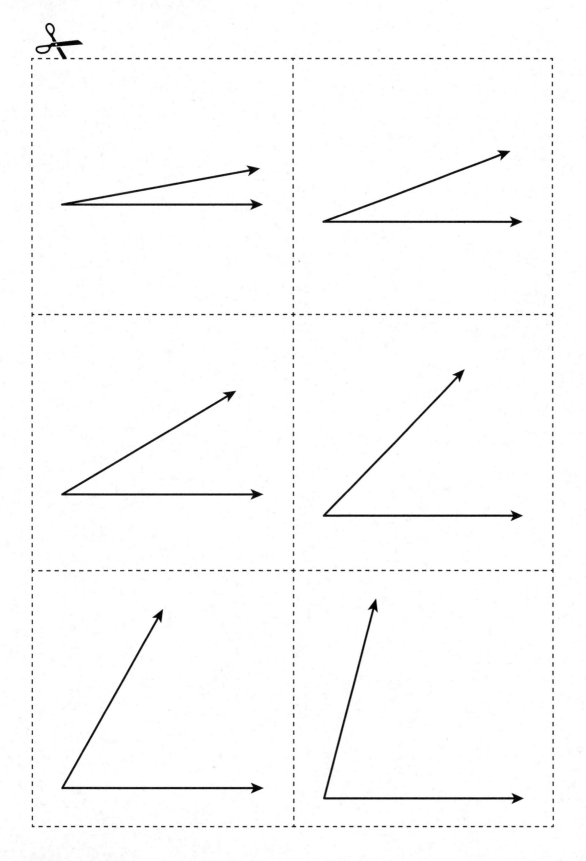

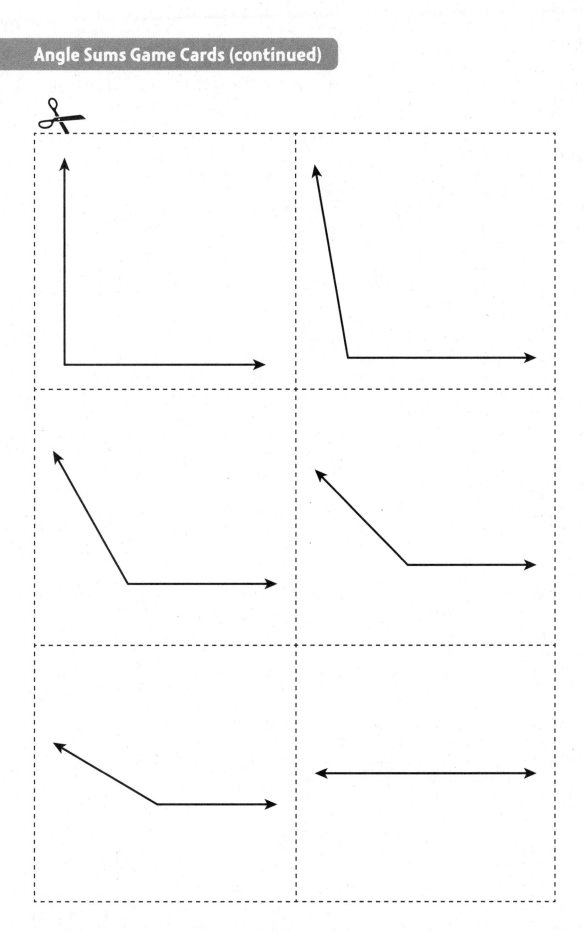

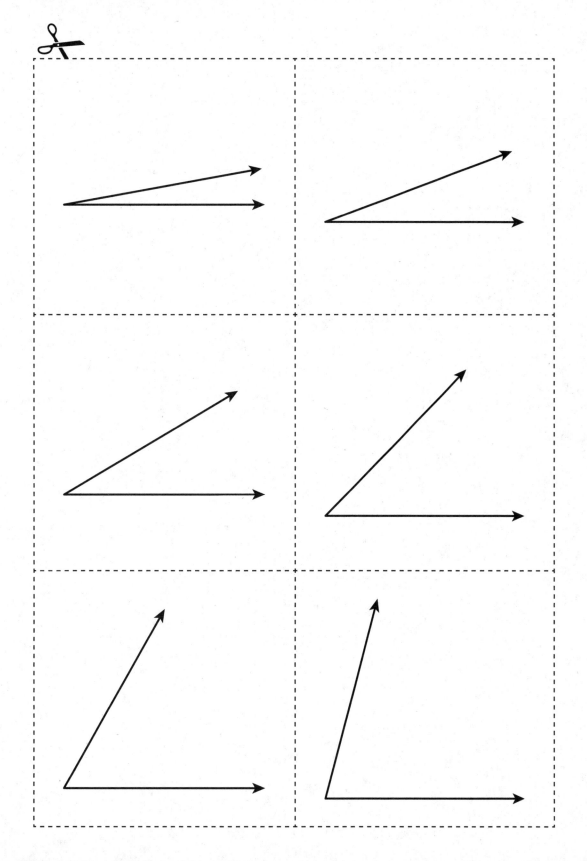

Angle Sums Game Cards (continued)

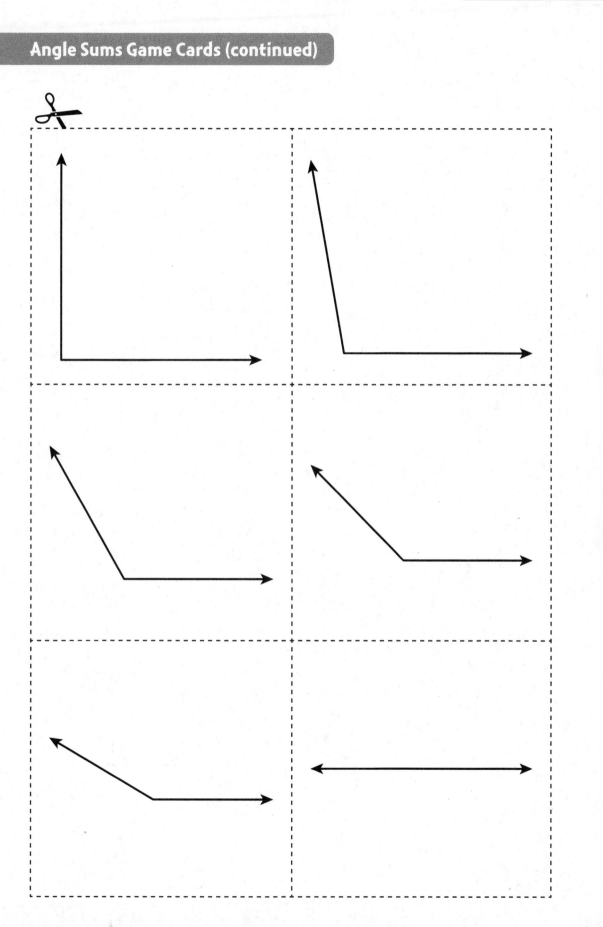

Unit 5 Practice

Name: _____

Measurement and Data

In this unit you learned to:	Lesson
convert units of length, weight, volume, and time, for example: 5 feet = 60 inches.	23, 24, 25
solve word problems about time, money, distances, volumes, and masses, for example: 4 L of juice + 300 mL of juice = 4,300 mL of juice.	24, 25, 27
use the area formula for rectangles, for example: $A = 3 \times 9$ for a rectangle with a length of 9 and a width of 3.	26
use the perimeter formula for rectangles, for example: $P = (2 \times 12) + (2 \times 5)$ for a rectangle with a length of 12 and a width of 5.	26
measure angles using a protractor, for example: an angle on a stop sign is 135°.	28, 29
solve addition and subtraction problems with angles, for example: 165° − 23° = 142°.	30

Use these skills to solve problems 1–5.

1 Tell whether each statement is *True* or *False*.

a. 12 yards = 4 feet

☐ True ☐ False

b. 2 kilograms = 2,000 grams

☐ True ☐ False

c. 1 hour = 360 seconds

☐ True ☐ False

d. 4,000 kilometers = 4 meters

☐ True ☐ False

e. 3 pounds = 48 ounces

☐ True ☐ False

2 The school library is holding a summer reading challenge. Students who meet a goal of reading 16 hours or more receive a prize. There are 10 weeks of summer break. If a student reads 4 days a week, how many minutes does a student need to read each day to meet the goal?

Show your work.

Solution: _____

Solve.

3 Find the area and perimeter of the shape.

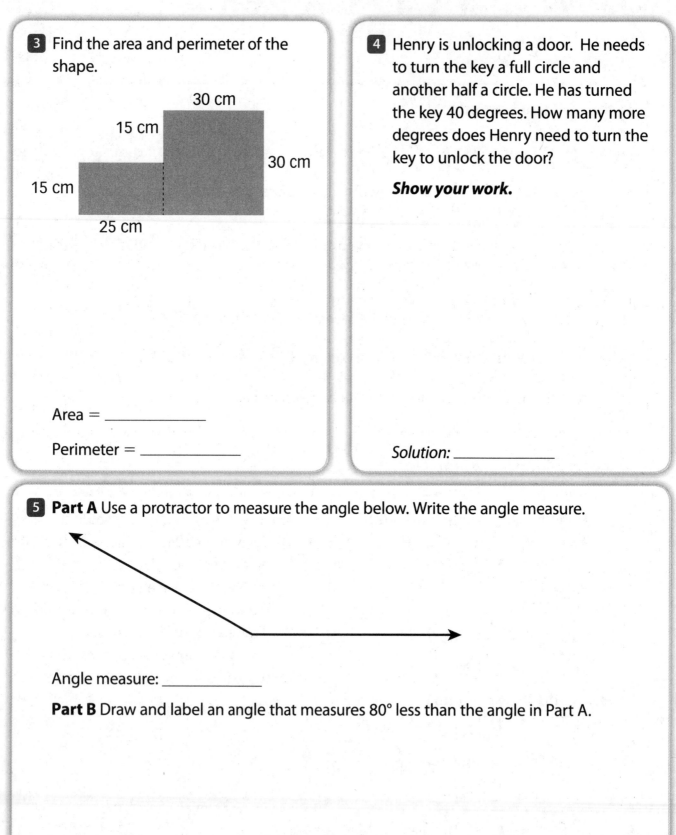

30 cm

15 cm

30 cm

15 cm

25 cm

Area = _____

Perimeter = _____

4 Henry is unlocking a door. He needs to turn the key a full circle and another half a circle. He has turned the key 40 degrees. How many more degrees does Henry need to turn the key to unlock the door?

Show your work.

Solution: _____

5 **Part A** Use a protractor to measure the angle below. Write the angle measure.

Angle measure: _____

Part B Draw and label an angle that measures 80° less than the angle in Part A.

Unit 5 Performance Task

Answer the questions and show all your work on separate paper.

Joey does yard and garden work for his neighbors on the weekend. He can mow a yard with 100 square meters of lawn in 10 minutes. He can weed a 5-meter long flower garden that borders a yard in 10 minutes.

The chart below shows the sizes of the yards and flower borders for four neighbors.

	Smith	**Jackson**	**Ruiz**	**Hall**
Length of Yard	40 meters	30 meters	20 meters	20 meters
Width of Yard	10 meters	20 meters	25 meters	35 meters
Size of Flower Border	Half of the width of the yard	Half of the width of the yard	Entire width of the yard	Half of the length of the yard

> **Checklist**
>
> Did you . . .
>
> ☐ organize the information?
>
> ☐ use a formula to find area?
>
> ☐ check that the results make sense?

Joey wants to work on some of the yards and flower borders this weekend. He plans to start work at 9 o'clock Saturday morning. He wants to finish by noon so that he can go to soccer practice.

Which yards and flower borders should Joey plan to work on Saturday? What time will he be finished with the work? Explain your reasoning.

Reflect on Mathematical Practices

After you complete the task, choose one of the following questions to answer.

1 **Reason Mathematically** How did you decide which yards and flower borders Joey should work on?

2 **Be Precise** How did you determine what time Joey would finish the work?

Performance Task Tips

Word Bank Here are some words that you might use in your answer.

length	equal	minutes
width	sum	hours
area	meters	square meters

Models Here are some models that you might use to find the solution.

Neighbor	Length of Yard	Width of Yard	Area of Yard	Minutes to Mow the Yard

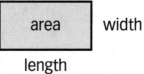

width

length

Sentence Starters Here are some sentence starters that might help you write an explanation.

The area of _____

It will take _____ minutes to _____

The total time _____

If Joey does _____ , then _____

©Curriculum Associates, LLC   Copying is not permitted.

Unit 5 Vocabulary

Name: _____

My Examples

convert

to change from one unit to another unit

line plot

a graph using marks along a number line to show how many objects are in a set

angle

a geometric shape made by two rays that meet at a common endpoint, called a vertex

right angle

an angle that looks like a square corner and measures 90°

We are accustomed to seeing *exeunt*, literally "they go out," as a stage direction in old plays, with the meaning "two or more actors leave the stage." When *exeunt* is followed by **omnes** (AWM-nays), the playwright is telling us that all the actors on stage at the time are to leave. The singular of *exeunt* is the familiar **exit** (EKS-it), a stage direction meaning "he (or she) leaves the stage."

exit

See EXEUNT.

exitus acta probat
EKS-ih-tuus AH-ktah PRAW-baht
the end justifies the means

Literally "the result validates the deeds." This proverb avers that any means—no matter how foul—may be used if the intended result is a good one. But take care.

ex libris
eks LIH-brees
from the library of

This familiar legend, also given as **e** (eh) **libris**, translated literally as "from the books," commonly appears on book plates. The phrase is followed by the owner's name.

ex mero motu
eks MEH-roh MOH-too
spontaneously

Literally "out of pure, simple impulse." "He insisted that no one had exerted pressure on him, that he acted *ex mero motu*."

ex more
eks MOH-reh
according to custom

ex nihilo nihil fit
eks NIH-hih-loh NIH-hihl fit
nothing comes from nothing

Lucretius, the first-century Roman poet, wrote in *De Rerum Natura* of the creation of the world: **Nil posse creari de nilo** (neel PAWS-seh kray-AH-ree day NEE-loh), "nothing can be created out of nothing," which is also rendered as *ex nihilo nihil fit*, suggesting that every effect must have a cause. Lucretius agreed with the fifth-century B.C. Greek philosophers who theorized that the world could not have been made from nothing. They thought it had been created from the accidental joining of atoms falling from space. The Latin **atomus** (AHT-awm-uus) means "atom" or—remember that this theory antedated quarks and mesons by more than two millennia—"that which is indivisible." But there is ambiguity in *ex nihilo nihil fit* and in its English translation. Thus, the Latin phrase is applied rather broadly today, and *ex nihilo nihil fit* may be used to suggest that a dull mind cannot be expected to produce great thoughts, anything worth doing requires hard work, you can't get bet blood from a stone, and the like. (See DE NIHILO NIHIL.)

ex officio
eks awf-FIH-kee-oh
by virtue of an office

Officers of an institution usually serve on many of its committees not because they have personal qualifications needed on the committees, but because they hold certain offices. Thus, the chief executive officer of a corporation usually is a member *ex officio* of all the important committees of the corporation. The phrase is so thoroughly part of the English language that it has an English pronunciation, eks ə-FISH-ee-oh.

ex parte
eks PAHR-teh
from one side only

A legal expression, literally "from a party," applied to a proceeding in which only one side of the case is presented, and the opposing side is absent. Naturally, there is the presumption of partisan testimony in an *ex parte* proceeding.

ex pede Herculem
eks PEH-deh HEHR-kuu-lem
from a sample we can judge the whole

This expression, literally "from the foot, a Hercules," means we can extrapolate accurately when we know a single pertinent fact. The phrase is an allusion to Pythagoras, the sixth-century B.C. Greek mathematician and philosopher, who calculated the height of Hercules by measuring and comparing the length of many Greek stadiums. Since Hercules' stadium at Olympia was longest by far, Pythagoras deduced that Hercules' foot was longer than the foot of lesser men (or gods). Knowing that a man's height is proportional to the length of his foot, Pythagoras was able to establish a credible height (the whole) for Hercules from the length of his foot (the sample). Inspector Maigret, Sherlock Holmes, Hercule Poirot, and Nero Wolfe may owe a great deal to Pythagoras. (See EX UNGUE LEONEM.)

experto credite
eks-PEHR-toh KRAY-dih-teh
trust me

In the absence of evidence to the contrary, we are adjured by Virgil, in the *Aeneid*, literally to "believe one who has experience." The fragility of this advice is implicit in its use: *Experto credite* is too often cited by the person who may understand little and have even less evidence to offer but has spent a long time practicing his trade. "That stock is a good buy, *experto credite*," said the broker.

ex post facto
eks pawst FAH-ktoh
from what is done afterward

We are all experts *ex post facto*, Monday morning quarterbacks who can always give the correct answers to all problems once we know how things have worked out. An *ex post facto* law, normally not permitted in United States constitutional law, is one that can be applied retroactively; even though such a law is passed after a particular case has been settled, it would be deemed applicable even to previously closed cases.

ex proprio motu
eks PRAW-pree-oh MOH-too
voluntarily

Anyone who acts entirely without encouragement or coercion does so *ex proprio motu*, literally "of one's own accord."

ex tempore
eks TEM-paw-reh
extemporaneously

Anyone speaking *ex tempore*, Cicero's phrase, with the meaning "without preparation," is winging it: "Two of the speakers were well prepared, but one surely spoke *ex tempore* and made a fool of himself." The phrase can also be used in the sense of "without premeditation."

extinctus amabitur idem

eks-TIN-ktuus ah-MAH-bih-tuur EE-dem

how quickly we forget

A marvelously insightful observation from the *Epistles* of Horace, with the literal meaning "the same man will be loved after he's dead." Horace understood how quickly a person's bad reputation is forgotten once he's safely underground, and we have ample evidence of the aptness of *extinctus amabitur idem* in the work of revisionist biographers and historians.

ex ungue leonem

eks UUN-gweh lay-OH-nem

from a sample we can judge the whole

Another way of saying that we can tell the whole from a single part, with the literal meaning "from a claw, the lion." (See EX PEDE HERCULEM.)

ex uno disce omnes

eks OO-noh DIH-skeh AWM-nays

from one example you may deduce the rest

This maxim, literally "from one, learn of all," advises us to generalize from one example, a precept that must be applied intelligently. *Ex uno disce omnes* may be useful for certain cases —if one oak leaf turns brown, they all will; if one quart of milk in a batch is sour, the entire batch will not be potable; if one war is hell, all wars will be hell—but if one child . . . others may not. . . . After all, S. I. Hayakawa long ago taught us that rose$_1$ is not rose$_2$ is not rose$_3$ despite Gertrude Stein's claim to the contrary, and we more recently identified the flaw in "if you've seen one ghetto, you've seen them all."

fabas indulcet fames
FAH-bahs in-DUUL-ket FAH-mays
hunger makes everything taste good

Literally "hunger sweetens beans," beans, of course, being the poor man's fare. *Fabas indulcet fames* is another way of saying *fames optimum condimentum*, "hunger is the best seasoning."

facile princeps
FAH-kih-leh PRIHN-keps
number one

A felicitous phrase, literally "easily first," used to designate the acknowledged leader in any field.

facilis descensus Averno
FAH-kih-lis deh-SKEHN-suus ah-WEHR-noh
the descent to hell is easy

Avernus (ah-WEHR-nuus), a lake in Campania, was considered by the Romans to be an entrance to hell. *Avernus*, literally "without a bird," is said to have been so named because poisonous vapors arose from it and were said to draw birds down into its waters, where they perished. Thus, *facilis descensus Averno*, a line from Virgil's *Aeneid*, cautions us that it is easy to fall, but once fallen, difficult to make one's way back up. Beware that first misstep!

facta non verba
FAH-ktah nohn WEHR-bah
actions speak louder than words

Facta non verba, literally "deeds, not words," holds that protestations of good intentions count for little: Action is what we need.

fama semper vivat

FAH-mah SEM-pehr WEE-waht

may his (or her) good name live forever

A useful expression when invoking the name of an illustrious or revered person. "This good woman, *fama semper vivat*, saw fit to remember us in a bequest that will help our cause for many years to come." (Notice the difference in the translation of *fama* in the next entry. In Latin, as in any other language, words acquire additional meanings through use.)

fama volat

FAH-mah WAW-laht

rumor travels fast

In the *Aeneid*, Virgil tells us that nothing travels faster than scandal: **Fama malum quo non aliud velocius ullum** (FAH-mah MAH-luum kwoh nohn AH-lee-uud way-LOH-kee-uus UUL-luum). *Fama volat*, another phrase from the *Aeneid*, provides a handier way to convey the same thought.

fames optimum condimentum

FAH-mays AW-ptih-muum kawn-dih-MEN-tuum

hunger is the best seasoning

See FABAS INDULCET FAMES.

Fata obstant

FAH-tah AWB-stahnt

the gods willed otherwise

The *Fata* were the three Roman goddesses of fate or destiny: Nona, Decuma, and Morta. Any human action that went amiss was blamed on the opposition of the *Fata*, "the Fates." So Virgil's phrase in the *Aeneid*, *Fata obstant*, literally "the Fates oppose," could be cited. Similarly, anything that concluded happily was ascribed to the cooperation of the Fata. Thus, the Romans had a foolproof device for refusing to take action or for turning down a request. *Fata obstant* beats "my hands were tied."

Fata viam invenient
FAH-tah WEE-ahm in-WEHN-ee-ent
the gods will find a way

Another saying (see the preceding entry) from Virgil's *Aeneid*, literally "the Fates will find a way," but this time an expression of optimism. Yet it is worth noting that the Romans here reveal once again their inclination to leave things in the laps of the gods. Modern man is more apt to say: "God helps those who help themselves." The Romans had more fun.

favete linguis
fah-WAY-teh LIHN-gwees
hold your tongue

This expression from Horace's *Odes*, with the literal meaning "favor with your tongues," is a warning to utter no words of bad omen during a religious rite: "Say nothing lest what you say hurt another or bring down on us an unfavorable act of the gods." The Latin for telling someone to keep silent under ordinary circumstances is **quin taces** (kween TAH-kays).

fecit
FAY-kit
made by

Fecit, literally "he or she made (it)," was an artist's way of signing a work. *Fecit* is followed by the artist's name. (See EXCUDIT.)

felicitas habet multos amicos
fay-LEE-kih-tahs HAH-bet MUUL-tohs ah-MEE-kohs
prosperity has many friends

When things are going well for us, we never lack for friends.
When our fortunes turn . . .

felix qui nihil debet
FAY-liks kwee NIH-hil DAY-bet
happy is he who owes nothing

If this proverb is accurate, Americans are among the unhap-
piest people of all time.

felix qui potuit rerum cognoscere causas
FEH-liks kwee PAW-too-it REH-ruum
kaw-GNAW-skeh-reh KOW-sahs
fortunate is he who has been able to learn the causes
of things

This line from Virgil's *Georgics* praises those of superior intel-
ligence who can grasp the secrets of nature and so raise themselves above reliance on superstition.

festina lente
feh-STEE-nah LEN-tay
make haste slowly

Suetonius, in *Divus Augustus*, attributes this bit of wisdom to
the emperor Augustus, who moved cautiously, step by step, to
transform Rome from a republic to an empire ruled virtually by
one man. Thus, what appears to be salutary advice worthy of
our own Ben Franklin may have Machiavellian overtones.

fiat iustitia (or justitia) ruat caelum
FEE-aht YUUS-tih-tee-ah ROO-aht KĪ-luum
let justice be done though the heavens fall

The unyielding precept that the law must be followed precisely, regardless of the circumstances and eventualities.

fiat lux
FEE-aht luuks
let there be light

The Latin version of one of the opening verses of Genesis.

fiat voluntas Tua
FEE-aht waw-LUUN-tahs TOO-ah
Thy will be done

Familiar words from the Latin version of the Lord's Prayer, from Matthew.

fide et amore
FIH-deh et ah-MOH-reh
by faith and love

fide et fiducia
FIH-deh et fee-DOO-kee-ah
by faith and confidence

Fidei Defensor
fih-DAY-ee day-FEN-sawr
Defender of the Faith

Fidei Defensor, abbreviated **F.D.**, is one of the many titles of British monarchs. Henry VIII was the first to have this one.

fides Punica
FIH-days POO-nih-kah
a double cross

This expression, literally "Punic faith," refers to the Carthaginians—the Latin name **Punicus** (POO-nih-kuus) means "Phoenician," and it was the Phoenicians who founded Carthage. The Punic Wars resulted in the destruction of Carthage by the Romans. The distrust of the Carthaginians by the Romans exemplified in *fides Punica*—the Romans intended the same meaning when they spoke of **ars** (ahrs) **Punica**, "the Punic art"; **fraus** (frows) **Punica**, "Punic deceit"; and **perfidia** (pehr-FEE-dih-ah) **Punica**, "Punic treachery"—may be a world-class proof of the aptness of "it takes one to know one." (See DELENDA EST CARTHAGO for an illustration of the trustworthiness of Rome.)

fidus Achates
FEE-duus ah-KAH-tays
bosom pal

In the *Aeneid*, Virgil characterized Achates, companion of Aeneas, as *fidus Achates*, literally "faithful Achates," giving us a convenient Latin substitute for "best friend."

finem respice
FEE-nem REH-spih-keh
look to the end

Appropriate advice for anyone about to take an irreversible step or launch a risky venture.

finis coronat opus
FEE-nis kaw-ROH-naht AW-puus
the end crowns the work

Easily understood by anyone who has completed a major project and rejoiced in its completion.

floruit
FLOH-roo-it
he [she] flourished

Floruit, often abbreviated fl., is used to date the period of a person's prime, particularly when exact birth and death dates are unknown: "Somadeva (*fl*. 11th century) was a Sanskrit author."

fluctuat nec mergitur
FLUUK-too-aht nek MEHR-gih-tuur
unsinkable

Fluctuat nec mergitur, literally "it is tossed by the waves but does not sink," is the motto of Paris, which has a ship as its emblem. Like any other city that has existed for a long time, Paris has had its ups and downs. In ancient times, for example, Paris was called **Lutetia** (luu-TEH-tee-ah), from the Latin word **lutum** (LUU-tuum), meaning "mud," reflecting the fact that the City of Lights was then only an aggregation of mud hovels. Anyone for Paris in the spring?

fons et origo
fawns et aw-REE-goh
the source and origin

forsan et haec olim meminisse iuvabit
FAWR-sahn et hīk OH-lim meh-mih-NIS-seh
yuu-WAH-bit
perhaps this will be a pleasure to look back on one day

Virgil, in the *Aeneid*, knowing that time cures all (see TEMPORIS ARS MEDICINA FERE EST), gives us this formula for surviving difficult times by looking ahead to what surely will be happier days.

fortes fortuna iuvat (or juvat)
FAWR-tays fawr-TOO-nah YUU-waht
fortune helps the brave

A proverb of Terence, in *Phormio*, given by others as **fortuna favet fortibus** (FAH-wet FAWR-tih-buus), "fortune favors the brave." We make our own luck.

fortiter in re, suaviter in modo
FAWR-tih-tehr in ray SWAH-wih-tehr in MAW-doh
resolutely in action, gently in manner

A characterization of the estimable person who does unhesitatingly what must be done, but accomplishes the deed as inoffensively as possible. An excellent motto for personnel managers.

fortuna favet fortibus
fawr-TOO-nah FAH-wet FAWR-tih-buus
fortune favors the brave

See FORTES FORTUNA IUVAT.

fronti nulla fides
FRAWN-tee NUUL-lah FIH-days
never judge a book by its cover

This advice from Juvenal's *Satires*, more literally "no reliance can be placed on appearance," warns us against hasty judgments of character made solely on what the eyes perceive.

fugaces labuntur anni
foo-GAH-kays lah-BUUN-tuur AHN-nee
you wake up one morning and find you are old

Literally "the fleeting years glide by." (See the next two entries and EHEU FUGACES LABUNTUR ANNI.)

fugit hora
FUU-git HOH-rah
time flies

Persius, a first-century A.D. Roman poet, used this expression, literally "the hour flies," to tell us that it's later than we think.

fugit irreparabile tempus
FUU-git ihr-reh-pah-RAH-bih-leh TEM-puus
we cannot stop time in its tracks

Tempus fugit, an expression we employ to mean "time flies" (in English pronounced TEM-pəs FYOO-jət), is taken from *fugit irreparabile tempus*—itself a slightly shortened form of a line from Virgil's *Georgics*—with the literal meaning "time irretrievably is flying." (See EHEU FUGACES LABUNTUR ANNI.)

fuit Ilium
FOO-it EE-lee-uum
Troy has had it

Virgil, declaring that Troy—called Ilium by the Romans—no longer existed, wrote *fuit Ilium*, literally "Troy has been," but better rendered as "Troy is no more." We now know a great deal about the riches of Troy, thanks to the work of Heinrich Schliemann, the gifted amateur archaeologist, so the lesson we learn from *fuit Ilium* is that if such a gem can fall, the rest of civilization—even IBM—had better watch out. What Virgil implied in *fuit Ilium* was "and now Rome is number one," that is, from a world destroyed a new world is created. But now that the Roman Empire is gone. . . .

furor

FUU-rawr

madness

This word concludes the entries for the sixth letter of the alphabet, but it is not to be taken as an indication that *furor* itself is of interest. Rather, *furor* combines with other Latin words to give us some useful phrases: **furor loquendi** (law-KWEN-dee), "a rage for speaking"; **furor poeticus** (poh-AY-tih-kuus), "poetic frenzy"; and **furor scribendi** (skree-BEN-dee), "a rage for writing."

gaudeamus igitur

gow-day-AH-muus IH-gih-tuur

let us therefore rejoice

The opening words of a student song of German origin, sung sometimes at academic exercises. Even without knowing what the words mean, anyone who looks back fondly at undergraduate life—proving that absence makes the heart grow fonder—will automatically choke up on hearing this song. After all, the words following are **iuvenes** (or **juvenes**) **dum sumus** (YUU-weh-nays duum SUU-muus), meaning "while we are young." (See EHEU FUGACES LABUNTUR ANNI for a bit of irony.) But to put college life in perspective, it is worthwhile to know that the English word "gaudeamus" (gaw-dee-AY-məs) means a revel by university students, who traditionally imbibe spirits and otherwise carouse to celebrate successful completion of their examinations. Those of us who are unfamiliar with the melody of *gaudeamus igitur* may hear it in the Brahms *Academic Festival Overture*.

genius loci
GEH-nee-uus LAW-kee
the guardian spirit of a place

The Romans believed that everybody born into this world was assigned a *genius*, a guardian spirit that accompanied that person from then on, determining the character and fortunes of the person until death—and beyond. The Romans also believed that every house and every institution had the same arrangement, a *genius loci*. The modern use of this term is intended to be taken as "the character of a place," for example, the *genius loci* (in English, JEEN-yəs LOH-sī) of one's alma mater.

genus irritabile vatum
GEH-nuus ihr-rih-TAH-bih-leh WAH-tuum
the irritable race of poets

Horace used this phrase in his *Epistles*, giving us a way to chide testy men of letters. The usual word for "poet" is **poeta** (POH-ay-tah). In replacing *poeta* with a form of **vates** (WAH-tays), which means "a prophet or seer who makes divine utterances," Horace—later poets also applied *vates* to members of their profession—was using a more honorific term, but one that conveys a vaguely sinister sense.

Gesta Romanorum
GEH-stah roh-mah-NOH-ruum
Deeds of the Romans

Title of a medieval collection of stories in Latin, with each story intended to teach a moral lesson.

Gloria in Excelsis Deo
GLOH-ree-ah in eks-KEL-sees DAY-oh
Glory be to God on high

The first words of the familiar hymn, from Luke.

Gradus ad Parnassum
GRAH-duus ahd pahr-NAHS-suum
a step to Parnassus

The title of a dictionary of prosody much used by past generations of English schoolboys learning to write Latin verse. A *gradus* (in English, GRAY-dəs), as any work of its type is known, supplies the length of syllables in spoken Latin, as well as suggesting poetic phraseology. Parnassus, a mountain in Greece, has two summits, one of which was consecrated to the Muses by the ancient Greeks. For this reason Parnassus is thought of as the seat of poetry.

grammatici certant
grahm-MAH-tih-kee KEHR-tahnt
grammarians dispute

The beginning of a line from Horace's *Ars Poetica*, concluding **et adhuc sub iudice** (or **judice**) **lis est** (et AHD-huuk suub YOO-dee-keh lees est), thus giving us: "Grammarians discuss, and the case is still before the courts." *Grammatici certant*, by itself, can be used to characterize any problem that is still to be resolved by the experts, in particular disagreement among critics over the quality of a work of art.

gratias tibi ago
GRAH-tee-ahs TIH-bee AH-goh
thank you

habeas corpus
HAH-beh-ahs KAWR-puus
you may have the body

Devotees of Hollywood movies know *habeas corpus* as something magical that a lawyer threatens to obtain when a district attorney appears to have the upper hand in a case. What the lawyer usually means is that he intends to apply to a court to obtain a judicial writ, fully described as a writ **habeas corpus ad subiciendum** (ahd suub-ih-kee-EN-duum), requiring the prosecutor in the case to bring the accused before a court to undergo (*ad subiciendum*) the action of the law. A "habeas corpus" (HAY-bee-əs KAWR-pəs), as this legal writ is commonly called in English—other writs carry these same opening words, but they are too numerous to list here—is a feature of British and United States law that protects an individual against arbitrary imprisonment by requiring that any person arrested be brought before a court for formal charge. When the writ is executed, the court hears the complaint under which the person has been detained and rules on the validity of the arrest. If the charge is considered valid, the person must submit to trial; if not, the person goes free. So when a Perry Mason or Joyce Davenport threatens, "I'll slap a habeas corpus on you so fast, it'll make your head swim," full protection of the law is being sought for the accused.

haec olim meminisse iuvabit (or juvabit)
hīk OH-lim meh-mih-NIS-seh yuu-WAH-bit
time heals all wounds

See FORSAN ET HAEC OLIM MEMINISSE IUVABIT.

Hannibal ad portas
HAHN-nih-bahl ahd PAWR-tahs
the Russians are coming

This expression, literally "Hannibal is at the gates," was used
to alert the citizens of Rome to imminent danger. Hannibal,
the commanding general of Carthaginian armies during the Second Punic War, was so feared by the Romans that *Hannibal ad portas* became a proverbial expression, in use well
after Hannibal and his armies no longer were a threat, and
carrying the meaning "our country's in danger." Compar-
able warnings—"missile gap" and "window of vulnerability"
spring to mind—are not unknown today. (See DELENDA EST
CARTHAGO.)

haud ignota loquor
howd ih-GNOH-tah LAW-kwawr
you know as well as I that . . .

A rhetorical expression, literally "I speak of things by no
means unknown," implying that an audience understands—
and agrees with—a speaker's interpretation of some aspect of
the subject under discussion, thus giving the speaker license to
gloss over the putative merits of the point being made.

hic et nunc
heek et nuunk
here and now

A person who demands immediate action, such as repayment
of a debt, would say he wants it *hic et nunc*.

hic et ubique
heek et oo-BEE-kweh
here and everywhere

hic iacet (or jacet)
heek YAH-ket
here lies

The opening words of many an old tombstone inscription.

hinc illae lacrimae
hihnk IHL-lī LAH-krih-mī
so that's what's eating you!

In the play *Andria*, Terence used this phrase, literally "hence those tears," to mean "so that is the true offense, the underlying reason for the annoyance." The rare modern father who finally grasps the reason for a child's display of moodiness might say, "*Hinc illae lacrimae*, you want to spend all your weekends with your mother."

hoc age
hawk AH-geh
get with it!

Literally "do this," but used to adjure people to apply themselves to their work.

hoc anno
hawk AHN-noh
in this year

hoc erat in votis
hawk EH-raht in WOH-tees
this is what I once longed for

These words from Horace's *Satires*, more literally "this was what I wished," introduce a listing of things he once wanted. The sense is that passage of time has altered his desires, so we use this phrase when looking back at our abandoned dreams.

hoc est vivere bis vita posse priore frui
hawk est wee-WEH-reh bihs WEE-tah PAWS-seh
pree-OH-reh FROO-ee
to live twice is to make useful profit from one's past

This epigram by Marcus Valerius Martialis (*c* A.D. 100), known today as Martial, may be interpreted in a variety of ways, all of them positive: Experience is the best teacher. Plan ahead. Don't look back, but capitalize on what you have been through. Who would dispute the efficacy of any of these?

hoc genus omne
hawk GEH-nuus AWM-neh
all this sort

A phrase from Horace's *Satires* that can be applied to people with the meaning "all people of that type," as well as in broader senses: "I quickly tire of discussions of home computers, word processors, and *hoc genus omne*."

hoc loco
hawk LAW-koh
in this place

hoc opus, hic labor est
hawk AW-puus hik LAH-bawr est
this is the tough part

Virgil, in the *Aeneid*, tells in this phrase, literally "this is work, this is labor," that once we go wrong, we will find it difficult to get back on the right track. Virgil was referring to how easy it is to fall into Avernus, the lower depths, and then how hard to make one's way back. (See FACILIS DESCENSUS AVERNO.) But we can use his phrase aptly to prescribe behavior for many difficult situations we encounter in life on earth.

hoc volo, sic iubeo (or jubeo), sit pro ratione voluntas
hawk WAW-loh seek YUU-bay-oh sit proh
rah-tee-OH-neh WAW-luun-tahs
the fact that I wish it is reason enough for doing it

This statement from Juvenal's *Satires* translates more literally as "this I will, thus I command; let my will serve as reason." Excellent text for a sampler destined for hanging at home or in the office of an editor or business executive.

hodie mihi, cras tibi
HAW-dee-ay MIH-hee krahs TIH-bee
my turn today, yours tomorrow

These words, literally "today to me, tomorrow to you," reflect the inevitability of change, so they are used in old epitaphs to remind viewers of their own mortality.

homo doctus in se semper divitias habet
HAW-moh DAW-ktuus in say SEM-pehr
dee-WIH-tee-ahs HAH-bet
a learned man always has wealth within himself

homo homini lupus
HAW-moh HAW-mih-nee LUU-puus
"man's inhumanity to man"

The bitter translation quoted above from Robert Burns has persisted in our culture with the same meaning as *homo homini lupus*, literally "man is a wolf to man," an observation adapted from the play *Asinaria*, by Plautus, and appropriate whenever one reads a newspaper.

honoris causa
haw-NOH-ris KOW-sah
honorary

An academic degree granted *honoris causa*, literally "for the sake of honor," is bestowed as recognition of merit without formal examination. As we know well, degrees awarded *honoris causa* too often are rewards for financial generosity: **pecuniae** (peh-KOO-nee-ī) **causa**, "for the sake of wealth." (For another point of view, see PECUNIA NON OLET.)

hora fugit
HAW-rah FUU-git
the hour flies

One of several Latin expressions reminding us that life passes all too quickly.

horas non numero nisi serenas
HAW-rahs nohn NUU-meh-roh NIH-sih seh-RAY-nahs
I do not count the hours unless they are bright

A favorite inscription for sundials.

horresco referens
hawr-REH-skoh reh-FEH-rens
I shudder to relate

In Virgil's *Aeneid*, Aeneas says these words as he recounts the death of Laocoön. A priest of Apollo, Laocoön saw that his sons were being attacked by serpents sent by Apollo or Athena. Good father that he was, Laocoön went to his children's defense and was killed along with them, supposedly for his role in attempting to dissuade the Trojans from accepting the horse the Greeks used to penetrate Troy. The only good thing about *horresco referens* is that it gives us a welcome relief from "you wouldn't believe it," "I kid you not," and "too horrible for words."

horribile dictu
hawr-RIH-bih-leh DIH-ktoo
horrible to relate

In describing a particularly bloody automobile accident, for example, one might interject *horribile dictu* just before launching into the most shocking details of the narrative. (See MIRA-BILE DICTU.)

hostis humani generis
HAW-stihs huu-MAH-nee GEH-neh-rihs
enemy of the human race

Few qualify for this appellation, suitable in our time for the likes of Adolf Hitler.

humanum est errare
hoo-MAH-nuum est ehr-RAH-reh
to err is human

See ERRARE HUMANUM EST.

iacta (or jacta) alea est
YAH-ktah AH-lay-ah est
the die is cast

See ALEA IACTA EST.

ianuis (or januis) clausis
YAH-noo-ees KLOW-sees
behind closed doors

Any private meeting can be called a meeting *ianuis clausis*, literally "with closed doors," the most celebrated examples being the meetings held by the college of cardinals in the Sistine Chapel to elect a pope.

ibid.

See next entry.

ibidem
IH-bih-dem (also ih-BEE-dem)
in the same place

A weapon in the arsenal of scholarly terms, used so often that it has acquired the English pronunciation IB-ə-dem. Abbreviated **Ibid.** in a footnote, and often italicized (underscored in manuscript) because it is Latin, *Ibid*. makes reference to an identical source cited in an immediately preceding footnote. For example, in the footnote "[16] *Ibid*., p. 77," the source referred to in footnote 15 is being referred to again, but this time citing page 77 of that source. Small wonder the young scholar complains: "Half my life is spent writing *Ibid.*, *op. cit*., and *loc. cit*."

idem
EE-dem
the same

Sometimes abbreviated **id.**, this scholarly term appears in footnotes containing more than one reference to works by the same author. It is used in place of the author's name after the initial reference. *Idem* has the English pronunciation ĪD-em.

id est
id est
that is

This scholarly term, abbreviated i.e., is used in identical fashion as its English translation: to clarify a statement just made. The abbreviation *i.e.* is heard more and more in the speech of those who do not know the Latin phrase—nor even the meaning of the term—so misuse is almost as common as correct use.

The most frequent mistake reflects confusion of *i.e.* with **e.g.**, the abbreviation of *exempli gratia*, "for example." Perhaps we are better advised to use the English equivalents in place of these abbreviations.

id genus omne
id GEH-nuus AWM-neh
all that sort

Used in the same way as HOC GENUS OMNE.

i.e.

See ID EST.

Iesus (or Jesus) Nazarenus Rex Iudaeorum (or Judaeorum)
YAY-suus nah-zah-RAY-nuus reks yoo-dī-OH-ruum
Jesus of Nazareth, King of the Jews

Abbreviated **I.N.R.I.**

ignis aurum probat, miseria fortes viros
IH-gnis OW-ruum PRAW-baht mih-SEH-ree-ah
FAWR-tays WIH-rohs
life is not a bowl of cherries

Seneca, in *De Providentia*, warns us that there will be trouble in our lives and we must learn to come to grips with it, telling us literally: "Fire tests gold; adversity (tests) strong men." (Seneca apparently knew something of the differential melting points of metals.)

ignis fatuus
IH-gnis FAH-too-uus
will-o'-the-wisp

Ignis fatuus, literally "foolish fire," signifying any misleading or deluding goal, is so called for the phosphorescent light sometimes seen at night above marshy ground and thought to be caused by the combustion of methane rising from decaying vegetable matter. Anyone who attempts to follow such light is misled, hence the meaning "will-o'-the-wisp."

ignorantia legis neminem excusat
ih-gnoh-RAHN-tee-ah LAY-gihs NEH-mih-nem
eks-KOO-saht
ignorance of the law excuses no one

Also given as **ignorantia iuris** (or **juris**) **non** (YOO-rees nohn) **excusat**, "ignorance of the law does not excuse." An even broader expression is **ignorantia non excusat**, "ignorance does not excuse," which goes beyond the realm of law, enabling us to upbraid an unfortunate who says, "But I didn't know. . . ."

ignoti nulla cupido
ih-GNOH-tee NUUL-lah kuu-PEE-doh
we don't want what we can't see

Ovid's thought in *Ars Amatoria*, literally "no desire (exists) for a thing unknown," is excellent for young parents to keep in mind if they want to preclude unreasonable requests from their children.

imo pectore
EE-moh PEH-ktaw-reh

See **AB IMO PECTORE**.

in absentia
in ahb-SEN-tee-ah
in (one's) absence

Pronounced in ab-SEN-shə in English. One may be awarded a university degree *in absentia* or convicted of a crime *in absentia*, in the former case because of inability to appear for the academic ceremony, in the latter because one is beyond the reach of the law.

in aeternum
in ī-TEHR-nuum
forever

in articulo mortis
in ahr-TIH-kuu-loh MAWR-tihs
at the point of death

A statement made *in articulo mortis*, literally "in the grasp of death," carries special weight, since it is believed that a person about to die has nothing to gain, perhaps much to lose, from lying.

in bello parvis momentis magni casus intercedunt
in BEL-loh PAHR-wees moh-MEN-tees MAH-gnee KAH-soos ihn-tehr-KAY-duunt
in war great events are the results of small causes

Anyone who has participated in war can affirm this observation, made by Caesar in his *Bellum Gallicum*: Battles are usually won by the armies that blunder least. Applied more broadly, Caesar's words tell us to pay attention to detail in any enterprise.

in camera
in KAH-meh-rah
in private

Literally "in a chamber," and applied especially to a hearing held by a judge in chambers or in a courtroom with public and press excluded.

in cauda venenum
in KOW-dah weh-NAY-nuum
watch out for the part you can't see

The Romans knew that the scorpion's sting was in its tail, so *in cauda venenum*, literally "in the tail is the poison," warns us to look beyond the obvious in judging potential danger. Thus, a speech that starts out innocuously may gather spite as it proceeds and climax in a malicious peroration: *in cauda venenum*.

incidis in Scyllam cupiens vitare Charybdim
IHN-kih-dihs ihn SKIH-lahm KUU-pee-ens
wee-TAH-reh kah-RIH-bdim
out of the frying pan into the fire

Scylla was a nymph who was changed into a sea monster, in Homer's *Odyssey* said to inhabit a rock in the strait of Messina —it separates Italy from Sicily—opposite the whirlpool that was the home of Charybdis, another sea monster. Scylla and Charybdis may be thought of as our modern rock and a hard place, because sailors careful to avoid one threat usually ended up being caught by the other: *incidis in Scyllam cupiens vitare Charybdim*, literally "you fall into Scylla in trying to avoid Charybdis." The message is clear: Although life usually demands that you face problems to attain any reasonable goal, exercise due caution lest you be blind-sided. In short, don't jump from the frying pan into the fire. But remember to see Italy before you die.

incipit
IN-kih-pit
here begins

The first word in many medieval manuscripts.

Index Librorum Prohibitorum
IN-deks lih-BROH-ruum praw-hih-bih-TOH-ruum
List of Prohibited Books

A list published by church authorities naming books currently out of bounds for most Catholics.

in dubio
in DUU-bee-oh
in doubt

in esse
in ES-seh
in being

Used to contrast things actually existing with those in **posse** (in PAWS-seh), literally "in potentiality."

in extenso
in ek-STEN-soh
word for word

An unabridged text is given *in extenso*, literally "in full."

in extremis
in ek-STRAY-mees
at the point of death

This unhappy phrase, also given as IN ARTICULO MORTIS, designates the final moments of a person's life.

in flagrante delicto
in flah-GRAHN-teh day-LIH-ktoh
red-handed

When someone is caught in the act of committing a crime, he has been caught *in flagrante delicto*, literally "while the crime is blazing." (The phrase is also applied to situations involving lesser embarrassments.) Our own "red-handed" is almost as vivid, if the red hands are thought of as hands covered with blood.

infra
IN-frah
below

A scholarly term used to call the reader's attention to something that follows in a text. It is usually preceded by **vide** (WIH-day, "see"). The opposite of **vide infra**, "see below," is **vide supra** (SOO-prah, "see above").

infra dignitatem
IN-frah dih-gnih-TAH-tem
undignified

This phrase, literally "beneath (one's) dignity," is used to indicate that a suggested or contemplated act does not befit one's character or standing. The phrase is shortened to *infra dig* by those in the know, who pronounce it in-frə dig.

in futuro
in fuu-TOO-roh
in the future

in hoc signo vinces
in hawk SIH-gnoh WIN-kays
in this sign thou shalt conquer

Emperor Constantine, on his way to battle, is said to have seen a cross appear in the sky, carrying these words. He had the message painted on his standard and went on to victory.

in limine
in LEE-mih-neh
on the threshold

Used to describe something that is about to happen or is beginning to happen.

in loco parentis
in LAW-koh pah-REN-tees
in the place of a parent

Anyone who serves *in loco parentis* may be considered to have responsibilities of guardianship, either formal or informal, over minors.

in lumine tuo videbimus lumen
in LOO-mih-neh TOO-oh wih-DAY-bih-muus
LOO-men
in thy light shall we see light

Motto of Columbia University.

in medias res
in MEH-dee-ahs rays
into the thick of it

Authors who eschew slow beginnings for their stories, but plunge right into the action, put their readers *in medias res*, literally "into the middle of things."

in medio tutissimus ibis
in MEH-dee-oh too-TIH-sih-muus EE-bis
you shall go safest in the middle course

Ovid counseling conservatism in *Metamorphoses*, and providing the prevailing political wisdom for candidates for high office in the United States.

in memoriam
in meh-MAW-ree-ahm
to the memory of

This expression, literally "in memory," is widely used in inscriptions, epitaphs, etc.

in naturalibus
in nah-too-RAH-lih-buus
stark naked

This phrase, literally "in a state of nature," fails to come to grips with its true meaning, just as the French *au naturel*, in its primary sense, plays games with the unclothed state—oops! with nakedness.

in nomine Patris et Filii et Spiritus Sancti
in NOH-mih-neh PAH-trihs et FEE-lee-ee et
SPEE-rih-toos SAHN-ktee
in the name of the Father and of the Son and of the Holy Spirit

in omnia paratus

in AWM-nee-ah pah-RAH-tuus

ready for anything

This phrase, literally "prepared for all things," echoes SEMPER PARATUS.

in ovo

in OH-woh

immature

This expression, literally "in the egg," can be used to characterize anything that is still in an undeveloped state. "Modern education too often leaves its beneficiaries just as it found them, *in ovo*."

in pace, ut sapiens, aptarit idonea bello

in PAH-keh uut SAH-pee-ens ah-PTAH-rit
ih-doh-NAY-ah BEL-loh

in peace, like a wise man, he appropriately prepares
for war

The advice of Horace in his *Satires*, used by modern advocates of a strong war machine as the best strategy for guaranteeing peace, even though it has been followed for centuries and has yet to produce lasting peace. (See QUI DESIDERAT PACEM PRAEPARET BELLUM.)

in partibus infidelium

in PAHR-tih-buus in-fih-DAY-lee-uum

in the lands of the infidels

This phrase, usually abbreviated *in partibus*, is used in English as part of an ecclesiastical title. For example, "Bishop *in partibus*" designates a bishop who bears the title of the office but has no religious jurisdiction, since he serves in an area under religious control of another group.

in pectore
in PEH-ktaw-reh
in secret

Anything done *in pectore* is done literally "in the breast," such as designation of a cardinal by a pope without public announcement. The designation is said to be *in pectore*.

in perpetuum
in pehr-PEH-too-uum
forever

Also given as **in perpetuo** (pehr-PEH-too-oh).

in pleno
in PLAY-noh
in full

Payment *in pleno* is payment in full.

in posse
in PAWS-seh
potentially

See IN ESSE.

in praesenti
in prī-SEHN-tee
at present

In praesenti means now rather than IN FUTURO.

in re
in ray
regarding

This phrase, literally "in the matter of," finds correct use in legal documents and notices.

in rerum natura
in REH-ruum nah-TOO-rah
in the nature of things

in saecula saeculorum
in SĪ-kuu-lah sī-kuu-LOH-ruum
forever and ever

Anything that has continued for a very long time can be said to have existed *in saecula saeculorum*, literally "for ages of ages."

insalutato hospite
in-sah-loo-TAH-toh HAW-spih-teh
without saluting one's host

This phrase refers to taking one's leave in a great hurry, for example, leaving a party without saying proper goodbyes. It also may be interpreted as "taking French leave," an old expression for leaving without announcement, for example, skipping town without paying one's debts. The French call this doubtful practice *filer à l'anglaise*, "to take English leave," an instance of the not-too-infrequent linguistic phenomenon of ascribing doubtful practices to the members of cultures other than one's own.

insanus omnis furere credit ceteros

in-SAH-nuus AWM-nis FOO-reh-reh KRAY-dit
KAY-teh-rohs

every madman thinks everybody else is mad

Syrus gave us this penetrating observation in his *Maxims*.
Who among us can see their own faults? The thief accuses
everybody else of dishonesty; the adulterer says we are all un-
faithful.

in se

in say

in itself

See PER SE.

in situ

in SIH-too

in its natural location

In situ, literally "in place," is an expression used by scholars,
who may say, for example, that an observation or experiment
was performed *in situ*, signifying that it was made in the natural
or original location of the material or process under study. "A
field examination of the archaeological find was performed *in
situ* before the shards were removed." The opposite of *in situ*
would be in vitro (WIH-troh), literally "in glass"—think of a test
tube, for example—and indicating a laboratory, hence artificial,
setting to which the material or process has been moved. "A
great deal is heard these days about *in vitro* fertilization." A
third expression, in vivo (WEE-woh), literally "in that which is
alive," is encountered in the writings of scientists. It describes
experiments performed in or on a living organism. All three
expressions have English pronunciations: *in situ* (in SĪ-too), *in
vitro* (in VEE-troh), *in vivo* (in VEE-voh).

instar omnium
IN-stahr AWM-nee-uum
worth all of them

Instar omnium is the expression Cicero used in speaking of Plato, to indicate that one Plato is worth all other men combined. The rest of us should be cautious in characterizing anyone as *instar omnium*.

in statu quo
in STAH-too kwoh
in the same state

In statu quo, literally "in the state in which," is used to refer to the condition of something at a particular time, for example, **in statu quo ante bellum** (AHN-teh BEL-luum), "in the same state as before the war," and **in statu quo ante**, "in the same state of things before they were changed." (See STATUS.)

integer vitae
IN-teh-gehr WEE-tī
blameless of life

These are the opening words of a beautiful sentence in Horace's *Odes*: **Integer vitae scelerisque purus non eget mauris iaculis neque arcu** (skeh-leh-REES-kweh POO-ruus nohn AY-get MOW-rees YAH-kuu-lees NAY-kweh AHR-koo), with the meaning "An upright man, free of guilt, needs no weapon to defend himself." The initial words, *integer vitae*, may be used alone to describe a person who lives an honorable life.

intelligenti pauca
in-tehl-lih-GEN-tee POW-kah
a word to the wise

This useful phrase, literally "to the intelligent, few words," is also expressed as **verbum sapienti** (WEHR-buum sah-pee-EN-tee), "a word is enough for a wise man," implying that the unwise will not heed even a lengthy, explicit warning.

in tempore opportuno
in TEM-paw-reh awp-pawr-TOO-noh
at the opportune time

inter alia
IN-tehr AH-lee-ah
among other things

"His views on women's rights and nuclear disarmament *inter alia* finally turned me against him."

inter alios
IN-tehr AH-lee-ohs
among other persons

inter nos
IN-tehr nohs
between or among us

The Latin equivalent of *entre nous*.

inter pares
IN-tehr PAH-rays
between or among equals

A discussion *inter pares* is one in which the participants consider one another peers.

inter pocula
IN-tehr POH-kuu-lah
over drinks

Literally "between cups." "Why don't we discuss this *inter pocula*?"

interregnum
in-tehr-REH-gnuum
a period between rulers

Now an English word (in-tər-REG-nəm), used to indicate a period in which there is no ruling authority. In the days of the Roman republic, it meant the time during the absence of the consuls or the time between the retirement or the death of the consuls and the election of their successors.

inter se
IN-tehr say
between or among themselves

inter vivos
IN-tehr WEE-wohs
between living persons

This legal phrase is used to designate a gift that is given by one living person to another, taking effect during their lifetimes. The English pronunciation is IN-tər VEE-vohs.

in toto
in TOH-toh
entirely

In toto can also be translated as "on the whole," "altogether," "in all," and "completely." The English pronunciation is the same as the Latin.

intra muros
IN-trah MOO-rohs
within the walls

In ancient times, sturdy walls built on the perimeters of cities protected their inhabitants against invasion, and the day-to-day life of the city was conducted *intra muros*.

in transitu
in TRAHN-sih-too
on the way

In transitu has its English counterpart in the phrase "in transit."

intra vires
IN-trah WEE-rays
within the powers

A matter that is *intra vires* is within the legal power or authority of an institution or individual, as opposed to one that is **ultra** (UUL-trah) **vires**, beyond the legal powers. The English pronunciation of *intra vires* is IN-trə VĪ-reez.

in utrumque paratus
in uu-TRUUM-kweh pah-RAH-tuus
ready, come what may

Regardless of the possible outcome for any human endeavor —success or defeat, life or death—the wise person is **in utrumque paratus**, Virgil's phrase in the *Aeneid*, with the literal meaning "prepared for either alternative."

in vacuo
in WAH-koo-oh
isolated

Physicists may study phenomena *in vacuo*, literally "in a vacuum," but the rest of us use the term in an extended meaning —just as we use the phrase *in a vacuum*—to indicate complete absence of communication with others, or separation from reality.

in vino veritas
in WEE-noh WAY-rih-tahs
wine loosens the tongue

There are sleeping drunks and fighting drunks and quiet drunks and talkative drunks. *In vino veritas*, an old Roman proverb, with the literal meaning "in wine the truth," tells us that people under the influence of wine or other spirits will say things they ordinarily try to conceal.

invita Minerva
in-WEE-tah mih-NEHR-wah
uninspired

Minerva, the Roman goddess of wisdom and patroness ot all the arts, obviously is someone to have on your team at all times if you work in the arts. If she deserts you on a given day, your work will suffer, but you can put the blame on her by saying *invita Minerva*, literally "Minerva being unwilling." The phrase may also be used by critics to characterize an artist or a work of art lacking inspiration.

in vitro
in WIH-troh

See IN SITU.

in vivo
in WEE-woh

See IN SITU.

ipsa quidem pretium virtus sibi
IH-psah KWIH-dem PREH-tee-uum WIHR-tuus
SIH-bee
virtue is its own reward

A saying of Claudian, a late-classical, fourth-century Roman
poet, who has been called the last of the Roman poets.

ipse dixit
IH-pseh DEE-ksit
an unsupported assertion

This phrase, literally "he himself said so" and pronounced
IP-see DIK-sit in English, labels a statement as authoritative
only to the extent that the reputation of its author merits trust,
with the implication that there is no other guarantee of its
validity: "All we have is his *ipse dixit*." When Cicero used this
phrase, he was referring to Pythagoras himself, and when Pythagoras is the *ipse* in *ipse dixit*, the authority cannot be ques-
tioned.

ipsissima verba
ih-PSIHS-sih-mah WEHR-bah
verbatim

Literally "the very words." "Did she say that?" "Yes, that is
what she said, *ipsissima verba*."

ipso facto
IH-psoh FAH-ktoh
by that very fact

Ipso facto has the meaning of "absolutely, regardless of all other considerations of right and wrong." "By ordering troops into the presidential palace, the general was *ipso facto* guilty of treason."

ira furor brevis est
EE-rah FOO-rawr BREH-wis est
anger is brief madness

Horace uses these words in his *Epistles* to tell us that anger is a momentary departure from rationality, and goes on to caution control over our passions lest they control us.

ite, missa est
EE-teh MEES-sah est
go, the mass is ended

The celebrant of the mass concludes with these words, literally "go, it has been sent on its way."

ius (or jus) est ars boni et aequi
yoos est ahrs BAW-nee et Ī-kwee
law is the art of the good and the just

An elegant characterization of the law, that much maligned profession. Contrast *ius est ars boni et aequi* with the characterization offered by Mr. Bumble in *Oliver Twist*: "The law is a ass, a idiot."

ius (or jus) primae noctis
yoos PREE-mī NAW-ktis
droit du seigneur

A feudal lord had the right, literally "right of the first night," to share the bed of his vassal's bride on her wedding night. This custom, not always practiced, one must believe, gave way to requiring payment of a sum of money to the lord in lieu of exercise of *ius primae noctis*.

iustitia (or justitia) omnibus
yuu-STIH-tee-ah AWM-nih-buus
justice for all

Motto of the District of Columbia.

jacta alea est

See ALEA IACTA EST.

januis clausis

See IANUIS CLAUSIS.

Jesus Nazarenus Rex Judaeorum

See IESUS NAZARENUS REX IUDAEORUM.

jus est ars boni et aequi

See IUS EST ARS BONI ET AEQUI.

jus primae noctis

See IUS PRIMAE NOCTIS.

justitia omnibus

See IUSTITIA OMNIBUS.

labor omnia vincit
LAH-bawr AWM-nee-ah WIHN-kiht
work conquers all things

Motto of Oklahoma, affirming that our pioneers knew how to tame the wilderness and, apparently, how to farm successfully. (Of course, there's nothing like an oil strike to make a farm really pay off.) The phrase is a shortened form—with the tense of the verb changed from *vicit* (perfect) to *vincit* (present)—of Virgil's statement in his *Georgics*: **labor omnia vicit improbus** (WIH-kiht ihm-PRAW-buus): "never-ending work conquered all things." Virgil was describing the harshness of life following the Golden Age, when the earth had yielded its fruits without labor. Jupiter then decided to change everything, making life hard so that men would learn and become independent. No welfare state from then on.

lacrima Christi
LAH-krih-mah KRIH-stee
the tear of Christ

This mournful expression is often given as **lacrimae** (LAH-krih-mī, "tears") **Christi** and as **Lachryma Christi**. In the latter spelling, we see the triumph of commercialism, Lachryma Christi being a sweet wine produced in Italy.

lapsus calami
LAH-psuus KAH-lah-mee
a slip of the pen

An error made through carelessness in writing is a *lapsus calami*. A calamus (KAH-lah-muus) was a reed that found use as a pen.

lapsus linguae
LAH-psuus LIHN-gwī
a slip of the tongue

lapsus memoriae

LAH-psuus meh-MAW-ree-ī

a lapse of memory

lares et penates

LAH-rays et peh-NAH-tays

Roman gods of the household

The *lares et penates* looked after the safety and well-being of the home. The *lares* were usually deified heroes or ancestors; the *penates* were the gods of the storeroom, with the special duty of keeping the house free of danger. Images of these gods were kept in a shrine in every home, and offerings were made to them on family occasions. Today, the phrase "lares and penates" (LAY-reez and pə-NAY-teez in English) has the meaning of "household effects and personal possessions."

laudator temporis acti

low-DAH-tawr TEHM-paw-rihs AH-ktee

a praiser of time past

Horace's expression in *Ars Poetica* for the bore who looks back always on the good old days, telling us that present times have nothing to recommend them. Revisionists of this stripe are always with us. Today's **laudatores** (low-dah-TOH-rays) **temporis acti** recall the good times we all enjoyed during the Great Depression; what will be said fifty years from now about the Glorious Eighties?

laudem virtutis necessitati damus

LOW-dem wihr-TOO-tisneh-keh-sih-TAH-tee DAH-muus

we give to necessity the praise of virtue

Marcus Fabius Quintilianus, known as Quintilian, was a Roman rhetorician of the first century A.D. In this marvelous saying, he recognized that people give themselves the courage to face adversity by finding some benefit in it. Chaucer spoke of making "vertue of necessitee," and Shakespeare followed with "there is no virtue like necessity." Without the ability to face our troubles this way, many more of us might founder.

laus Deo
lows DAY-oh
praise (be) to God

lex loci
leks LAW-kee
the law of the place

The Latin equivalent of "the law of the land."

lex non scripta
leks nohn SKRIH-ptah
the unwritten law

Lex non scripta refers to what we call common law, the body of law derived in the English tradition from precedent without the formality of statutes and regulations, but nonetheless binding. *Lex scripta*, it follows logically, is the body of written, or statutory, law.

lex salica
leks SAH-lih-kah
Salic law

Lex salica is the law of the ancient Salian Franks, a people who inhabited a region in the Rhine valley near the North Sea. *Lex salica* became part of the French legal tradition, and the aspect of Salian law that became particularly well known is that forbidding the inheritance of an estate by female members of a family. It was because of an interpretation of this law that the French monarchy never had women as rulers.

lex scripta
leks SKRIH-ptah

See LEX NON SCRIPTA.

lex talionis
leks tah-lee-OH-nis
an eye for an eye, a tooth for a tooth

Lex talionis, literally "the law of retaliation," is the practice of punishment in kind, dating back at least to the Old Testament, yet much in vogue today in some societies.

licentia vatum
lih-KEN-tee-ah WAH-tuum
poetic license

Literally "the license of poets." (See GENUS IRRITABILE VATUM.)

licet
LIH-keht
it is allowed

Licet, pronounced LĪ-set in English, is the formal expression used in granting permission. "May I be relieved of my academic responsibilities during the coming semester?" "*Licet*." (Or "*Non licet*.")

ligonem ligonem vocat
lih-GOH-nem lih-GOH-nem WAW-kaht
he or she calls a spade a spade

A *ligo* (LIH-goh) is really a hoe, but the phrase is construed as a compliment regardless of the tool employed. Many of us prefer people who are outspoken even to the point of rudeness,

compared with pussyfooters who never let us know where they
stand.

lis sub iudice (or judice)
lees suub YOO-dih-keh
a case not yet decided

A matter before the courts that has not yet been disposed of
is a *lis sub iudice*, literally "a lawsuit before the judge." (See
ADHUC SUB IUDICE LIS EST.)

litterae humaniores
LIHT-teh-rī huu-mah-nee-OH-rays
the humanities

The Latin phrase, literally "the more humane letters (or
learning)," designating the Greek and Latin classics, grammar,
poetry, and rhetoric—all considered polite learning conducive
to culture, contrasted with **litterae divinae** (dee-WEE-nī), "the-
ology."

Litterarum Doctor
lih-teh-RAH-ruum DAW-ktawr
Doctor of Letters

An honorary degree, abbreviated **Litt.D.**

loco citato
LAW-koh kih-TAH-toh
in the place cited

This phrase, in English pronounced LOH-koh sī-TAY-toh, is
a tool of the scholar. Abbreviated **loc. cit.**, it is used in footnotes
to refer the reader to a passage previously cited: "Morrison, *loc.
cit.*"

locum tenens
LAW-kuum TEH-nens
a substitute or deputy

Locum tenens, pronounced LOH-kəm TEN-enz in English, and literally "one holding the place," refers to someone who is filling in temporarily for another person. The expression is said most often of pinch-hitting physicians and clergymen.

locus classicus
LAW-kuus KLAHS-sih-kuus
the most authoritative or most frequently cited passage

A *locus classicus*, pronounced LOH-kəs KLAS-si-kəs in English, and literally "a classical source," is a passage commonly cited to explain or illustrate a subject.

locus delicti
LAW-kuus day-LIH-ktee
the scene of the crime

A CORPUS DELICTI establishes that a crime has been committed. A *locus delicti*, pronounced LOH-kəs də-LIK-tī in English, is the place where the crime occurred. Now all we need is the perpetrator.

locus in quo
LAW-kuus in kwoh
the place in question

A *locus in quo*, literally "the place in which," refers to a place where something of interest has occurred, or where a passage under discussion may be found.

locus poenitentiae
LAW-kuus poy-nih-TEN-tee-ī
a place or opportunity for repentance

A legal expression, pronounced LOH-kəs pen-ih-TEN-shih-ee in English, denoting the period within which a person may withdraw from an assumed obligation before it becomes binding.

locus sigilli
LAW-kuus sih-GIHL-lee
the place of the seal

The *locus sigilli*, abbreviated l.s., is the place on a document for affixing the seal of the notary public or other official.

loquitur
LAW-kwih-tuur
he or she speaks

A stage direction, abbreviated **loq.**

lucri causa
LUU-kree KOW-sah
for the sake of gain

Anything done in hope of financial reward or profit is done *lucri causa*. Before leaving the subject of money, it is worthwhile to cite Juvenal, in his *Satires*: **Lucri bonus est odor** (BAW-nuus est AW-dawr), "sweet is the smell of money," and the line concludes **ex re qualibet** (eks ray KWAH-lih-bet), "obtained from any source."

lucus a non lucendo
LOO-kuus ah nohn loo-KEN-doh
a paradoxical or absurd etymology

This expression, literally "(called) a grove from the absence of light," can be used to characterize anything whose essence is the opposite of what its name suggests, but it is most frequently used to describe a paradoxical or false word derivation. It has this latter use because the words *lucus* and *lucendo* are not derived from the same root, even though the unwary may assume that they are.

lupus est homo homini
LOO-puus est HAW-moh HAW-mih-nee
man is a wolf to man

Plautus, in his *Asinaria*, recognized man's inhumanity to man in this phrase, suggesting that pride and avarice are the cause of lupine behavior in humans. The wolf epitomizes predatory behavior, of course, but we must regretfully take note that while wolves are not known to attack one another, human beings too often do.

lusus naturae
LOO-suus nah-TOO-rī
a freak

Literally "a sport of nature."

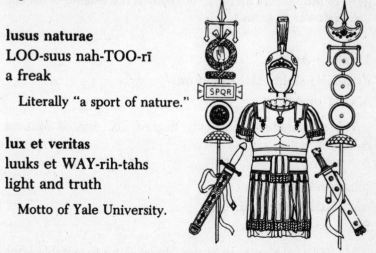

lux et veritas
luuks et WAY-rih-tahs
light and truth

Motto of Yale University.

macte virtute
MAH-kteh wihr-TUU-teh
well done!

This phrase, literally "be increased in merit," gives us a Latin equivalent for "bravo" or "hooray." *Macte virtute*, like its English counterparts, commends and encourages.

magis mutus quam piscis
MAH-gihs MOO-tuus kwahm PIH-skis
silent as the grave

Literally "quieter than a fish."

magister artis ingeniique largitor venter
mah-GIH-stehr AHR-tihs in-gen-ee-EE-kweh
lahr-GEE-tawr WEN-tehr
necessity is the mother of invention

The Roman satirist Aulus Persius Flaccus, known as Persius, gave us this maxim, literally "the belly is the teacher of art and the bestower of genius."

Magister Artium
mah-GIH-stehr AHR-tee-uum
Master of Arts

The intermediate university degree, abbreviated **M.A.** or **A.M.**

magister dixit
mah-GIH-stehr DEEK-sit
the master has spoken

Medieval scholastics used this phrase as an irrefutable argument, invoking Aristotle.

magister ludi
mah-GIH-stehr LOO-dee
schoolteacher

Literally "master of public games in honor of the gods." A **ludus litterarius** (LOO-dis liht-teh-RAH-ree-uus) was an elementary school. Modern readers know *Magister Ludi* as the title of a novel by Hermann Hesse.

magna cum laude
MAH-gnah kuum LOW-deh
with great praise

Second honors in a university degree. (See CUM LAUDE.)

magna est veritas et praevalet
MAHG-nah est WEH-rih-tahs et PRĪ-wah-let
great is truth, and it prevails

A proverb from Esdras, also given with **praevalebit** (PRĪ-wah-lay-bit, "will prevail") as the final word.

magnificat
mah-GNIH-fih-kaht
it magnifies

A hymn to the Virgin Mary, "My soul doth magnify the Lord," begins in Latin: **Magnificat anima mea Dominum** (AH-nih-mah MAY-ah DAW-mih-nuum). Any song of praise may be called a *magnificat*, pronounced mag-NIF-i-kat in English.

magni nominis umbra
MAH-gnee NAW-mih-nihs UUM-brah
an unworthy descendant of an illustrious family

Literally "the shadow of a great name," an unfortunate appellation for anyone who struggles unsuccessfully to emulate the achievements of senior members of his family. The expression is from Lucan's *Pharsalia*.

magnum bonum
MAH-gnuum BAW-nuum
a great good

magnum opus
MAH-gnuum AW-puus
one's crowning achievement

An artist's or a writer's masterpiece may be called his *magnum opus*, literally "a great work." The English pronunciation for this happy expression is MAG-nəm OH-pəs.

maior (or major) e longinquo reverentia
MAH-yawr ay lawn-GIHN-kwoh reh-weh-REN-tee-ah
no man is a hero to his valet

Literally "greater reverence from afar," *maior e longinquo reverentia* calls attention to our inclination to fail to observe faults when we consider people or things from a distance—distance lends enchantment—and our inclination to find fault with everyone and everything close at hand. And, conversely, familiarity breeds contempt—faults are exaggerated when we observe them often, as in someone we love.

mala fide
MAH-lah FIH-deh
in bad faith

Anything done *mala fide*, as opposed to BONA FIDE, is done fraudulently.

mala in se
MAH-lah in say
inherently bad

> Literally "bad in themselves."

malesuada fames
mah-leh-SWAH-dah FAH-mays
hunger that leads to crime

In a description of Hell in the *Aeneid*, Virgil tells us that outside Hell's doors live Grief, Suffering, Disease, Age, Fear, Hunger, and Want. Hunger (*fames*) is described as *malesuada*, literally "persuading to evil." A sobering thought for those who make social policy.

malis avibus
MAH-lees AH-wih-buus
under unfavorable signs

The Roman propensity for employing soothsayers when planning an important move is nowhere better illustrated than in this phrase, literally "with bad birds." The birds referred to are birds of divination, and since they are **malae** (MAH-lī), the omens are bad. *Avibus bonis*, literally "with good birds," means "under favorable signs." Roman soothsayers often based their predictions and advice on their observations of birds, particularly birds in flight.

malo animo
MAH-loh AH-nih-moh
with evil intent

The legal phrase "with malice aforethought" is based on the Latin *malo animo*.

malum in se
MAH-luum in say
inherently bad

> Literally "bad in itself." (See MALA IN SE.)

mandamus
mahn-DAH-muus
we command

> A writ of *mandamus*, pronounced man-DAY-məs in English, is an order of a higher court directing a lower court to enforce performance of a legal duty.

manibus pedibusque
MAH-nih-buus peh-dih-BUUS-kweh
with all one's might

> Literally "with the hands and feet." This colorful expression reminds one of the expression "jumping in with both feet."

manu propria
MAH-noo PRAW-pree-ah
with one's own hand

> Anything done without assistance is accomplished *manu propria*. Medieval artists who affixed this legend to a work were telling the world they had done their work without help from apprentices.

mare clausum
MAH-reh KLOW-suum
a closed sea

This phrase describes a body of navigable water entirely within the jurisdiction of a nation, therefore closed to foreign shipping.

mare liberum
MAH-reh LEE-beh-ruum
an open sea

Mare liberum is a body of navigable water open to ships of all nations.

mare nostrum
MAH-reh NAW-struum
the Mediterranean

The Romans referred to the Mediterranean as *mare nostrum*, literally "our sea."

margaritas ante porcos
mahr-gah-REE-tahs AHN-teh PAWR-kohs
pearls before swine

Matthew cautions against offering the uncultured anything of quality: "Give not that which is holy to dogs; neither cast ye your pearls before swine." Serving Mexican cocktails to those who habitually swill six-packs is a more modern application of *margaritas ante porcos*.

mater dolorosa
MAH-tehr daw-law-ROH-sah
sorrowful mother

Any mother who has lost her child is a *mater dolorosa*, but the term is applied particularly to the Virgin Mary, mourning the death of her son.

materfamilias
mah-tehr-fah-MIH-lee-ahs
matriarch

This term can be used to describe the mistress of a household or a matron. The meaning "matriarch" is more appropriate for *materfamilias* because the Latin word *familia* is usually applied to an extended family. (See PATERFAMILIAS.)

materia medica
mah-TEH-ree-ah MEH-dih-kah
substances used as medicine

Materia medica, literally "medical material," comprises the drugs and other substances physicians prescribe to cure illness. *Materia medica*, pronounced mə-TEE-ri-ə MED-i-kə in English, is also used to mean "pharmacology."

mea culpa
MAY-ah KUUL-pah
I am to blame

This phrase, literally "through or by my fault," is heard in the confessional and in certain Christian prayers. When **maxima** (MAH-ksih-mah) is added, the resulting phrase, **mea maxima culpa**, literally means "through or by my very great fault."

medice, cura te ipsum
MEH-dih-keh KOO-rah tay IH-psuum
physician, heal thyself

Excellent advice from Luke for those who give advice they themselves should heed.

Medicinae Doctor
meh-dih-KEE-nī DAW-ktawr
Doctor of Medicine

The familiar university degree, abbreviated **M.D.**

medio tutissimus ibis
MEH-dee-oh too-TIHS-sih-muus IH-bihs
avoid extremes

This proverb from Ovid's *Metamorphoses* translates literally as "you will go safest in the middle," typically Roman advice and the conventional political wisdom for those who aspire to high office in the United States. (See IN MEDIO TUTISSIMUS IBIS.)

me iudice (or **judice**)
may YOO-dih-keh
in my opinion

membrum virile
MEHM-bruum wih-REE-leh
the male member

A euphemism for **penis** (PAY-nihs), with the meaning of our own word spelled identically but pronounced PEE-nis. The Latin word *penis* also means "tail."

memento, homo, quia pulvis es et in pulverem revertis
meh-MEN-toh HAW-moh KWEE-ah PUUL-wihs es et in PUUL-weh-rem reh-WEHR-tees
remember, man, that dust thou art, and to dust shalt thou return

A Latin rendering of words in Genesis spoken by God to Adam. They are repeated on Ash Wednesday each year by

priests marking the foreheads of the faithful. (See TERRA ES,
TERRAM IBIS.)

memento mori
meh-MEN-toh MAW-ree
remember that you must die

A grim reminder, literally "remember to die," telling all of us
that we must be prepared for death. A *memento mori* (mə
-MEN-toh MOHR-ee in English) is a human skull or any other
object serving as a reminder of the inevitability of death: It's
later than you think.

memoriter
meh-MAW-rih-tehr
by rote

Literally "by or from memory." When we learn something
memoriter, we learn it by heart.

mendacem memorem esse oportet
men-DAH-kem MEH-maw-rem ES-seh aw-PAWR-tet
liars should have good memories

This saying of Quintilian's, literally "it is fitting that a liar
should be a man of good memory," recognizes a difficulty the
inveterate liar faces every day of his life, that of keeping his fa-
brications consistent. "Oh, what a tangled web we weave . . ."

mens sana in corpore sano
mens SAH-nah in KAWR-paw-reh SAH-noh
a sound mind in a sound body

Juvenal, in his *Satires*, suggests to us that we must pray for
attainment of *mens sana in corpore sano*, and his phrase has

found use for many centuries as the stated educational goal of many schools: to train the body as well as the mind. Public statements by some near-illiterate college athletes suggest that the sound body is too often achieved without accompanying improvement of mind.

miles gloriosus
MEE-lehs gloh-ree-OH-suus
A Boastful Soldier

Title of a comedy by Plautus.

minima de malis
MIH-nih-mah day MAH-lees
choose the lesser of two evils

A proverb, literally "of evils, the least," to bear in mind when we are forced to choose between less than desirable alternatives.

mirabile dictu
mih-RAH-bih-leh DIH-ktoo
wonderful to relate

The phrase to use when one wishes to express astonishment while recounting an event of overwhelming significance or accomplishment or irony. "Then, as the child watched, the figure, *mirabile dictu*, rose high in the air and vanished." "As he left the penitentiary, where he had just completed a two-year sentence for stealing public funds, he announced, *mirabile dictu*, that he would be a candidate for a second term in the United States Senate."

mirabile visu
mih-RAH-bih-leh WEE-soo
wonderful to behold

A companion phrase for MIRABILE DICTU. "There before me, *mirabile visu*, stood Bethlehem itself. My dream had been fulfilled."

mirabilia
mih-rah-BIH-lee-ah
wonders

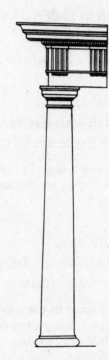

misericordia
mih-seh-rih-KAWR-dee-ah
mercy

The classic plea.

Missa solemnis
MIHS-sah saw-LEM-nihs
High Mass

Literally "solemn mass."

mobile perpetuum
MAW-bih-leh pehr-PEH-too-uum
something perpetually in motion

The impossible dream of the inventor who rejects the laws of thermodynamics.

mobile vulgus
MAW-bih-leh WUUL-guus
the fickle crowd

A phrase, literally "the movable public," that recognizes the inconstancy of popular taste and the ease with which adroit politicians can influence the great mass of voters—and can lose the support of the same voters when circumstances turn against them. It is interesting to note that the English word "mob" is a contraction of *mobile vulgus*.

modus operandi
MAW-duus aw-peh-RAHN-dee
manner of working

Every devotee of crime stories knows this phrase and the police abbreviation for it, **M.O.**, designating the pattern a criminal typically follows in pursuing his felonious ways. But *modus operandi* is not restricted to police use. Any work plan or scheme for doing a job may be termed a *modus operandi*, pronounced MOHD-əs ahp-ə-RAN-dee in English.

modus vivendi
MAW-duus wee-WEN-dee
a way of getting along together

When partners in any human enterprise must somehow manage to get along with one another despite the fact that they are not on the best of terms, they reach an accommodation, a *modus vivendi*, literally "a way of living," which makes possible the continuing relationship. The English pronunciation of *modus vivendi* is MOHD-əs vi-VEN-dee.

montani semper liberi
mawn-TAH-nee SEM-pehr LEE-beh-ree
mountaineers are always freemen

Motto of West Virginia.

morituri te salutamus
maw-rih-TOO-ree tay sah-loo-TAH-muus
we who are about to die salute you

See AVE CAESAR, MORITURI TE SALUTANT.

mors tua, vita mea
mawrs TOO-ah WEE-tah MAY-ah
you must die so that I may live

One who can preserve his own life only by taking the life of another—think of the hired assassin or the desperately ill patient awaiting an organ transplant from a dying donor—may employ this dismal expression, literally "your death, my life."

mortis causa
MAWR-tihs KOW-sah
in prospect of death

A legal expression, literally "because of death," used to describe a decision made in anticipation of one's death. The phrase is seen in old wills.

mortui non mordent
MAWR-too-ee nohn MAWR-dent
dead men carry no tales

In its literal meaning, "dead men don't bite," an especially colorful expression.

mox nox in rem
mawks nawks in rem
let's get on with it

For anyone who believes that things are moving too slowly, an excellent call to action, akin to "let's get this show on the road," but literally "soon night, to the business."

multi sunt vocati, pauci vero electi

MUUL-tee suunt waw-KAH-tee POW-kee WAY-roh
eh-LEH-ktee

many are called, but few are chosen

The words of Matthew.

multum in parvo

MUUL-tuum in PAHR-woh

much in little

A useful phrase for praising a message or a reference book that conveys much information in few words.

mundus vult decipi

MUUN-duus wuult DAY-kih-pee

there's a sucker born every minute

Mundus vult decipi, literally "the world wants to be deceived," concludes **et decipiatur** (et day-kih-pee-AH-tuur), "and let it be deceived." This thought, from an unknown Roman P. T. Barnum, shows that twentieth-century man did not invent cynicism or opportunism.

mutatis mutandis

moo-TAH-tees moo-TAHN-dees

after making the necessary changes

This phrase can be rendered as "when what must be changed has been changed," or translated more literally as "things having been changed that had to be changed," in the sense "with alterations to fit the new circumstances." Thus, we may write a sentence such as: "The new regulations governing our men's athletic teams are to apply as well to our women's teams, *mutatis mutandis*."

mutato nomine
moo-TAH-toh NAW-mih-neh
with the name changed

Literally "the name having been changed." This phrase becomes more interesting when we add the rest of Horace's line from his *Satires*: **de te fabula narratur** (day tay FAH-buu-lah NAHR-rah-tuur). Now we have "with the name changed, the story applies to you." Can you see the opportunities *mutato nomine* offers?

nam et ipsa scientia potestas est
nahm et IH-psah skee-EN-tee-ah paw-TES-tahs est
knowledge is power

Francis Bacon's much repeated and often borrowed aphorism, literally "for knowledge too is itself power."

nascentes morimur
nah-SKEN-tays maw-REE-muur
every day we die a little

This sobering thought from Manilius, in *Astronomica*, translates literally as "from the moment of birth we begin to die." It concludes **finisque ab origine pendet** (fih-NIHS-kweh ahb aw-REE-gih-neh PEN-det), "and the end hangs from the beginning."

naturam expelles furca tamen usque recurret
nah-TOO-rahm ek-SPEL-lays FUUR-kah TAH-men
UUS-kweh reh-KUUR-ret
the leopard cannot change its spots

This proverb from Horace's *Epistles*, literally "you may drive nature out with a pitchfork, but it will still return," states the nature side of the nature vs. nurture debate.

natura non facit saltum
nah-TOO-rah nohn FAH-kiht SAHL-tuum
nature makes no leaps

This aphorism suggests the continuity and consistency of natural phenomena. Great changes that become evident as time goes by are achieved slowly and gradually, and always in consonance with underlying natural principles. Alexander Pope, in *An Essay on Man*: "Order is heaven's first law."

ne Aesopum quidem trivit
nay Ī-saw-puum KWIH-dem TREE-wit
he doesn't know beans about anything

Aesop's *Fables* was used as a primer for Roman schoolboys, so *ne Aesopum quidem trivit*, literally "he has not even thumbed through Aesop," is strong condemnation.

ne cede malis
nay KAY-deh MAH-lees
do not yield to misfortunes

nec pluribus impar
nek PLOO-rih-buus IHM-pahr
a match for anyone

The motto, literally "not unequal to most," of Louis XIV of France, who used the sun as his emblem and was known as *le Roi Soleil*, "the sun king." "Not unequal to most" and its Latin counterpart are good examples of litotes, understatement in which an affirmative thought is expressed by stating the negative of the contrary thought.

nefasti dies
neh-FAH-stee DEE-ays
legal holidays

Certain days in the Roman religious calendar were *nefasti dies*, days in which official business of any kind was proscribed.

nemine contradicente
NAY-mih-neh kawn-trah-dih-KEN-teh
unanimously

Literally "no one contradicting."

nemine dissentiente
NAY-mih-neh dihs-sen-tih-EN-teh
unanimously

Literally "no one dissenting."

nemo liber est qui corpori servit
NAY-moh LEE-behr est kwee KAWR-paw-ree
SEHR-wit
no one is free who is a slave to his body

Seneca's observation may have been intended for those who indulged in the unbridled pursuit of pleasure (and other excesses), but it can just as easily be applied to frenzied dieters, dogged joggers, natural food faddists, and those who enrich manufacturers of vitamins.

nemo malus felix
NAY-moh MAH-luus FAY-liks
"there is no peace unto the wicked"

Isaiah provides this observation, literally "no bad man is happy."

nemo me impune lacessit
NAY-moh may im-POO-neh lah-KES-sit
no one provokes me with impunity

Motto of the kings of Scotland.

nemo repente fuit turpissimus
NAY-moh reh-PEN-teh FOO-it tuur-PIHS-sih-muus
no one ever became extremely wicked suddenly

Juvenal, in his *Satires*, telling us we can always find a history of mischief in anyone who goes wrong in a big way.

ne plus ultra
nay ploos UUL-trah
perfection

Ne plus ultra may be translated formally as "the acme" or "the highest attainable point," literally as "not more beyond." The literal sense of the phrase enables it to be used as a term expressing prohibition, in the sense of "no further may you go," but its primary use remains that of indicating the supremacy of a product, a literary work, a system, and the like.

ne quid nimis
nay kwid NIH-mihs
nothing in excess

Yet another Roman expression advocating the middle ground in all things.

ne supra crepidam sutor iudicaret (or judicaret)
nay SUU-prah KREH-pih-dahm SOO-tawr
yoo-dih-KAH-ret
cobbler, stick to your last

These wise words, literally "the cobbler should not judge above the sandal," of Pliny the Elder, first-century A.D. Roman naturalist and writer, advise us not to make judgments in areas in which we have no special competence. The story behind the expression concerns a cobbler's encounter with Apelles, a Greek painter, fourth century B.C. The cobbler correctly criticized the representation of a sandal in a painting Apelles was working on. Unfortunately, he went on to criticize the way in which the subject's legs were being painted. This was too much for Apelles, who responded with his memorable rebuke: *ne supra crepidam sutor iudicaret* (also given as *sutor, ne supra crepidam*).

nigro notanda lapillo
NIH-groh naw-TAHN-dah lah-PIHL-loh
marking (a day) with a black pebble

In ancient Rome, a sad day or an unlucky day was marked with a black pebble, **niger lapillus** (NIH-gehr lah-PIHL-luus), a happy or lucky day with a white pebble, **albus** (AHL-buus) **lapillus**. (See ALBO LAPILLO NOTARE DIEM.) Black pebbles were also used at Roman trials to signify a guilty verdict, white stones acquittal.

nihil agendo homines male agere discunt
NIH-hihl ah-GEN-doh HAW-mih-nays MAH-lay
AH-geh-reh DIH-skuunt
the devil finds mischief for idle hands

Literally "by doing nothing, men learn to act wickedly."

nihil obstat
NIH-hihl AWB-staht

nothing stands in its way

Nihil obstat—the complete expression is **nihil obstat quo-minus imprimatur** (KWOH-mih-nuus ihm-prih-MAH-tuur), "nothing hinders it from being published"—are the words used by a Roman Catholic censor to indicate that a book has been found to contain nothing morally offensive or contrary to the faith. A *nihil obstat*, therefore, is a clean bill of health.

nil admirari
neel ahd-mee-RAH-ree

to wonder at nothing

According to Horace's *Epistles*, *nil admirari*, which also translates as "to admire nothing," may be the only way a person can become happy and remain happy. Stolid indifference is strange counsel, but is not *nil admirari* the slogan of the truly cool?

nil desperandum
neel deh-spay-RAHN-duum

never say die

The old college spirit, as expressed by Horace in his *Odes*, meaning literally "nothing is to be despaired of." As Yogi Berra so aptly puts it, "The game ain't over until it's over."

Nil habet infelix paupertas durius in se,
Quam quod ridiculos homines facit.
neel HAH-bet in-FAY-liks POW-pehr-tahs DOO-ree-uus
in say
kwahm kwawd ree-DIH-kuu-lohs HAW-mih-nays
FAH-kit
"Nothing in poverty so ill is borne
As its exposing men to grinning scorn."

The translation of two lines from Juvenal's *Satires* is by John
Oldham, 1653–1683, sometimes called the English Juvenal. The
thought is as apt today—uncaring politicians take note—as it
was in ancient Rome.

nil nisi bonum
neel NIH-sih BAWN-uum
nothing unless good

See DE MORTUIS NIHIL NISI BONUM.

nil novi sub sole
neel NAW-wee suub SOH-leh
nothing new under the sun

This well-known phrase from Ecclesiastes reads fully: "That
which hath been is that which shall be, and that which hath
been done is that which shall be done; and there is nothing new
under the sun."

nil sine numine
neel SIH-neh NOO-mih-neh
nothing without divine will

Motto of Colorado.

nolens, volens

NOH-lens WAW-lens

whether willing or not

Literally "being unwilling, willing." Anyone who does something he really does not want to do does it *nolens, volens*. The phrase is used also to mean "willy-nilly," in the sense of "haphazardly."

noli me tangere

NOH-lee may TAHN-geh-reh

touch me not

John has it that Christ said these words when he was approached by Mary Magdalene after the resurrection. Today, a picture representing this scene is called a *noli me tangere*, and the impatiens plant is also called by this name, as well as by "touch-me-not."

nolo contendere

NOH-loh kawn-TEN-deh-reh

I do not wish to contend

The plea of a defendant in a criminal proceeding who does not admit guilt but states that he will offer no defense against the charges. The defendant may then be declared guilty, yet retain the right to deny the validity of that finding in related proceedings. "Spiro Agnew pled *nolo contendere* to a charge of income tax evasion."

non bis in idem

nohn bihs in IH-dem

not twice for the same thing

The Latin expression proscribing double jeopardy in the courts. Also a boy's defense against further punishment by his father after being punished by his mother.

non compos mentis
nohn KAWM-paws MEN-tihs
not of sound mind

The legal expression used for any form of mental unsoundness. (See COMPOS MENTIS.)

non erat his locus
nohn EH-raht hees LAW-kuus
that was inappropriate

Literally "that was not the place for these things."

non est tanti
nohn est TAHN-tee
it's no big deal

Literally "it is not of such great importance."

non est vivere sed valere vita est
nohn est WEE-weh-reh sed wah-LAY-reh WEE-tah est
life is more than just being alive

From Martial's *Epigrams*, literally "life is not being alive but being well." A suitable motto for those who value physical fitness. (But see NEMO LIBER EST QUI CORPORI SERVIT.)

non ignara mali, miseris succurrere disco
nohn ih-GNAH-rah MAH-lee mih-SEH-rees
suuk-KUUR-reh-reh DIH-skoh
I've been there myself

One rationale for helping people in distress, from Virgil's *Aeneid*. Dido, Queen of Carthage, greets Aeneas and his companions, who are in exile: *Non ignara mali*, "no stranger to misfortune myself," *miseris succurrere disco*, "I learn to relieve the sufferings of others."

non licet omnibus adire Corinthum
nohn LIH-ket AWM-nih-buus ahd-EE-reh
kaw-RIHN-tuum
circumstances deny us certain pleasures

From Horace's *Epistles*, literally "not everyone is permitted to go to Corinth." Why? Corinth was the Paris of its day, but its pleasures were too costly for the pocketbooks of many people. The expression is also given as **non cuivis homini contingit** (nohn KOOEE-wihs HAW-mih-nee kawn-TIHNG-it) **adire Corinthum**, "it does not fall to every man's lot to go to Corinth."

non mihi, non tibi, sed nobis
nohn MIH-hee nohn TIH-bee sed NOH-bees
not for you, not for me, but for us

non nova sed nove
nohn NAW-wah sed NAW-way
not new things but in a new way

non obstante
nohn awb-STAHN-teh
notwithstanding

non omnia possumus omnes
nohn AWM-nee-ah PAWS-suu-muus AWM-nays
we cannot all do everything

Virgil, in the *Aeneid*, gives us this way to acknowledge a fact of life: No one can reasonably be expected to become expert in all things.

non omnis moriar
nohn AWM-nihs MAW-ree-ahr
I shall not wholly die

This was Horace's way, in the *Odes*, of telling the world that his works would live forever. Not a bad call.

non placet
nohn PLAH-ket
nay

A formal way of indicating dissent, literally translated as "it does not please."

non possumus
nohn PAWS-suu-muus
no way!

The answer, literally "we cannot," given by Peter and John when they were asked to stop preaching, and now used by a pope to reject a suggested innovation in doctrine. *Non possumus* may be used by the rest of us in pleading inability to honor a request.

non semper ea sunt quae videntur
nohn SEM-pehr AY-ah suunt kwī wih-DEN-tuur
things are not always what they appear to be

Phaedrus, first-century A.D. Roman fabulist, came up with this gem to warn the unwary. In *H.M.S. Pinafore*, William S. Gilbert put it this way: "Things are seldom what they seem, Skim milk masquerades as cream."

non semper erit aestas
nohn SEM-pehr EH-rit Ī-stahs
be prepared for hard times

Literally "it will not always be summer." A similar bit of advice, this one from Seneca, is **non semper Saturnalia erunt** (sah-tuur-NAH-lee-ah EH-ruunt), literally "the Saturnalia will not last forever," more freely "every day is not a holiday." The Saturnalia, one of the principal festivals of the Romans, was celebrated in December. A time of merrymaking—often debauchery—the period of the Saturnalia saw suspension of all public business: Schools and courts were shut down, criminals were not punished, and even slaves enjoyed a taste of liberty. But the implication of Seneca's words and of *non semper erit aestas* is not lost on us: The day of reckoning will come.

non sequitur

nohn SEH-kwih-tuur

it does not follow

A familiar way of indicating a logical fallacy: A conclusion offered cannot justly be inferred from the premises. The English pronunciation of *non sequitur* is non SEK-wə-tər.

non sum qualis eram

nohn suum KWAH-lihs EH-rahm

I'm a different person today

Horace gave us this line in his *Odes*, literally translated as "I am not the sort of person I was," and we may use it whenever there is a need to explain why our character and behavior have changed. The full line from Horace is **non sum qualis eram bonae sub regno Cinarae** (BAW-nī suub REH-gnoh kih-NAH-rī), literally "I am not what I was under the reign of good Cynara." The poet is pleading with Venus, the goddess of love, to stop tempting him with love, since he is no longer the man he once was. It is worthwhile to recall Cynara now for reasons that soon will become clear. In the poem "Cynara," the nineteenth-century English poet Ernest Dowson used as a refrain "I have been faithful to thee, Cynara, in my fashion"—recall the song from *Kiss Me, Kate*—and in one of the stanzas wrote: "I have forgot much, Cynara! gone with the wind. . . ." Need one say more?

non teneas aurum totum quod splendet ut aurum
nohn TEH-nay-ahs OW-ruum TOH-tuum kwawd
SPLEN-det uut OW-ruum
all that glitters is not gold

Literally "do not take as gold everything that shines like gold." In *The Merchant of Venice*, Shakespeare gave the line as "All that glisters is not gold."

nosce te ipsum
NAW-skeh tay IH-psuum
know thyself

Plutarch attributed this advice to Plato, but a score of candidates may claim original authorship. Plutarch reported that *nosce te ipsum* was inscribed—in Greek, of course—at the oracle at Delphi.

nota bene
NAW-tah BEH-neh
take notice

The familiar way of calling attention to something of importance in a letter or other document one is writing, and abbreviated **N.B.** The literal meaning is "note well." "*N.B.* The alliance had already begun to fall apart by that time."

notatu dignum
naw-TAH-too DIH-gnuum
worthy of note

novissima verba

naw-WIHS-sih-mah WEHR-bah

final words

Latin for a person's last utterance.

novus homo

NAW-wuus HAW-moh

a Johnny-come-lately

Literally "a new man," but used to describe a *parvenu*. In the days of the Roman republic, a *novus homo* was the first man in a family to hold a consulship, thus ennobling both himself and his family.

novus ordo seclorum

NAW-wuus AWR-doh seh-KLAW-ruum

a new order of the ages (is created)

Motto on the great seal of the United States. (See ANNUIT COEPTIS and any one-dollar bill.)

nudum pactum

NOO-duum PAH-ktuum

an invalid agreement

Literally "a nude pact." This legal phrase describes a contract made without a consideration—that is, without passing something of value sufficient to make the contract binding and therefore resulting in no contract at all. In Roman law, **nudus** (NOO-duus) was used either to describe a promise made without formal agreement or to describe a type of ownership that did not include the right to convey a property to others.

nulla dies sine linea
NUUL-lah DEE-ays SIH-neh LIH-nay-ah

you've got to keep at it

This expression, applied by Pliny to the Greek painter Apelles (see NE SUPRA CREPIDAM SUTOR IUDICARET), described the painter's admirable steadfastness in practicing his art, and is translated literally as "not a day without a line."

nulli secundus
NUUL-lee seh-KUUN-duus

second to none

nullius filius
NUUL-lee-uus FEE-lee-uus

a bastard

Literally "no one's son."

nullum quod tetigit non ornavit
NUUL-luum kwawd TEH-tih-giht nohn awr-NAH-wiht

he touched nothing he did not adorn

From Dr. Johnson's epitaph on Goldsmith: "To Oliver Goldsmith, A Poet, Naturalist, and Historian, who left scarcely any style of writing untouched, and touched none [a better translation of *nullum*] he did not adorn."

numerus clausus
NUU-meh-ruus KLOW-suus

a quota

This ugly phrase, literally "closed number," veils in Latin the idea of limiting membership of classes of people deemed undesirable for a club, school, or the like. "When a *num-*

erus clausus is condoned for any group, your group may be next."

nunc aut nunquam
nuunk owt NUUN-kwahm
now or never

An excellent phrase for anyone to use when trying to force someone into making a decision.

nunc dimittis
nuunk dee-MIHT-tihs
permission to leave

From Luke: **nunc dimittis servum tuum, Domine** (SEHR-wuum TOO-uum DAW-mih-neh), "Lord, now let thy servant depart." To receive one's *nunc dimittis* is, therefore, to receive permission to depart.

nunc est bibendum
nuunk est bih-BEN-dum
break out the champagne

Horace's call to merrymaking, literally "now it's time to drink," from the *Odes*.

nunc pro tunc
nuunk proh tuunk
now for then

A wage settlement or other agreement made *nunc pro tunc* is retroactive to some time prior to the date of the settlement.

nunc scripsi totum pro Christo da mihi potum

nuunk SKRIH-psee TOH-tuum proh KRIH-stoh dah MIH-hee PAW-tuum

Now I have written so much for Christ, give me a drink!

With this inscription, monk-copyists marked the end of a manuscript or perhaps the end of a day's work.

nunquam non paratus

NUUN-kwahm nohn pah-RAH-tuus

never unprepared

A less direct way to say SEMPER PARATUS.

obiit

AWB-ih-iht

he or she died

An inscription found on tombstones and in church records. All that remains to be done is to supply the date of the unhappy event.

obiit sine prole

AWB-ih-iht SIH-neh PROH-leh

he or she died without issue

Even unhappier than the preceding entry.

obiter dictum

AW-bih-tehr DIH-ktuum

an incidental remark

A legal phrase, designating a statement made in passing by a judge on a tangential matter in connection with a judicial opinion he is rendering. While an *obiter dictum*—the plural is **obiter dicta** (DIH-ktah)—has no legal bearing on the opinion to which it is appended, it may have considerable effect in later cases, since it may be read and considered along with the full opinion, and in some circumstances become even more important than the opinion itself. The English pronunciation of *obiter dictum* is OH-bit-ər DIKT-əm.

obsta principiis
AWB-stah prihn-KIH-pee-ees
nip it in the bud

Ovid advises in *Remedia Amoris* that we take immediate steps, literally that we "resist the beginnings," once we know we have fallen into difficulties: It is much easier to root out evil as soon as it appears than to try to do so after its effects have become pervasive.

obstupui, steteruntque comae, et vox faucibus haesit
awb-STUU-poo-ee steh-teh-RUUNT-kweh KAW-mī et wawks FOW-kih-buus HĪ-siht
I was scared stiff

A description of the physical effects of fear, from Virgil's *Aeneid*, literally "I was stupefied, and my hair stood on end, and my voice stuck to my throat." How about that?

occasionem cognosce
awk-kah-see-OH-nem kaw-GNAW-skeh
strike while the iron is hot

Literally "recognize opportunity."

oderint dum metuant
OH-deh-rihnt duum MEH-too-ahnt
let them hate, provided they fear

A motto attributed to Emperor Tiberius, now appropriate for any despot or misguided business executive.

odi et amo
OH-dee et AH-moh
I hate and I love

Catullus, verbalizing the love-hate relationship. His thoughts continue: "I don't know why, and I am in agony."

odium
AW-dee-uum
hatred

This word, in English pronounced OHD-ee-əm, plays a part in several Latin phrases of interest. **Odium aestheticum** (ī-STEH-tih-kuum) designates the bitter rivalry among artists and writers; **odium medicum** (MEH-dih-kuum), the hatred of physicians for one another—consider the attitude of the medical establishment toward radical practitioners; **odium theologicum** (tay-aw-LAW-gih-kuum), mutual hatred among theologians, the result of differences in doctrinal interpretation.

O fortunatos nimium, sua si bona norint, agricolas.
oh fawr-too-NAH-tohs NIH-mee-uum SOO-ah see
BAW-nah NOH-rihnt ah-GRIH-kaw-lahs
Oh, blessed beyond all bliss, the farmers—did they but know their happiness.

Virgil, in the *Georgics*, apparently expressing a romantic view of bucolic life. In fairness to Virgil, the farmers he had in mind in this characterization were not perceived as blessed because of the nature of their work or their surroundings, but because they were far removed from the dangers experienced by warriors.

oleo tranquillior
AW-lay-oh trahn-KWIHL-lee-awr
smoother than oil

An interesting phrase from the Psalms: "His mouth was as smooth as butter, but his heart was war; his words were smoother than oil, yet they were drawn swords."

olet lucernam
AW-let luu-KEHR-nahm
it smells of the lamp

Any labored literary work may be condemned with this phrase, also given as **redolet** (REH-daw-let) **lucernam**. So while students are advised to burn the midnight oil, poets and other creative writers must avoid giving the impression that they have labored too long over a piece of work. (See OLEUM PERDISTI.)

oleum addere camino
AW-lay-uum AHD-deh-reh kah-MEE-noh
to make bad things worse

Literally "to pour fuel on the stove."

oleum perdisti
AW-lay-uum pehr-DIH-stee
you've wasted your time

Like *olet lucernam*, this phrase refers to the oil lamps used by Romans, this time in the literal meaning "you have lost oil," telling a writer that whatever oil he burned while working on a manuscript was ill spent. A useful phrase for anyone intent on critical attack.

olim meminisse iuvabit (or juvabit)
OH-lihm meh-mih-NIHS-seh yuu-WAH-biht
it will be pleasant to look back on things past

Shades of Shakespeare and Proust:

> When to the sessions of sweet silent thought
> I summon up remembrance of things past. . . .

(See FORSAN ET HAEC OLIM MEMINISSE IUVABIT.)

omne ignotum pro magnifico est
AWM-neh ih-GNOH-tuum proh mah-GNIH-fih-koh est
distance lends enchantment

Tacitus, in *Agricola*, gives us this useful phrase, literally "everything unknown is thought magnificent." But it can also be interpreted as "everything unknown is thought to be more difficult or challenging than it really is."

omnem movere lapidem
AWM-nem maw-WAY-reh LAH-pih-dem
keep trying

This saying, literally "to move every stone" or "to leave no stone unturned" adjures us to do our level best in any enterprise.

omnes deteriores sumus licentia
AWM-nays day-teh-ree-OH-rays SUUM-uus
lih-KEN-tee-ah
too much freedom debases us

A saying attributed to Terence. Applied to child rearing, today sometimes called "mothering" or "fathering," these words recall "spare the rod and spoil the child."

omne trinum est perfectum
AWM-neh TREE-nuum est pehr-FEH-ktuum
everything in threes is perfect

An old adage, reflecting the mystical power ascribed to the number three. Three fates, three graces, three muses, the trinity, three kings, Jonah in the whale's belly for three days and three nights, three cardinal colors, three cheers—the list is a long one.

omne tulit punctum qui miscuit utile dulci
AWM-neh TUU-liht PUUN-ktuum kwee MIH-skoo-iht OO-tih-leh DUUL-kee
he has gained every point who has combined the useful with the agreeable

Horace, in *Ars Poetica*.

omnia mutantur nos et mutamur in illis
AWM-nee-ah moo-TAHN-tuur nohs et moo-TAH-muur in IHL-lees
all things change, and we change with them

Unless we want to be left behind.

omnia vincit amor
AWM-nee-ah WIHN-kiht AH-mawr
love conquers all

See AMOR VINCIT OMNIA.

omnia vincit labor
AWM-nee-ah WIHN-kiht LAH-bawr
work conquers all things

> See LABOR OMNIA VINCIT.

onus probandi
AW-nuus praw-BAHN-dee
the burden of proof

> Literally "the burden of proving."

op. cit.

> See OPERE CITATO.

ope et consilio
AW-peh et kawn-SIH-lee-oh
with help and counsel

opere citato
AW-peh-reh kih-TAH-toh
in the work cited

Known better in its abbreviated form, **op. cit.**, this scholarly phrase is used in a footnote to indicate reference to a work previously cited. For example, "Flexner, *op. cit.*, p. 242."

opere in medio
AW-peh-reh in MEH-dee-oh
in the midst of work

> A useful phrase: "You caught me *opere in medio*."

optat supremo collocare Sisyphus in monte saxum
AW-ptaht suu-PRAY-moh kawl-law-KAH-reh
SIH-sih-puus in MAWN-teh SAH-ksuum
someone up there doesn't love me

The literal translation of this phrase is "Sisyphus tries to place the boulder atop the mountain," but the phrase does not end there: **sed vetant leges Iovis** (sehd WEH-tahnt LEH-gays YOH-wihs), "but Jove's decrees forbid." Poor Sisyphus (in English pronounced SIS-ə-fəs), mythological ruler of Corinth, was known for his cunning. In one version of the myth, the gods decided to punish him for showing disrespect to Zeus. They compelled him forever to push a boulder to the top of a mountain. Each time Sisyphus tried, he moved it closer to the top, but at the last moment the boulder would slip from his grasp and roll farther down the mountain from where he had started. Thus, when anyone is confronted with a task that seems to become harder and harder to complete, the task is termed Sisyphean (sis-ə-FEE-ən). Have the gods taken offense?

opus magnum
AW-puus MAH-gnuum
a masterpiece

Literally "a great work." Also given as *magnum opus*.

ora et labora
OH-rah et lah-BOH-rah
pray and work

ora pro nobis
OH-rah proh NOH-bees
pray for us

orator fit, poeta nascitur
AWR-ah-tawr fiht PAW-eh-tah NAHS-kih-tuur
poets are born, not made

Literally "an orator is made, a poet is born."

origo mali
aw-REE-goh MAH-lee
the source or origin of evil

Choose your own uses for this phrase.

O si sic omnia
oh see sihk AWM-nee-ah
oh, if everything were thus

A happy phrase for those rare times when one completes a task without a hitch, enjoys an ideal vacation, or. . . .

O tempora! O mores!
oh TEM-paw-rah oh MOH-rays
these are bad times

Literally, "Oh, the times! Oh, the habits!" Speaking in the Roman Senate, Cicero opened an attack on Catiline—he was accusing Catiline of conspiracy—with a rhetorical question, "How long will you abuse our patience, Catiline?" and then exclaimed, "*O tempora! O mores!*" The phrase has become a legacy for all who wish to decry the times they live in.

otium cum dignitate
OH-tee-uum kuum dih-gnih-TAH-teh
leisure with dignity

The best kind.

pace tua

PAH-keh TOO-ah

with your permission

Paete, non dolet

PĪ-teh nohn DAW-leht

don't worry, it doesn't hurt

Literally "Paetus, it does not hurt." The classic way to firm up the wavering resolve of the second principal in a double-suicide team to fulfill the rest of the agreement after the first member has taken the irretrievable step. **Paetus** (PĪ-tuus), who had made the mistake of criticizing Emperor Nero, was number two in a husband-and-wife suicide team. He watched while **Arria** (AHR-ree-ah), his wife, opened a vein in her arm. She then handed him the dagger and said, *"Paete, non dolet."* It is an obvious advantage to know the right words to say under such circumstances.

pallida Mors

PAH-lih-dah mawrs

pale Death

The opening words of a sobering observation from Horace's *Odes*: "Pale Death with impartial foot knocks at the doors of poor men's lodgings and of king's castles."

panem et circenses

PAH-nehm et kihr-KEN-says

bread and circus games

Juvenal said that the Romans, once rulers of the world, had come to care for nothing but handouts and spectacles, and *panem et circenses* was the favorite formula for Roman leaders who wanted to keep the allegiance of the masses.

paterfamilias
PAH-tehr-fah-MIH-lih-ahs
a patriarch

Literally "father of a family." *Paterfamilias* can also be taken as "head of a household." (See MATERFAMILIAS.)

pater noster
PAH-tehr NAW-stehr
our father

The opening words of the Lord's Prayer, in Latin called the *Paternoster*: "Our Father, which art in heaven . . ."

pater patriae
PAH-tehr PAH-tree-ī
father of his country

The Romans sometimes used this expression to designate distinguished statesmen.

patris est filius
PAH-trihs est FEE-lee-uus
a chip off the old block

Literally "he is his father's son."

pauca sed bona
POW-kah sed BAWN-ah
few things, but good

An excellent precept for Christmas shoppers.

paucis verbis
POW-kees WEHR-bees
in brief

Literally "in few words."

paupertas omnium artium repertrix
POW-pehr-tahs AWM-nee-uum AHR-tee-uum
reh-PEHR-trihks
necessity is the mother of invention

Literally "poverty is the inventor of all the arts."

pax
pahks
peace

This Latin word gives us the core of many expressions. **Pax Britannica** (brih-TAHN-nih-kah), literally "the peace of Britain," reflects the terms imposed by the British—a British peace —on members of their colonial empire. **Pax in bello** (in BEL-loh) is "peace in war," a peace in which fighting continues but at a reduced rate. **Pax regis** (REH-gihs) is "the king's peace." **Pax Romana** (roh-MAH-nah), literally "the Roman peace," denotes the peace dictated by the impressive strength of the Roman military. **Pax vobiscum** (woh-BEES-kuum) is a greeting, literally "peace be unto you." Christ greeted the apostles with these words on the first Easter morning. **Pax tecum** (TAY-kuum), literally "peace be unto you," is the singular form of *pax vobiscum*.

peccavi
pehk-KAH-wee
I have sinned

The pleasurable aspect of this frank admission, normally made in the confessional (see MEA CULPA), lies in its use in a dispatch by Sir Charles Napier, a British general, while on campaign in 1843 in northwest India. Having taken Miani, in central Sind, he wrote the single word *Peccavi* as his entire message to his superiors, announcing conquest—in actuality at that point still incomplete—of the entire region. Listen closely: *Peccavi*. (I have sinned? No, I have Sind.)

pecuniae obediunt omnia
peh-KOO-nee-ī awb-AY-dee-uunt AWM-nee-ah
money makes the world go round

Literally "all things yield to money." *Obediunt* is also seen as **oboediunt**, pronounced awb-OY-dee-unt.

pecunia non olet
peh-KOO-nee-ah nohn AW-leht
money doesn't smell

A Roman proverb counseling us not to concern ourselves with the source of any money that may come our way: Don't look a gift horse in the mouth.

penates
peh-NAH-tays
household gods

See LARES ET PENATES.

pendente lite
pehn-DEHN-teh LEE-teh
while the suit is pending

A legal phrase. "*Pendente lite*, I shall say make no public statements." Unless I see a way to help my cause by speaking out?

penetralia mentis
peh-neh-TRAH-lee-ah MEN-tihs
heart of hearts

Literally "the innermost recesses of the mind."

per acria belli
pehr AH-kree-ah BEL-lee
through the harshness of war

The word *acria* may also be translated as "bitterness" or "savagery."

per angusta ad augusta
pehr ahn-GUU-stah ahd ow-GUU-stah
through difficulties to honors

Also given as AD AUGUSTA PER ANGUSTA.

per annum
pehr AHN-nuum
annually

Literally "by the year." The English pronunciation of *per annum* is pər AN-əm.

per ardua ad astra
pehr AHR-doo-ah ahd AH-strah
through difficulties to the stars

Motto of the Royal Air Force. The thought is also conveyed by *per aspera ad astra*. (See AD ASTRA PER ASPERA.)

per capita
pehr KAH-pih-tah
individually

Literally "by the head." The English pronunciation of *per capita* is pər KAP-ət-ə.

per centum
pehr KEHN-tuum
on each hundred

Literally "by the hundred." The English pronunciation of *per centum* is pər SENT-əm.

per contra
pehr KAWN-trah
on the contrary

This expression is used today most often to mean "on the opposite side of the argument."

per diem
pehr DEE-em
daily

Literally "by the day." The English pronunciation of *per diem* is pər DEE-əm.

per fas et nefas
pehr fahs et NEH-fahs
justly or unjustly

Literally "through right and wrong." "This is what I plan to do, *per fas et nefas*."

periculum in mora

peh-REE-kuu-luum ihn MAW-rah

danger in delay

A good expression to use when counseling against inaction.

per impossibile

pehr ihm-paws-SEE-bih-leh

as is impossible

An elegant way to qualify a proposition that cannot now or ever be true: "Assume, *per impossible,* that you were born in Shakespeare's time."

per incuriam

pehr ihn-KOO-ree-ahm

through carelessness

per interim

pehr IHN-teh-rihm

meanwhile

The English noun *interim* (IN-tə-rəm) is visible here.

per Iovem (or Jovem)

pehr YOH-wehm

by Jupiter

Also rendered in English by the phrase "by Jove," Jove being another name for Jupiter.

per mensem

pehr MEN-sehm

monthly

per minas
pehr MIH-nahs
by threats

permitte divis cetera
pehr-MIHT-teh DEE-wees KAY-teh-rah
leave the rest to the gods

Horace gives us this line in the *Odes*, suggesting that there is just so much we can do to order our lives, make our plans, and the like. "When you have done all you can in the interest of prudence, *permitte divis cetera* and take the plunge."

per se
pehr say
intrinsically

Literally "by or in itself." The English pronunciation of *per se* is pər say.

persona grata
pehr-SOH-nah GRAH-tah
an acceptable person

While this term can be taken to mean "a welcome guest" or "a favorite person," it is most generally used to describe a diplomatic representative who is acceptable to the government to which he or she is accredited. When a diplomat is no longer *persona grata*, he or she becomes **persona non** (nohn) **grata**.

persta atque obdura
PEHR-stah AHT-kweh awb-DOO-rah
be steadfast and endure

pessimum genus inimicorum laudantes
PEHS-sih-muum GEH-nuus ihn-ihm-ih-KOH-ruum
low-DAHN-tays
flatterers are the worst type of enemies

petitio principii
peh-TEE-tee-oh prihn-KIH-pee-ee
begging the question

The logical fallacy, literally "begging of the principle," of taking for granted that which remains to be proved. For example, stating as a matter of proof that parallel lines will never meet because they are parallel assumes as fact the very thought one is supposed to prove.

pictor ignotus
PIH-ktawr ih-GNOH-tuus
painter unknown

A way of indicating an anonymous work of art.

pinxit
PIN-ksiht
he or she painted it

This word, preceded by the name of the artist, is found on many old paintings.

placet
PLAH-keht
it pleases

Used as an affirmative vote or an expression of assent. (See NON PLACET.)

plaudite, cives
PLOW-dih-teh KEE-ways
let's hear it for the cast

Literally "applaud, citizens," *plaudite, cives* was the call addressed to an audience at the end of a Roman play.

plures crapula quam gladius
PLOO-rays KRAH-puu-lah kwahm GLAH-dee-uus
more people die partying than fighting wars

The Romans knew the toll taken by overindulgence: This grim expression translates literally as "drunkenness (kills) more than the sword."

poeta nascitur, non fit
paw-AY-tah NAH-skih-tuur nohn fiht
a poet is born, not made

See ORATOR FIT, POETA NASCITUR for yet another reminder for unpublished poets.

pollice verso
PAWL-lih-keh WEHR-soh
thumbs down

When a gladiator in a Roman amphitheater had an opponent at his mercy, he customarily looked toward the spectators for guidance on whether to administer the *coup de grâce*. If the spectators turned their thumbs toward their chests—*pollice verso*, literally "with thumb turned"—they were making clear that they wanted to see the opponent killed. If they wanted the opponent to live, they kept their thumbs in their fists—**pollice compresso** (kawm-PRES-soh), literally "with thumb folded." Our modern phrases of approval and disapproval, "thumbs up" and "thumbs down," do not ordinarily apply to situations of life and death, but they may derive from the Roman practice.

posse comitatus
PAWS-seh kaw-mih-TAH-tuus
a posse

Western fans will be pleased to know that a *posse comitatus*, literally "the power of a county," is the full phrase from which derives the word "posse" (pronounced PAHS-ee in English). Members of any self-respecting posse—in reality, too often a group of vigilantes—are enlisted on the spot by a sheriff just after the local bank has been robbed or some other outrage has been committed. Fortunately, everyone in a Hollywood Western has a horse to ride on and a rifle to fire at the bad guys, who are heading for the hills and soon will be ensconced behind boulders that will prove no more than a temporary barrier against the bullets of the posse's guns.

possunt quia posse videntur
PAWS-suunt KWEE-ah PAWS-seh wih-DEN-tuur
they can do it because they think they can do it

The power of positive thinking, as expressed by Virgil in the *Aeneid*, with the literal meaning "they can because they seem to be able to." The appearance of power bestows power.

post equitem sedet atra cura
pawst EH-kwih-tem SEH-det AH-trah KOO-rah
behind the horseman sits black care

One of the less appealing thoughts from Horace's *Odes*. The implication is that no one is free of anxiety.

post festum venisti
pawst FEH-stuum way-NIH-stee
sorry, too late!

Literally "you have arrived after the feast." This expression can be invoked whenever the overly cautious have let opportunity slip through their fingers. (See CARPE DIEM.)

post hoc, ergo propter hoc
pawst hawk EHR-goh PRAW-ptehr hawk
after this, therefore because of this

The logical fallacy that because one event follows another, the former must have caused the latter. For example, ingestion of a large quantity of vitamin C upon the first sign of a cold may well be followed by complete remission of cold symptoms, yet the true explanation of the phenomenon could lie elsewhere: a mistaken diagnosis, removal of an offending allergen, an improvement in astrological signs—heaven knows what. But until the jury returns on this one, perhaps it's better to take the megadose and risk the consequences of *post hoc, ergo propter hoc*.

post meridiem
pawst meh-REE-dee-em
after noon

The phrase we all know in its abbreviated form, **P.M.** (See ANTE MERIDIEM.)

post mortem
pawst MAWR-tehm
an autopsy

Literally "after death." The English noun "postmortem" is pronounced pohst-MAWRT-əm.

post nubila Phoebus
pawst NOO-bih-lah POY-buus
every cloud has a silver lining

Literally "after clouds, Phoebus." Phoebus, one of the names for Apollo, god of the sun, was used by poets to mean "the sun."

post partum
pawst PAHR-tuum
after childbirth

The period after delivery of a child. In English, we may hear of "postpartum depression." (See ANTE PARTUM.)

post scriptum
pawst SKRIH-ptuum
written afterward

Better known as **P.S.**

potius mori quam foedari
PAW-tee-uus MAW-ree kwahm foy-DAH-ree
death before dishonor

Literally "rather to die than to be dishonored." Whenever one expresses oneself in this vein, there is a tendency to run wild. Consider New Hampshire's "live free or die" and the once-current "better dead than red."

praemonitus praemunitus
prī-MAW-nih-tuus prī-MOO-nih-tuus
forewarned, forearmed

praestat sero quam nunquam
PRĪ-staht SAY-roh kwahm NUUN-kwahm
better late than never

prima facie
PREE-mah FAH-kee-eh
at first sight

This phrase, which finds frequent use in the law, has an English pronunciation: PRĪ-mə FAY-shə. *Prima facie* can be taken as "at first view or appearance" or "on first consideration." It suggests that thorough investigation has not been conducted, but an inference can be drawn that appears to be valid: "Notes found in the possession of a student sitting for an examination are considered *prima facie* evidence of intent to cheat." In law, therefore, a *prima facie* case is one based on facts legally sufficient to establish the case unless the facts presented are disproved.

primus inter pares
PREE-muus IHN-tehr PAH-rays
the first among equals

This paradoxical phrase finds use in describing the pecking order within a group of males of equal rank. The full professors in a university department are a good example. No individual professor stands above the others in rank, but the professor who is designated chairman may be said while holding that position to be *primus inter pares*. While he may not fire or otherwise affect the careers of the other professors, since they all are of equal rank, for the period of his chairmanship he presides over departmental meetings and has certain prerogatives not enjoyed by the others. There is a corresponding Latin phrase for a woman who is first among equals: **prima** (PREE-mah) **inter pares.**

probitas laudatur et alget
PRAW-bih-tahs low-DAH-tuur et AHL-geht
honesty is praised and is neglected

A cynical observation from Juvenal's *Satires*, sometimes rendered as "virtue is praised and then left to freeze." The implication is clear: Society may approve goodness of character but won't reward it.

pro bono publico
proh BAW-noh POO-blih-koh
for the public good

The full phrase for the expression **pro bono** (pronounced in English proh BOH-noh), often heard these days. Some attorneys devote a portion of their working time to cases *pro bono publico*, usually called *pro bono* cases, in which they represent the indigent or seek redress for public grievances, and a necessary condition of true *pro bono* work requires forgoing one's customary professional fees. Attorneys who take positions in firms that concentrate exclusively on such cases are said to be *pro bono* attorneys, and they can expect fewer of the legal life's customary rewards for their efforts. Undoubtedly there are countervailing rewards.

profanum vulgus
praw-FAH-nuum WUUL-guus
the common people

Literally "the profane multitude." (See MOBILE VULGUS.)

pro forma
proh FAWR-mah
as a formality

Literally "for form." "They made a *pro forma* appeal for a stay of execution, knowing they had little chance of saving their client's life."

promotor fidei
proh-MOH-tawr fih-DEH-ee
promoter of the faith

See ADVOCATUS DIABOLI.

pro patria
proh PAH-tree-ah
for one's country

Literally "for the country."

proprio motu
PRAW-pree-aw MOH-too
by one's own initiative

Literally "on one's own motion."

proprium humani ingenii est odisse quem laeseris
PRAW-pree-uum huu-MAH-nee ihn-GEN-ee-ee est oh-DIHS-seh kwehm LĪ-seh-rihs
it is human nature to hate a person whom you have injured

An insightful observation from Tacitus, in the *Agricola*.

pro rata
proh RAH-tah
in proportion

The English pronunciation of *pro rata* is proh RAYT-ə.

prosit
PROH-siht
l'chaim

A Latin toast, literally "may it benefit you," but freely trans-
latable as "to you," "your good fortune," "to life"—as rendered
above—and any of the multitude of expressions we use to wish
someone good health when we lift a glass of spirits or, in these
times, a glass of white wine. Perrier water does not qualify.

pro tempore
proh TEM-paw-reh
temporarily

The full phrase for **pro tem**, pronounced in English proh tem.
A chairperson *pro tem* is chairperson *pro tempore*, to serve until
a permanent chairperson is selected.

proxime accessit
PRAW-ksih-may ahk-KEHS-siht
he or she came nearest

See ACCESSIT.

P.S.

See POST SCRIPTUM.

punctatim
puun-KTAH-tihm
point for point

Punica fides
POO-nih-kah FIH-days
treachery

This ironic phrase, which translates literally as "Punic [Carthaginian] faith," reflects the Roman attitude toward their rivals in the Punic Wars. (See DELENDA EST CARTHAGO.)

Q.E.D.

Abbreviation of QUOD ERAT DEMONSTRANDUM.

Q.E.F.

Abbreviation of QUOD ERAT FACIENDUM.

qua
kwah
in the capacity of

A form of the pronoun **qui** (kwee), literal meaning "who," and pronounced kway or kwah in English. "He puts his duties *qua* citizen above other loyalties."

quae nocent docent
kwī NAW-kent DAW-kent
things that hurt teach

The rhyming way to indicate the educational validity of the curriculum offered by the College of Hard Knocks.

quaerenda pecunia primum est, virtus post nummos
kwī-REN-dah peh-KOO-nee-ah PREE-muum est
WIHR-toos pawst NUUM-mohs
let's keep our eye on the bottom line

A practical thought from Horace's *Epistles*, with the literal meaning "money is the first thing to be sought, good reputation after wealth."

quaere verum
KWĪ-reh WAY-ruum
seek the truth

qualis artifex pereo
KWAH-lihs AHR-tih-feks PEHR-ay-oh
what an artist dies in me

Suetonius reports that Nero—he who is said to have fiddled while Rome burned—spoke these words shortly before committing suicide. While Nero is known to have loved music, there is no indication that he was a man of great talent.

qualis pater talis filius
KWAH-lihs PAH-tehr TAH-lihs FEE-lee-uus
like father, like son

quando hic sum, non ieiuno (or jejuno) Sabbato;
quando Romae sum, ieiuno (or jejuno) Sabbato
KWAHN-doh heek suum nohn yay-YOO-noh
SAHB-bah-toh KWAHN-doh ROH-mī suum
yay-YOO-noh SAHB-bah-toh
when in Rome, do as the Romans do

The Latin for this thought is rendered in various ways, but the thought is always attributed to St. Ambrose. The version supplied above may be translated literally as "when I'm here [in Milan] I do not fast on Saturday; when I'm in Rome I fast on Saturday." No matter how the Latin reads, the advice is the same: Follow local customs.

quandoque bonus dormitat Homerus
kwahn-DOH-kweh BAW-nuus DAWR-mih-taht
haw-MAY-ruus
sometimes even good Homer sleeps

These words from Horace's *Ars Poetica* are generally taken to suggest rather gently that even good writers are not always at their best. You win some, you lose some.

quantum
KWAHN-tuum
as much

This word gives us several useful phrases. **Quantum libet** (LIH-beht), "as much as one pleases." **Quantum meruit** (MEH-roo-iht), "as much as one has deserved." **Quantum placeat** (PLAH-kay-aht), "as much as pleases." **Quantum satis** (SAH-tihs), "as much as is sufficient." **Quantum sufficit** (SUUF-fih-kiht), "as much as suffices." **Quantum valeat** (WAH-lay-aht), "as much as it may be worth." **Quantum vis** (wees), "as much as you wish."

quare impedit?
KWAH-ray IHM-peh-diht
why is he fighting us?

Literally "why does he obstruct?"

quem di diligunt, adolescens moritur
kwem dee DEE-lih-guunt ah-daw-LEH-skens
MAW-rih-tuur
only the good die young

The literal translation of this consoling line is "whom the gods love dies young." *Quem di diligunt, adolescens moritur* is a translation into Latin made by Plautus in the *Bacchides* of a line by Menander, a fourth-century B.C. Greek dramatist.

qui bene amat bene castigat
kwee BEH-neh AH-maht BEH-neh KAH-stih-gaht
he who loves well chastises well

The Latin argument opposing permissiveness in raising children and favoring frankness of expression in dealing with all people one loves or respects.

qui desiderat pacem praeparet bellum
kwee day-SEE-deh-raht PAH-kem prī-PAH-reht
BEL-luum
let him who wants peace prepare for war

Vegetius, a Roman military writer, advocating anything but arms control.

quid faciendum?
kwihd fah-kee-EHN-duum
what's to be done?

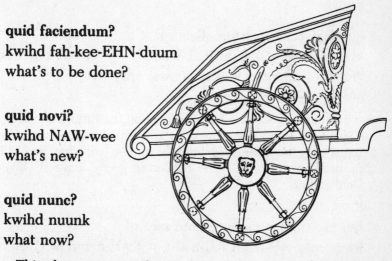

quid novi?
kwihd NAW-wee
what's new?

quid nunc?
kwihd nuunk
what now?

This phrase gives us the English word "quidnunc" (KWID-nunk), "a busybody."

qui docet discit
kwee DAW-keht DIH-skiht
the best way to learn a subject is to teach it

Literal translation, "he who teaches learns." Every experienced teacher knows the truth of this aphorism.

quid pro quo
kwihd proh kwoh
something given in return for something

Literally "something for something." "I will not give up that privilege without a *quid pro quo*." The phrase has been taken into English, with the pronunciation unchanged.

quidquid agas prudenter agas
KWIHD-kwihd AH-gahs proo-DEN-tehr AH-gahs
whatever you do, do with caution

See RESPICE FINEM.

qui fugiebat rursus proeliabitur
kwee fuu-gee-AY-baht RUUR-suus proy-lee-AH-bih-tuur
"for he who fights and runs away may live to fight another day"

Tertullian, quoting a Greek source on the futility of making a last-ditch stand when the odds are heavily against one. The Latin may be translated literally as "he who has fled will do battle once more." The rendering given above is Oliver Goldsmith's.

qui me amat, amat et canem meam
kwee may AH-maht AH-maht et KAH-nehm MAY-ahm
love me, love my dog

The Latin words for telling the world that it will have to take you as you are. The literal translation is "who loves me loves my dog as well."

qui nescit dissimulare nescit vivere
kwee NEH-skiht dihs-sih-muu-LAH-reh NEH-skiht WEE-weh-reh
he who doesn't know how to fib doesn't know how to survive

More formally, "he who does not know how to dissemble does not know how to live." This same Latin line, with the last word replaced by **regnare** (reh-GNAH-reh, "to rule"), may give us some insight into the way nations large and small are governed.

qui scribit bis legit
kwee SKREE-biht bihs LEH-giht
he who writes reads twice

This maxim recognizes the effectiveness of writing out something one wishes to learn thoroughly.

quis custodiet ipsos custodes?
kwihs kuu-STOH-dee-eht IH-psohs kuu-STOH-days
who will guard the guards themselves?

Juvenal, in his *Satires*, poses this vexing question, suitable today for situations in which we have little confidence in the people appointed to positions of trust, for example, those who are duty-bound to watch over public funds. Juvenal may actually have been more concerned with the problem of hiring guards to prevent infidelity among women whose husbands were out of town. The modern challenge more likely is to avoid assignment of a fox to guard the henhouse.

quis fallere possit amantem?
kwihs FAHL-leh-reh PAWS-siht ah-MAHN-tehm
who can deceive a lover?

Virgil, in the *Aeneid*, giving us wisdom about the human condition.

qui tacet consentit
kwee TAH-keht kawn-SEN-tiht
silence implies consent

Literally "he who remains silent consents." This observation may be applied to a range of situations, from silence at an everyday business meeting to silence of an entire people in a country that is pursuing an inhumane policy.

qui timide rogat docet negare
kwee TIH-mih-day RAW-gaht DAW-keht neh-GAH-reh
don't be afraid to ask

Literally "he who asks timidly teaches to refuse." In better translation, "he who asks timidly invites refusal."

qui transtulit sustinet
kwee trahn-STOO-liht SUU-stih-neht
he who transplanted sustains

Motto of Connecticut: God brought us here and still looks after us.

quo animo?
kwoh AH-nih-moh
with what intention?

Even when we report all the words someone has used in telling us something, we may not be conveying a true reflection of what was intended. Facial expression, emphasis, and the like may be as significant as the words themselves in revealing the full story. Thus, we are not surprised when we are asked, "*Quo animo?*"

quod avertat Deus!
kwawd ah-WEHR-taht DAY-uus
God forbid!

Literally "which may God avert."

quod cibus est aliis, aliis est venenum
kwawd KIH-buus est AH-lee-ees AH-lee-ees est weh-NAY-nuum
one man's meat is another man's poison

Literally "what is food to some is poison to others." What you and I find attractive, others may well find abhorrent. (See DE GUSTIBUS NON EST DISPUTANDUM.)

quod cito acquiritur cito perit
kwawd KIH-taw ahk-KWEE-rih-tuur KIH-taw PEHR-iht
easy come, easy go

Literally "that which is quickly acquired quickly vanishes."

quod erat demonstrandum
kwawd EH-raht day-mawn-STRAHN-duum
which was to be demonstrated

The statement, abbreviated **Q.E.D.**, that is appended to a mathematical solution, with the meaning "we have proved the proposition we set out to prove."

quod erat faciendum
kwawd EH-raht fah-kee-EN-duum
which was to be done

The statement, abbreviated **Q.E.F.**, that is appended to a mathematical solution, with the meaning "we have done the work we were required to do."

quod vide
kwawd WIH-deh
which see

See Q.V.

quo iure (or jure)?
kwoh YOO-reh
by what right?

A challenge: "Why have you done this? *Quo iure?*"

quomodo vales?
KWOH-maw-daw WAH-lays
how are you?

A Roman greeting.

quondam
KWAWN-dahm
former

Used in English and pronounced KWAHN-dəm: "my quondam [erstwhile] friend."

quorum
KWOH-ruum
of whom

Given here primarily to show the origin of the English noun *quorum*, "the minimum number of people that must be present at a meeting before its proceedings are to be regarded as valid." In commissions written in Latin appeared the words **quorum vos . . . unum [duos, etc.] esse volumus** (waws . . . OO-nuum ES-seh waw-LUU-muus), "of whom we will that you . . . be one [two, etc.]." The intent was to designate the person (or persons) so addressed as member (or members) of an official body, without whose presence work could not go on. And that's how *quorum* was born.

quos Deus vult perdere prius dementat
kwohs DAY-uus wuult PEHR-deh-reh PREE-uus
day-MEN-taht
whom God wishes to destroy, he first makes mad

A Latin rendering of a line from Euripides.

quot homines, tot sententiae
kwawt HAW-mih-nays tawt sehn-TEN-tee-ī
complete lack of agreement

A phrase from Terence's *Phormio*, literally "so many men, so many opinions," leaving one as far from consensus as possible.

quo vadis?
kwoh WAH-dihs
whither goest thou?

The well known question from John.

q.v.

The abbreviation of **quod vide** (kwawd WIH-deh), literally "which see," a scholar's way of providing a cross-reference. For example, "*quondam, q.v.*" indicates to the reader who does not know the meaning of *quondam* that the term is explained elsewhere in the text, in the case of the present book in its alphabetical location.

radit usque ad cutem
RAH-diht UUS-kweh ahd KUU-tehm
he drives a hard bargain

Literally "he shaves all the way to the skin."

radix omnium malorum est cupiditas
RAH-dihks AWM-nee-uum mah-LOH-ruum est
kuu-PIH-dih-tahs
the love of money is the root of all evil

Please notice that this observation from Timothy is not concerned with wealth, but with avarice: Money *per se* is not the root of evil.

rara avis
RAH-rah AH-wihs
a rarity

A prodigy or anything that is quite out of the ordinary may be described as a *rara avis* (English pronunciation RAIR-ə AY-vis), literally "a rare bird." Juvenal used the phrase in his *Satires*: **rara avis in terris nigroque simillima cycno** (ihn TEHR-rees nih-GROH-kweh sih-MIHL-lih-mah KIH-knoh), "a rare bird upon the earth and very much like a black swan." Black swans were unknown to the Romans. They were discovered in modern times.

raram facit misturam cum sapientia forma
RAH-rahm FAH-kiht mih-STOO-rahm kuum
sah-pee-EN-tee-ah FAWR-mah
beauty and brains don't mix

We have Petronius's *Satyricon* to blame for this canard, literally "beauty and wisdom are rarely found together." The myth of "beautiful but dumb" is destroyed by university teachers each time they look up from their notes. What they see is a lecture hall filled with intelligent and attractive students. What the students see may be another matter.

re
ray
concerning or regarding

rebus sic stantibus
RAY-buus seek STAHN-tih-buus
as matters stand

A phrase, literally "things staying as they are," that lawyers use as one criterion for determining that an obligation or a contract remains in force.

recte et suaviter
REH-ktay et SWAH-wih-tehr
justly and mildly

recto
REH-ktoh
right

Pronounced in English REK-toh. This term is used to denote a right-hand page of a book, the full Latin phrase be-

ing **recto folio** (FAW-lee-oh), "the page being straight." See
VERSO.

reddite quae sunt Caesaris Caesari, et quae sunt Dei Deo
REHD-dih-teh kwī suunt KĪ-sah-rihs KĪ-sah-ree et kwī
suunt DAY-ee DAY-oh
render unto Caesar the things that are Caesar's, and
unto God the things that are God's

Matthew recounting Christ's response to the Pharisees, who
asked whether they should pay tribute to the Romans.

redime te captum quam queas minimo
REH-dih-meh tay KAH-ptuum kwahm KWAY-ahs
MIH-nih-moh
only name, rank, and serial number

The Latin prescription for soldierly behavior following cap-
ture by enemy troops, literally "when taken prisoner, pay as
little as you can to buy your freedom." In ancient times, the
enemy wanted money, not information, but the principle was
the same: Give the enemy as little help as possible.

redivivus
reh-dih-WEE-wuus
brought back to life

In English pronounced red-ə-VEE-vəs. This word gives us an
opportunity to call "a second Beethoven" a Beethoven *redivi-
vus*—and probably be wrong in both languages.

redolet lucernam
REH-daw-leht luu-KEHR-nahm
it's labored

This destructive phrase may be used by critics to convey the literal thought "it smells of the lamp," suggesting that a composer or writer stayed up nights—that is, worked too hard—to create the work. The implication is that genius doesn't sweat in creating a masterpiece—do you believe it? When critics have exhausted the possibilities of this phrase, they can always describe a work of art as "careless." (See OLET LUCERNAM.)

reductio ad absurdum
reh-DUU-ktee-oh ahd ahb-SUUR-duum
reduction to absurdity

In English pronounced ri-DUK-tee-oh ad əb-SURD-əm. Disproof of a principle or proposition by showing that it leads to an absurdity when followed to its logical conclusion.

regina
reh-GEE-nah
queen

rem acu tetigisti
rehm AH-koo teh-tih-GIH-stee
right on!

Where the old-fashioned among us might say, "You've hit the nail right on the head," Romans would have said *rem acu tetigisti*, literally "you've touched the thing with a needle."

remis velisque
RAY-mees weh-LEES-kweh
giving one's best

Literally "with oars and sails," a phrase that reminds us that the airplane is a modern invention. "He took out after them *remis velisque*."

repente dives nemo factus est bonus
reh-PEN-teh DIH-wehs NAY-moh FAH-ktuus est
BAW-nuus
no one who is rich is made suddenly good

Publilius Syrus, as shown in this aphorism, was a keen observer of people and their ways. Of course, Syrus lived before the era of multimillion-dollar contracts for sports heroes, million-dollar payoffs in lotteries, oil wells in one's backyard, etc. The intent of his observation applies even now, however, absent any of the legitimate ways to strike it rich overnight: When someone you know appears suddenly to have made a quantum improvement in his style of living, don't be surprised if the law shows up one day to ask him embarrassing questions.

requiescat in pace
reh-kwee-EH-skaht ihn PAH-keh
may he or she rest in peace

The plural form of this final thought is **requiescant** (reh-kwee-EH-skahnt) **in pace**, "may they rest in peace." The abbreviation for both the singular and the plural is **R.I.P.**

res age, tute eris
rays AH-geh TOO-tay EH-rihs
wash that man right out of your hair

Ovid gives advice to the lovelorn in *Remedia Amoris*, saying literally "be busy and you will be safe." Who needs Ann Landers?

res angusta domi
rays ahn-GUU-stah DAW-mee
Daddy has lost his job

This sad statement, literally "straitened circumstances at home," is useful in itself, but one may also find it instructive to recall a line from Juvenal's *Satires* in which the words appear: **Haud facile emergunt quorum virtutibus opstat** (howd FAH-kih-leh ay-MEHR-guunt KWOH-ruum wihr-TOO-tih-buus AWP-staht) **res angusta domi,** "by no means is it easy for those to rise from obscurity whose noble qualities are hindered by straitened circumstances at home." Juvenal, in expressing concern for the unfortunate among us, was far ahead of many hard-nosed people in positions of power today, who insist that the poor have only themselves to blame.

res in cardine est

rays ihn KAHR-dih-neh est

the next twenty-four hours will tell the story

Literally "the matter is on a door hinge," or as we are apt to say more conventionally, "we are facing a crisis."

res inter alios

rays IN-tehr AH-lee-ohs

it's no concern of ours

Literally "a matter between other people."

res ipsa loquitur

rays IH-psah LAW-kwih-tuur

the facts speak for themselves

Literally "the thing itself speaks." A complainant in an automobile accident case who appears in court swathed in bandages and escorted by nurses should not have to go to great lengths to establish that he has been injured: *res ipsa loquitur*.

respice, adspice, prospice
REH-spih-keh AHD-spih-keh PRAW-spih-keh
look to the past, the present, the future

Motto of the City College of New York, literally "examine the past, examine the present, examine the future."

respice finem
REH-spih-keh FEE-nehm
look before you leap

Literally "examine the end." The full proverb, **quidquid agas prudenter agas et** (KWIHD-kwihd AH-gahs proo-DEN-tehr AH-gahs et) **respice finem**, may be translated as "whatever you do, do with caution, and look to the end."

respondeat superior
reh-SPAWN-day-aht suu-PEHR-ee-awr
the buck stops here

The tradition of accountability, literally "let the superior answer," more freely "a supervisor must take responsibility for the quality of a subordinate's work."

res publica
rays POO-blih-kah
the commonwealth

Literally "the affairs of the people." What the Romans meant when they said *res publica*—it is the origin of the English word "republic"—was "the state" (in the sense of "the body politic"), "the republic," or, as given above, "the commonwealth." However interpreted, by *res publica*, the Romans meant their own commonwealth. *Res publica* was also written as a single word, **respublica**.

resurgam
reh-SUUR-gahm
I shall rise again

retro Satana!
REH-troh sah-TAH-nah
get thee behind me, Satan!

   The abbreviated form of VADE RETRO ME, SATANA. (See also
APAGE SATANAS.)

rex non potest peccare
reks nohn PAW-test pehk-KAH-reh
the king can do no wrong

rex regum
reks REH-guum
king of kings

R.I.P.

   See REQUIESCAT IN PACE.

ruat caelum
ROO-aht KĪ-luum
come what may

   Literally "though the heavens fall." (See FIAT IUSTITIA RUAT
CAELUM.)

rus in urbe
roos ihn UUR-beh
country in city

The phrase is used most often to describe a city building, garden, or view that suggests the countryside. "How can they leave their *rus in urbe* for a loft in SoHo with a view of Canal Street?" *Rus in urbe* is also used, but less often, to denote the creating of an illusion of countryside in a city setting. "In her designs for urban buildings, she specializes in *rus in urbe*."

sal Atticum
sahl AHT-tih-kuum
wit

This phrase from Pliny's *Historia Naturalis*, and often given in English as "Attic wit," is literally "Attic salt," reflecting the refined elegance, the taste—no pun is intended—of the ancient Athenian (Attic) intelligentsia. The wit denoted is often taken as "acerbity" or "intellectual wit." Byron, in his *English Bards and Scotch Reviewers*, referred to a taste for punning as "Attic salt."

salus mundi
SAH-loos MUUN-dee
the welfare of the world

salus populi suprema lex esto
SAH-loos PAW-puu-lee suu-PRAY-mah leks EH-stoh
let the welfare of the people be the supreme law

Motto of Missouri. Cicero, in *De Legibus*, had it this way: **Salus populi suprema est lex**, "the welfare of the people is the supreme law."

salus ubi multi consiliarii
SAH-loos UU-bih MUUL-tee kawn-sih-lee-AH-ree-ee
where there are many advisers there is safety

An excellent reminder for politicians whose words and actions hold hostage the future of the world. (See SALUS MUNDI.)

salve!
SAHL-weh
hail!

A Roman greeting.

sanctum sanctorum
SAHN-ktuum sahn-KTOH-ruum
a place of inviolable privacy

Sanctum in English is a noun meaning "a retreat or a private room" and pronounced SANK-təm. In Latin, *sanctum* is a neuter adjective meaning "sacred." Combining the Latin *sanctum* with *sanctorum* gives us a phrase that can be translated literally as "holy of holies," useful in denoting a place in a house of worship proscribed for all but the high priests, or a room in a home that is off limits to everyone but the master or mistress —either one, not both—of the establishment.

sapiens nihil affirmat quod non probat
SAH-pee-ehns NIH-hihl ahf-FIHR-maht kwawd nohn
PRAW-baht
don't swear to anything you don't know firsthand

Excellent advice, translated literally as "a wise man states as true nothing he does not prove."

Sartor Resartus
SAHR-tawr reh-SAHR-tuus
The Tailor Reclothed

Title of a book by Thomas Carlyle that examines life under the guise of expounding a philosophy of clothing. Not to be confused with *Dress for Success* or others of that ilk.

satis
SAH-tihs
enough

Satis gives us several interesting phrases. **Satis superque** (suu-PEHR-kweh), "enough and to spare." **Satis verborum** (wehr-BAWR-uum), "enough of words"; by extension: "let's have some action." The most satisfying is **satis eloquentiae, sapientiae parum** (eh-law-KWEN-tee-ī sah-pee-EN-tee-ī PAH-ruum), "enough eloquence, too little wisdom." Ah, the joys of Latin.

Saturnalia
sah-tuur-NAH-lee-ah
a real wingding

We know the English word "saturnalia," pronounced sat-ər-NAYL-yə, as "unrestrained revelry," but the Latin original is worth reviewing. The *Saturnalia* was the week-long Roman festival said to have begun in mid-December—sometimes given as the seventeenth of the month, sometimes as the nineteenth. The nature of the festival is not in dispute: public spectacles and banquets, freedom from restraint, general merrymaking, debauchery, and exchanges of presents. Indeed, during *Saturnalia* masters waited on slaves, courts and schools were closed, and sentencing of criminals was suspended. Who could ask for anything more? And all this in honor of Saturn, in Latin **Saturnus** (sah-TUUR-nuus), the god of planting and harvest, among other things.

scientia est potentia

skee-EN-tee-ah est paw-TEN-tee-ah

knowledge is power

An appropriate maxim for illicit wiretappers and those who record their telephone conversations without informing the people they speak with that they are doing so.

scilicet

SKEE-lih-keht

namely

Used in English in place of "to wit" and pronounced SIL-ə-set. *Scilicet* is the Latin abbreviation of **scire licet** (SKEE-reh LIH-keht), "it is permitted to know."

scripsit

SKRIH-psiht

he or she wrote it

With the author's name given first, a way to sign a literary work.

sculpsit

SKUUL-psiht

he or she carved (or cut) it

With the artisan's name given first, a way to sign a carving, engraving, etc.

scuto bonae voluntatis tuae coronasti nos

SKOO-toh BAW-nī waw-luun-TAH-tihs TOO-ī kaw-roh-NAH-stee nohs

with the shield of thy good favor, thou hast encompassed us

Motto on the Great Seal of Maryland.

semel insanivimus omnes
SEH-mehl ihn-sah-NEE-wih-muus AWM-nays
we have all been mad once

A good point to keep in mind when dealing with someone who has committed an antisocial act or made an egregious error. No one goes through life without slipping now and then.

semper fidelis
SEM-pehr fih-DAY-lihs
always faithful

Motto of the United States Marine Corps.

semper idem
SEM-pehr IH-dehm
always the same thing

A descriptive phrase suitable for characterizing something whose appearance does not change. *Semper idem*, the identical Latin phrase, but pronounced SEM-pehr EE-dehm, means "always the same person."

semper paratus
SEM-pehr pah-RAH-tuus
always ready

Motto of the United States Coast Guard.

Senatus Populusque Romanus
seh-NAH-tuus paw-puu-LUUS-kweh roh-MAH-nuus
the Roman Senate and People

Abbreviated **S.P.Q.R.** and, for the Romans, emblematic of their constitution.

senex bis puer
SEH-neks bihs POO-ehr
second childhood

This disagreeable Latin phrase, evocative of Shakespeare's characterization of the final stage of man—he called it "second childishness"—literally translates as "an old man is twice a boy."

seniores priores
seh-nee-OH-rays pree-OH-rays
elders first

A civilized precept.

seq.

Abbreviation of **sequens** (SEH-kwens) and **sequentes** (seh-KWEN-tays), respectively the singular and plural forms meaning "the following," and of **sequitur** (see the next entry). The plural of *seq*. is sometimes written as *seqq*.

sequitur
SEH-kwih-tuur
it follows

This word can be used to mean "it follows logically" (see NON SEQUITUR) or to mean "the following remark."

seriatim
seh-ree-AH-tihm
in series

A scholar's term, used to indicate that a publication is part of a series.

sero venientibus ossa
SAY-roh weh-nee-EN-tih-buus AWS-sah
sorry, too late

The Latin version of "the early bird catches the worm." Literally "for latecomers, the bones." (See POST FESTUM VENISTI.)

sesquipedalia verba
seh-skwih-peh-DAH-lee-ah WEHR-bah
oppressively long words

The English word "sesquipedalian" (ses-kwi-pi-DAY-li-ən) is an adjective carrying the meanings "having many syllables" and "tending to use long words." The Latin phrase, from Horace's *Ars Poetica*, literally means "words a foot and a half long." If Horace was referring to metrical feet, the phrase would describe words having at least four or five syllables, but he could also have had linear measure in mind, in which event the length of such words would boggle the mind. In either case, the meaning is clear, and Horace has given us an excellent way to characterize writers whose vocabularies are so pretentious that their readers must go repeatedly to an unabridged dictionary in order to understand what they are reading. *Sesquipedalia verba* may also be used to characterize the writing of such authors. John Simon, are you listening?

sic
seek
thus

This common word is used by writers and editors to indicate an apparent misspelling or a doubtful word or phrase in a source being quoted. "This dessiccant [*sic*] is useless." "The meeting was the most fortuitous [*sic*] I ever attended." Insertion of *sic* in these examples absolves the quoter of misspelling the word "desiccant" and misusing the word "fortuitous," and lays the blame—if blame it is—on the source quoted.

sic itur ad astra
seek IH-tuur ahd AH-strah
this is the path to immortality

Literally "thus one goes to the stars."

sic semper tyrannis
seek SEM-pehr tih-RAH-nees
thus ever to tyrants

Motto of Virginia, and said to be the words shouted by John Wilkes Booth after assassinating Abraham Lincoln. Booth is also said to have added, "The South is avenged."

sic transit gloria mundi
seek TRAHN-siht GLOH-ree-ah MUUN-dee
so passes away the glory of the world

Thomas à Kempis, in *De Imitatione Christi*, commenting on the transitory nature of human vanities. The Latin phrase is used at the coronation of a pope: A rope bundle is burned during the ceremony and, as the flame dies, the words "**Pater sancte** (PAH-tehr SAHN-kteh, "holy father") **sic transit gloria mundi**" are intoned.

sicut patribus, sit Deus nobis
SEE-kuut PAH-trih-buus siht DAY-uus NOH-bees
as with our fathers, may God be with us

Motto of Boston.

si dis placet
see dees PLAH-keht
if it pleases the gods

The equivalent of "God willing." (See DEO VOLENTE.)

si fecisti nega!
see fay-KIH-stee NEH-gah
stonewall!

Literally "if you did it, deny it."

si finis bonus est, totum bonum erit
see FEE-nihs BAW-nuus est TOH-tuum BAW-nuum
EH-riht
"all's well that ends well"

Literally "if the end is good, everything will be good."
Shakespeare couldn't have said it better.

sigillum
sih-GIHL-luum
a seal

Seen on the seals of states, cities, universities, etc.

silent leges enim inter arma
SIH-lent LAY-gays EH-nihm IHN-tehr AHR-mah
laws don't count in wartime

The principle used to justify imposition of martial law. This
maxim, found in Cicero's *Pro Milone*, translates literally as "for
laws are silent in the midst of war."

similia similibus curantur
sih-MIH-lee-ah sih-MIH-lih-buus koo-RAHN-tuur
fight fire with fire

Literally "like things are cured by likes," more freely "similar
ailments are treated successfully by similar remedies." This is
the doctrine of homeopathy, which advocates treatment of a
disease by giving the sick person small amounts of substances

that would produce symptoms of the same disease if they were given to a healthy person. It is also the basis for the putative hair-of-the-dog cure of a hangover, in which the afflicted person is encouraged to imbibe small amounts of the same substance that caused the unfortunate condition in the first place. (See CONTRARIA CONTRARIIS CURANTUR.)

sine die
SIH-neh DEE-ay
until an unspecified date

When a meeting adjourns *sine die*, literally "without a day," don't hold your breath until it reconvenes. For example, when a national convention of one of the major political parties in the United States adjourns *sine die* (pronounced sī-ni-DĪ in English), you can bet you'll have to wait four years for that party's next national convention. For this reason, it is only at the end of the final day of such a convention that the chairman declares the convention adjourned *sine die*.

sine dubio
SIH-neh DUU-bee-oh
without doubt

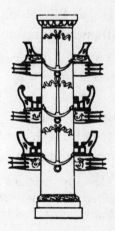

sine invidia
SIH-neh ihn-WIH-dee-ah
without envy

sine ira
SIH-neh EE-rah
without anger

sine loco et anno
SIH-neh LAW-koh et AHN-noh
without place and date

A bibliographer's term. A book that does not provide information concerning its place and date of publication is said to have been published *sine loco et anno*. Modern books normally supply such information.

sine mora
SIH-neh MAW-rah
without delay

sine praeiudicio (or **praejudicio**)
SIH-neh prī-yoo-DIH-kee-oh
without prejudice

sine prole
SIH-neh PROH-leh
without children

A legal term, often translated as "without issue," encountered in some wills.

sine qua non
SIH-neh kwah nohn
an indispensable condition

Literally "without which not." Anything that may be described accurately as *sine qua non* is absolutely necessary. "Warm outer clothing is a *sine qua non* at the North Pole."

si post fata venit gloria non propero

see pawst FAH-tah WEH-niht GLOH-ree-ah nohn
PRAW-peh-roh

if one must die to be recognized, I can wait

One of Martial's epigrams, literally "if glory comes after death, I'm not in a hurry." For a writer, this means "better unread than dead."

si quaeris peninsulam amoenam circumspice

see KWĪ-rihs peh-NIHN-suu-lahm ah-MOY-nahm
kihr-kuum-SPIH-keh

if you seek a lovely peninsula, look about you

Motto of Michigan.

si sic omnes

see seek AWM-nays

why couldn't it last forever?

A wistful expression, literally "if everything had been thus."

siste viator

SIH-steh wee-AH-tawr

stop, traveler

A favorite inscription on Roman tombstones.

sit non doctissima coniux (or conjux)

siht nohn daw-KTIHS-sih-mah KAWN-yuuks

a Roman formula for a happy marriage

One of Martial's epigrams, literally "may my wife not be very learned," revealing more than we would like to know about one Roman's attitude toward women.

sit tibi terra levis
siht TIH-bih TEHR-rah LEH-wihs
may the earth be light upon you

An ancient Roman tombstone inscription.

si vis me flere dolendum est primum ipsi tibi
see wees may FLAY-reh daw-LEN-duum est
PREE-muum IH-psee TIH-bih
if you wish me to weep, you yourself must first feel
grief

Method acting? Horace, in *Ars Poetica*, explaining to the
writer that emotion must be felt in order to be conveyed successfully in words.

si vis pacem para bellum
see wees PAH-kehm PAH-rah BEL-luum
if you want peace, prepare for war

A traditional justification for an arms buildup, from Vegetius,
a Roman military writer, in his *Epitoma Rei Militaris*. Stand by
for further developments.

socius criminis
SAW-kee-uus KREE-mih-nihs
a partner in crime

soli Deo gloria
SOH-lee DAY-oh GLOH-ree-ah
glory to God alone

sol lucet omnibus
sohl LOO-keht AWM-nih-buus
the sun shines for everyone

spectatum veniunt, veniunt spectentur ut ipsae
speh-KTAH-tuum WEH-nee-uunt WEH-nee-uunt
speh-KTEN-tuur uut IH-psī
they wish as much to be seen as to see

An observation by Ovid, in *Ars Amatoria*, literally "they come to see, they come that they themselves be seen," making it clear that the beautiful people have not changed much in two millennia.

spolia opima
SPAW-lee-ah AW-pee-mah
how sweet it is!

This phrase, literally "the choicest spoils," was used by Livy to denote the booty personally taken by a victorious general who has slain the commanding general of an enemy army.

sponte sua
SPAWN-teh SOO-ah
of one's own accord

Usually given as **sua sponte**.

S.P.Q.R.

Abbreviation of SENATUS POPULUSQUE ROMANUS, "the Roman Senate and People." *S.P.Q.R.* is often seen in depictions of Roman military standards.

stans pede in uno
stahns PEH-deh ihn OO-noh
effortlessly

Horace used this expression, literally "standing on one foot," in his *Satires*. Some of us use the equivalent expression in English: "I can do that standing on one foot." Now we can do it *stans pede in uno*.

status
STAH-tuus
condition or state

This Latin word, which can also be translated as "status" (in English, STAY-təs), is used commonly in a handful of Latin expressions: **statu quo** (STAH-too-kwoh), "as things were before"; **status quo**, "the state in which anything is (or was)"; **status quo ante bellum** (AHN-teh BEL-luum), "the condition (or military boundaries) that existed before the war"; and **status quo ante**, an abbreviated version of the previous phrase, with the same meanings. "Even though the couple had reunited, both husband and wife knew that too many recriminations had been exchanged, too much bitterness remained. They would never return to *status quo ante*."

stet
steht
let it stand

An editor or proofreader's mark, pronounced stet in English, canceling a deletion or other change previously made in a manuscript or proof. *Stet* also appears in various Latin expressions, including two of quite different intent. **Stet fortuna domus!** (fawr-TOO-nah DAW-muus) means "may the good fortune of the house endure!" **Stet pro ratione voluntas** (proh rah-tee-OH-neh waw-LUUN-tahs) means "let my will stand as a reason," giving a person in command a way of dismissing any arguments advanced to question his judgment; in English, "end of discussion, we'll do it my way."

stillicidi casus lapidem cavat
stihl-LIH-kih-dih KAH-suus LAH-pih-dehm KAH-waht
slow and steady does it

A Roman proverb, literally "dripping moisture hollows out a stone."

stultorum calami carbones moenia chartae
stuul-TOH-ruum KAH-lah-mee kahr-BOH-nays
MOY-nee-ah KAHR-tī
no graffiti, please

The Romans, in this saying, literally "chalk is the pen of fools, walls (their) paper," reveal that the graffiti artist is far from a modern phenomenon. Archaeologists have found graffiti on walls of buildings in many ancient Roman cities, including Pompeii, and the nature of the literary, artistic, political, and cultural content revealed in these ancient graffiti does not vary substantially from what can be seen today in many American cities. O TEMPORA! O MORES!

sua cuique voluptas
SOO-ah KWEE-kweh waw-LUU-ptahs
to each his own

Literally "everyone has his own pleasures." A related expression is **sua cuique sunt vitia** (suunt WIH-tee-ah), "everyone has his own vices."

sua sponte
SOO-ah SPAWN-teh
of one's own accord

Sometimes given as **sponte sua.**

suaviter in modo, fortiter in re
SWAH-wih-tehr ihn MAW-daw FAWR-tih-tehr ihn ray
he does what has to be done, but with the necessary compassion

In our everyday lives, we must inevitably do things we would prefer not to do. It is then that we are called on to be *suaviter in modo, fortiter in re*, literally "gentle in manner, resolute in deed," or to behave *suaviter in modo, fortiter in re*, literally "gently in manner, resolutely in deed." Thus, *suaviter in modo, fortiter in re* describes the model parent, executive, personnel manager, *et al*.

sub iudice (or judice)
suub YOO-dih-keh
before the courts

This legal phrase, literally "under consideration," is used so often that it has an English spelling, *sub judice*, and an English pronunciation, sub JOOD-ə-see. When a matter is before the courts, that is, still under litigation, the case generally is not discussed publicly by those directly involved. The intent is to avoid prejudicing the legal process. (See ADHUC SUB IUDICE LIS EST.)

sub poena
suub POY-nah
under penalty

Add "of a fine" or "of imprisonment" or what you will after this phrase, and the result is threatening. The derivation of the English noun "subpoena" (sə-PEE-nə), "a writ commanding a person to appear in a law court," reflects the opening words of such documents: *Sub poena* . . ., "under penalty . . . ," which go on to specify that the person summoned will be punished if the writ is not obeyed.

sub quocunque titulo
suub kwoh-KUUN-kweh TIH-tuu-loh
under whatever title

sub rosa

suub RAW-sah

in strict confidence or secretly

In this age of covert operations, *sub rosa* is understood all too well and said all too often in English, with the pronunciation sub ROHZ-ə. The phrase is of interest primarily because it has the literal meaning "under the rose." The rose is a symbol of secrecy, perhaps deriving from a story involving Cupid, the Roman god of love, who is said to have given a rose to Harpocrates, the god of silence, as a bribe for not revealing the amorous activities of Venus, the goddess of sensual love, well known for practicing what she preached. Roman dining room ceilings were decorated with roses to remind guests not to make public things that might be said **sub vino** (suub WEE-noh, "under the influence of wine"). And the American press frequently reports that Presidents walk with important visitors in the White House rose garden in order to gain privacy for discussion of matters of state. The power of the rose?

sub verbo

suub WEHR-boh

under the word

A scholar's term, abbreviated s.v., for example, "*s.v. sine prole*," used for making a cross-reference to an entry in a dictionary, encyclopedia, index, or other portion of a text.

sufficit

SUUF-fih-kiht

it is sufficient

sui generis
SOO-ee GEH-neh-rihs
one of a kind

This phrase, literally "of its (or his or her or their) own kind," is pronounced SOO-ee JEN-ə-rəs in English. One should take some care in applying *sui generis*, lest the phrase lose its value. Properly used, *sui generis* requires that the person, place, or thing be of an entirely distinctive character. Jimmy Durante comes to mind, perhaps the Grand Canyon, maybe Bach's Mass in B Minor—do you see how difficult it is to qualify?

summa cum laude
SUUM-mah kuum LOW-deh
with highest praise

See CUM LAUDE.

summa sedes non capit duos
SUUM-mah SAY-days nohn KAH-piht DOO-ohs
there's only room for one at the top

Literally "the highest seat does not hold two." And that's the story in all corporations.

summum bonum
SUUM-muum BAW-nuum
the highest good

summum ius (or jus) summa iniuria (or injuria)
SUUM-muum yoos SUUM-mah ihn-YOO-ree-ah
extreme law, extreme injustice

Lawmakers and judges beware: Strict enforcement of a law sometimes results in great injustice.

summum nec metuas diem nec optes
SUUM-muum nek MEH-too-ahs DEE-ehm nek
AW-ptays
neither fear nor wish for your last day

One of Martial's epigrams.

sumptus censum ne superet
SUUM-ptuus KEN-suum neh SUU-pehr-eht
live within your means

One of Martial's epigrams, literally "let not your spending exceed your income." Good advice for all but modern governments. It is worthwhile to reflect on the word *censum* in this epigram. The Roman **census** (KEN-suus), conducted every five years, registered all citizens in classes according to their property holdings. So *census* came to mean "wealth" and "property," and a poor Roman could be called **homo sine censu** (HAW-moh SIH-neh KEN-soo), literally "a man without property."

suo iure (or jure)
SOO-oh YOO-reh
in one's own right or in its own right

suo motu
SOO-oh MOH-too
spontaneously

Literally "by one's own motion" or "by its own motion."

suo tempore
SOO-oh TEM-paw-reh
at one's own time or at its own time

supra
SUU-prah
above

A scholar's word, used to make reference to an earlier portion of a text, usually in the phrase **vide** (WIH-deh) **supra**, "see above."

supremum vale
suu-PRAY-muum WAH-lay
farewell for the last time

Before death, that is.

sursum corda
SUUR-suum KAWR-dah
lift up your hearts

Heard in the mass.

sutor, ne supra crepidam
SOO-tawr nay SUU-prah KREH-pih-dahm
cobbler, stick to your last

See NE SUPRA CREPIDAM SUTOR IUDICARET.

suum cuique pulchrum
SOO-uum KWEE-kweh PUUL-kruum
love is blind

Literally "to everyone, his own is beautiful." Alone, *suum cuique* may be rendered as "to each his own."

s.v.

Abbreviation of **sub verbo,** "under the word." A lexicographer or encyclopedist's phrase, informing readers that the entry for a specified word or topic, for example, *"s.v. quorum,"* contains information germane to the subject under discussion to which reference is made.

tabula rasa
TAH-buu-lah RAH-sah
a clean slate

This phrase, literally "a scraped writing tablet," is used most often to denote a mind devoid of preconceptions. Thus, a person who has practiced hunt-and-peck typewriting for most of his adult life must become a *tabula rasa* before he can learn to use the touch system, and a newborn child is presumed to be a *tabula rasa.*

tacent, satis laudant
TAH-kent SAH-tihs LOW-dahnt
silence is praise enough

A line from Terence's *Eunuchus*, literally "they are silent, they praise enough," recognizing that rapt attention in an audience can be more flattering than applause.

tacet
TAH-keht
be silent

A musical notation, literally "it is silent," directing a singer or instrumentalist to maintain silence during the portion of a score so marked.

taedium vitae
TĪ-dee-uum WEE-tī
ennui or Weltschmerz

Literally "weariness of life."

tam facti quam animi
tahm FAH-ktee kwahm AH-nih-mee
as much in deed as in intention

tamquam alter idem
TAHM-kwahm AHL-tehr EE-dem
as if a second self

See ALTER IDEM.

tangere ulcus
TAHN-geh-reh UUL-kuus
to touch a sore

This expression is used with the meaning of "to hit the nail on the head" and with the meaning of "to touch a sore spot."

tarde venientibus ossa
TAHR-day weh-nee-EN-tih-buus AWS-sah
for latecomers, the bones

See SERO VENIENTIBUS OSSA.

telum imbelle sine ictu
TAY-luum ihm-BEL-leh SIH-neh IH-ktoo
an ineffectual argument

In Virgil's *Aeneid*, aged Priam throws a *telum imbelle sine ictu*, literally " a feeble weapon without a thrust," giving us a metaphor for an argument that falls short of the mark or misses it altogether.

tempora mutantur nos et mutamur in illis
TEM-paw-rah moo-TAHN-tuur nohs eht
moo-TAH-muur ihn IHL-lees
times change and we change with them

Attributed to John Owen, died 1622, a Welshman known for his Latin epigrams.

tempori parendum
TEM-paw-ree pah-REN-duum
one must keep abreast of the times

An essential thought—literally "one must yield to time"—for anyone who wishes to remain in the swim. A related expression is **temporibus inserviendum** (tehm-PAW-rih-buus ihn-sehr-wee-EN-duum), literally "one must pay attention to the times."

temporis ars medicina fere est
TEM-paw-rihs ahrs meh-dih-KEE-nah FEH-ray est
time is a great healer

This phrase, literally "time usually is the best means of healing," may have application in the field of medicine, but it appears in Ovid's *Remedia Amoris*, which is concerned with the amatory rather than the medical arts.

tempus abire tibi est
TEM-puus ahb-EE-reh TIH-bee est
make way for someone else

Horace, in his *Epistles*, giving all of us excellent advice: When we have ceased being productive, it is time to make room for those who are. Horace put it this way: "You have played enough, eaten and drunk enough." Now *tempus abire tibi est*, literally "it is time for you to go away." Senior faculty, superannuated executives, old soldiers and politicians, hearken unto Horace.

tempus edax rerum
TEM-puus EH-dahks RAY-ruum
time, the devourer of all things

Ovid, in *Metamorphoses*, calling our attention to the irreversible results—both good and bad—of the passage of time.

tempus fugit
TEM-puus FUU-giht
time flies

Who doesn't know this? Pronounced TEM-pəs FYOO-jət in English.

tempus ludendi
TEM-puus loo-DEN-dee
a time for playing

Workaholics, take heed. All work and no play . . .

tempus omnia revelat
TEM-puus AWM-nee-ah reh-WAY-laht
time reveals all things

So wait.

tenax propositi
TEH-nahks proh-PAW-sih-tee
resolute

Literally "tenacious of purpose."

tenere lupum auribus

teh-NAY-reh LUU-puum OW-rih-buus

to take the bull by the horns

This phrase, literally "to hold a wolf by the ears," implies fearlessness in confronting a dangerous situation or boldness in dealing with a difficulty.

te nosce

tay NAWS-keh

know thyself

A Latin translation of a precept incised in the stone of the temple of the oracle at Delphi, reflecting the oracle's interest in individual morality.

teres atque rotundus

TEH-rehs AHT-kweh raw-TUUN-duus

well-rounded

Horace's phrase, in the *Satires*, literally "polished and round," describing the Stoics' conception of a wise man as one who rolls smoothly through life. The full phrase is **totus** (TOH-tuus) **teres atque rotundus**, "complete, polished, and round."

terra es, terram ibis

TEHR-rah es TEHR-rahm EE-bihs

"dust thou art, to dust thou shalt return"

This entry comprises a well-known line from Genesis as rendered in Latin in the Vulgate and in English in the King James Version. The edition of the Bible known as the Vulgate, from the Latin **editio vulgata** (ay-DIH-tee-oh wuul-GAH-tah), "the common edition," first appeared in print in 1456, after translation more than a thousand years earlier by St. Jerome. The King James Version, also known as the King James Bible (1611), was produced at the direction of King James I (1566–1625) by a team of scholars who worked for several years, relying on exist-ing English translations. The line *terra es, terram ibis* is the one in which God explains the consequences of Adam's disobedi-ence. In one stanza of "A Psalm of Life," Longfellow incorpo-rated the King James translation of this melancholy line:

> Life is real! Life is earnest!
> And the grave is not its goal;
> Dust thou art, to dust returnest,
> Was not spoken of the soul.

(See MEMENTO, HOMO, QUIA PULVIS ES ET IN PULVEREM REV-ERTIS.)

terra firma
TEHR-rah FIHR-mah
dry land

This well-known phrase, in English pronounced TER-rə FIR-mə, literally means "solid land." It is used to differentiate land from sea.

terra incognita
TEHR-rah ihn-KAW-gnih-tah
unknown territory

This phrase is used to designate a subject or place about which nothing or next to nothing is known. "Modern phy-sics, by its nature, continually concerns itself with *terra incog-nita*."

testis unus, testis nullus
TEH-stihs OO-nuus TEH-stihs NUUL-luus
one witness, no witness

A legal maxim indicating that unsupported testimony is no better than complete absence of testimony, and suggesting to all of us that we not give full credence to a story we hear from one source only.

timeo Danaos et dona ferentes
TIH-may-oh DAH-nah-ohs et DOH-nah feh-REN-tays
when an enemy appears friendly, watch out

This advice, literally "I fear the Greeks [ancient name Danai], even when bearing gifts," comes from Virgil's *Aeneid* and is addressed to the men of Troy. The Trojans were told by one of their priests to mistrust the huge wooden horse—the fabled Trojan horse—left behind by the departing soldiers of Greece, ostensibly as an offering to the gods to secure safe passage for Ulysses during his return to Greece. Ignoring the advice, the Trojans did not look the gift horse in the mouth, but dragged it inside their city, with predictable results. Recall that it contained a contingent of Greek soldiers sufficiently numerous to open the city gates and admit enough additional troops to destroy Troy. The irony is that Troy, not Greece, is stigmatized in the naming of the wooden horse: To this day, "a Trojan horse" is a thing or person that subverts from within. The Greeks come in for their share of opprobrium in the expression "Greek gifts," today scarcely cited, except as *timeo Danaos et dona ferentes* and its translation.

timeo hominem unius libri
TIH-meh-oh HAW-mih-nehm OO-nee-uus LIH-bree
I fear the man of one book

An observation attributed to Aquinas, with two possible interpretations. The older, more customary interpretation has it that a person steeped in a single source is a formidable opponent in debate. In a more recent interpretation, *timeo hominem unius libri* expresses fear in confronting a man for whom the knowledge, opinions, and dogma of a single book are sufficient and who recognizes no truths but the literal statements of his own book.

toga
TAW-gah
a toga

The *toga* (English pronunciation TOH-gə) is well known as the standard Roman outer garment. It was a white woolen upper garment worn in public by men in times of peace as a sign of their status as citizens. Freedmen and freedwomen also wore the *toga*, but women of higher status wore the **stola** (STAW-lah), a long outer garment. The adjective **togata** (taw-GAH-tah) was applied to women of doubtful reputation, an indication that the practice of judging a book by its cover, or a person by the way he or she dresses, did not originate in modern times.

totidem verbis
TAW-tih-dem WEHR-bees
in so many words

totis viribus
TOH-tees WEE-rih-buus
with all one's powers

toto caelo
TOH-toh KĪ-loh
diametrically opposite

We say the views of two people or two governments are "worlds apart," but the Romans said they were separated *toto caelo*, literally "by the entire heavens."

totus teres atque rotundus
TOH-tuus TEH-rehs AHT-kweh raw-TUUN-duus
well-rounded

See TERES ATQUE ROTUNDUS.

tu ne cede malis sed contra audentior ito
too nay KAY-deh MAH-lees sed KAWN-trah
ow-DEN-tee-awr EE-toh
yield not to misfortunes, but advance all the more
boldly against them

Advice for all of us, from Virgil's *Aeneid*.

tu quoque
too KWAW-kweh
you too

A retort to an accusation: You are guilty of the very misdeeds
or mistakes you attribute to me; it takes one to know one.

ubi bene ibi patria
UU-bee BEH-neh IH-bee PAH-tree-ah
I owe my allegiance to the country in which I prosper

A patriotic Roman sentiment, also expressed as **ubi libertas**
(LEE-behr-tahs, "liberty") **ibi patria,** "where there is freedom,
there is my fatherland."

ubi mel ibi apes
UU-bee mel IH-bee AH-pays
honey attracts bees

This saying from Plautus, literally "where there is honey,
there will be bees," reminds us that there is a surefire way to
attract followers.

ubi solitudinem faciunt pacem appellant
UU-bee soh-lih-TOO-dih-nehm FAH-kee-uunt
PAH-kehm AHP-pel-lahnt
they create desolation and call it peace

A more literal translation of this line from Tacitus's *Agricola* is "where they create a desert, they call it peace." Tacitus was quoting the leader of the Britons, who had made the mistake of coming out second best in a war against the invading armies of the Romans. While the Romans customarily treated conquered peoples with respect, their destruction of Carthage and sack of Corinth were notable exceptions.

ultima forsan
UUL-tih-mah FAWR-sahn
it's later than you think

These words, literally "perhaps the last," are sometimes inscribed on the face of a clock, to convey the thought that the moment of death—indeed, the moment of eternal judgment—may be at hand. The prudent person treats every hour as though it were his last.

ultima ratio
UUL-tih-mah RAH-tee-oh
the final argument

This phrase has literal applications, for example, "We find many reasons for denying your loan application, but your four bankruptcies are the *ultima ratio*." Louis XIV of France, recognizing that force is the final argument, directed that his cannons carry the legend ultima ratio regum (RAY-guum, "of kings"). As a result, *ultima ratio regum* signifies "war."

ultima Thule
UUL-tih-mah TOO-lay
the end of the world

Ancient mariners believed that the northern end of the world was an island called Thule, which stood six days' sail from Britain. The precise location of Thule is not known today, but *ultima Thule*, mentioned in Virgil's *Georgics*, survives as a useful expression for describing any place whose appearance gives one the feeling of standing at the end of the world.

ultimum vale
UUL-tih-muum WAH-lay
farewell for the last time

See SUPREMUM VALE.

ultra vires
UUL-trah WEE-rays
beyond legal authority

A court or other agency of government that exceeds its legal authority in a particular matter is said to be acting *ultra vires* (pronounced UL-trə VĪ-reez in English), literally "beyond the powers."

una salus victis nullam sperare salutem
OO-nah SAH-luus WIH-ktees NUUL-lahm
spay-RAH-reh sah-LOO-tehm
knowing there is no hope can give one the courage to fight and win

Virgil, in the *Aeneid*, gives us this insight, which translates more literally as "the one safety for the vanquished is to abandon hope for safety." Thus, when we know we are doomed, we take risks we would dismiss as imprudent if we thought we still had a chance. This is the stuff that brings dazed prizefighters back to their feet at a count of nine.

una voce
OO-nah WAW-keh
unanimously

Literally "with one voice."

unguibus et rostro
UUN-gwih-buus et RAW-stroh
with all one's might

When the Romans fought *unguibus et rostro*, they fought "with claws and beak." After all, they used the eagle as their device on banners etc. We moderns sometimes are said to fight "tooth and nail," which implies that we bite and scratch, and some of us have been known to claw our way to the top. Civilization marches on.

unus vir nullus vir
OO-nuus wihr NUUL-luus wihr
two heads are better than one

This Roman proverb translates literally as "one man, no man" giving the sense shown above. But it also can be taken in a second sense: Before machines came along, many heavy tasks were beyond the strength of a person working alone, so *unus vir nullus vir*, "one man, no man."

urbi et orbi
UUR-bee et AWR-bee
to the city and the world

In papal blessings and documents addressed *urbi et orbi*, the city is Rome, the world the rest of humanity.

urbs in horto
uurbs ihn HAWR-toh
a city in a garden

Motto of Chicago.

usque ad aras
UUS-kweh ahd AH-rahs
even to the altars

See AMICUS USQUE AD ARAS.

usque ad nauseam
UUS-kweh ahd NOW-say-ahm
even to the point of (inducing) nausea

See AD NAUSEAM.

usus promptos facit
UU-suus PRAWM-ptohs FAH-kiht
practice makes perfect

Literally "use makes men ready." A related proverb is **usus te plura docebit** (tay PLOO-rah DAW-kay-biht), "experience will teach you many things." And then there is **usus est optimum magister** (est AW-ptih-muum mah-GIH-stehr), "experience is the best teacher."

utcumque placuerit Deo
UUT-kuum-kweh plah-KOO-eh-riht DAY-oh
howsoever it shall please God

ut fata trahunt
uut FAH-tah TRAH-huunt
at the mercy of destiny

Literally "as the fates drag." This expression recognizes that we have limited control over our lives. "We have done all we can; from here on, it's *ut fata trahunt*."

ut infra
uut IHN-frah
as cited below

A scholar's phrase, literally "as below." See UT SUPRA and VIDE.

uti non abuti
UU-tee nohn ahb-OO-tee
treat with respect

Literally "to use, not abuse."

uti possidetis
UU-tee paws-sih-DAY-tihs
we stole it fair and square

The principle, literally "as you possess," that one is entitled to keep what one has acquired. It is applied most often during diplomatic negotiations prior to a peace treaty. According to *uti possidetis*, the territory a country has won during a war may be retained by that country from then on. The principle works well because strong countries usually win wars and can continue to work their will. It does not work well when a comparatively weak nation happens to win a war against an even weaker adversary. At that point, the great powers usually team up to arrange for return of conquered territory to the defeated nation. So *uti possidetis*, "as you possess," depends on who the "you" is.

ut supra
uut SUU-prah
as cited above

A scholar's phrase, literally "as above." See UT INFRA and VIDE.

vade in pace
WAH-deh ihn PAH-keh
go in peace

A Roman way to say goodbye.

vade mecum
WAH-deh MAY-kuum
go with me

A *vade mecum*, in English pronounced VAY-dee MEE-kəm, is usually a small manual or reference book that is regularly carried in one's pocket—today, a *vade mecum* as often as not travels in a handbag or in the ubiquitous attaché case—because it contains information that is frequently consulted. A *vade mecum* may also be something other than a small book: a pocket calculator, a portable dictating machine, even a personal computer.

vade retro me, Satana
WAH-deh REH-troh may sah-TAH-nah
get thee behind me, Satan

The well-known phrase in Mark, in which Jesus rebukes Peter, concluding "for thou mindest not the things of God, but the things of men." (See APAGE SATANAS.)

vae soli
wī SOH-lee
woe to the solitary men

Bachelors, take heed.

vae victis
wī WIH-ktees
it's tough to be a loser

The words, literally "woe to the vanquished," attributed by Livy to Brennus, a chief of the Gauls arranging terms of peace with the Romans in 390 B.C. According to Livy, when the Romans complained that the Gauls were using excessive weights in measuring the amount of gold the Romans were to pay, Brennus threw his sword onto the weights, exclaiming, "*Vae victis.*" Brennus was telling the Romans that he, not they, had the upper hand.

vale
WAH-lay
farewell

See AVE ATQUE VALE.

valeat quantum valere potest
WAH-lay-aht KWAHN-tuum wah-LAY-reh PAW-test
take it for what it's worth

Literally "let it stand for what it is worth." Appropriate when passing information of doubtful authenticity.

valete ac plaudite
wah-LAY-teh ahk plow-DEE-teh
let's hear it for the cast

The words, literally "farewell and applaud," said at the end of a Roman play. Remember that theaters were not equipped with curtains in those days. (See PLAUDITE, CIVES.)

vanitas vanitatum, omnis vanitas
WAH-nih-tahs wah-nih-TAH-tuum AWM-nihs
WAH-nih-tahs
everything man does is in vain

This phrase from Ecclesiastes is often given the literal translation "vanity of vanities, all is vanity," leading to a misunderstanding of what is intended. When it is understood that *vanitas* means "emptiness" or "fruitlessness," the true intention of Ecclesiastes is perceived.

varia lectio
WAH-ree-ah LEH-ktee-oh
a variant reading

A scholar's phrase. The plural is **variae lectiones** (WAH-ree-ī leh-ktee-OH-nays).

variorum
wah-ree-OH-ruum
of various persons

The English word "variorum," pronounced va-ree-OH-rəm and also given as "variorum edition," is a shortened form of the Latin **cum notis** (kuum NAW-tees) **variorum,** "with the notes of various persons." "Variorum" has two applications in English. It is used to designate an edition or a text containing the notes of various scholars, and to designate an edition supplying variant readings of a text. The full Latin phrase for a variorum or a variorum edition is **editio** (ay-DIH-tee-oh) **cum notis variorum.** Variorums generally supply both comments by various scholars and variant readings of a text.

varium et mutabile semper femina
WAH-ree-uum et moo-TAH-bih-leh SEM-pehr
FAY-mih-nah
la donna è mobile

This is the argument, literally "woman is ever fickle and changeable," advanced to Aeneas as a sound reason for leaving Dido, and thanks to Virgil—and to Giuseppe Verdi's *Rigoletto* —it has been parroted ever since, perhaps primarily by men. Let the record—according to Virgil at least—show that lovelorn Dido committed suicide by fire after Aeneas departed. So who was fickle? On the other hand, if the story can be believed, it does appear that old flames die.

vel caeco appareat
wel KĪ-koh ahp-PAH-ray-aht
it's obvious

Literally "it would be apparent even to a blind man."

velis et remis
WAY-lees et RAY-mees
an all-out effort

Literally "with sails and oars," also given as **remis velisque** (way-LEES-kweh). What would the Romans have said if they had invented the jet airplane?

veni, vidi, vici
WAY-nee WEE-dee WEE-kee
I came, I saw, I conquered

The best-known Latin sentence of them all, freely rendered as "a piece of cake," reported by Plutarch to have been uttered by Julius Caesar by way of reporting his victory in 47 B.C. over Pharnaces, king of Pontus.

verbatim et litteratim
wehr-BAH-tihm et liht-teh-RAH-tihm
accurately rendered

Literally "word for word and letter for letter." To this phrase is sometimes appended **et punctatim** (et puun-KTAH-tihm), "and point for point."

verba volant, scripta manent
WEHR-bah WAW-lahnt SKREE-ptah MAH-nent
get it down on paper

Literally "spoken words fly away, written words remain."

verbum sat sapienti
WEHR-buum saht sah-pee-EN-tee
a word to the wise

Literally "a word is enough for a wise man."

veritas
WAY-rih-tahs
truth

Motto of Harvard.

veritas odium parit
WAY-rih-tahs AW-dee-uum PAH-riht
truth breeds hatred

Terence, in *Andria*, telling us it is not always wise to be frank with one's friends.

veritas simplex oratio est
WAY-rih-tahs SIHM-pleks aw-RAH-tee-oh est
the language of truth is simple

By contrast, with apologies to Sir Walter Scott: "Oh, what a tangled web we weave, When first we practice to deceive!"

veritas vos liberabit
WAY-rih-tahs wohs lee-beh-RAH-biht
the truth shall make you free

Motto of The Johns Hopkins University.

verso
WEHR-soh
left

This term (pronounced VUR-soh in English) is used to indicate a left-hand page of a book, the full Latin phrase being **verso folio** (FAW-lee-oh, in English FOH-lee-oh), literally "the page being turned." (See RECTO.)

versus
WEHR-suus
against

In English pronounced VUR-səs.

via
WEE-ah
a way

This word gives us several interesting combinations. **Via Appia** (AHP-pee-ah), "the Appian Way," leads from Rome to Brindisi (ancient name **Brundisium**, bruun-DIH-see-uum). **Via**

Dolorosa (daw-law-ROH-sah), "the road of sadness," is the road Jesus followed on the way to his crucifixion. **Via media** (MEH-dee-ah), "the middle way," is the moderate course so frequently recommended in Latin proverbs. Another bit of Roman advice is **via trita** (TREE-tah), **via tuta** (TOO-tah), which translates as "the beaten path is the safe path." *Via* has also given us an English preposition, pronounced VEE-ə or VĪ-ə, meaning "by way of" or "through."

vice versa
WIH-keh WEHR-sah
conversely

A phrase we all know in English. The Latin words translate literally as "the change being turned."

victis honor
WIH-ktees HAW-nawr
let's hear it for the losers

Literally "honor to the vanquished."

vide
WIH-day
see

Vide gives us several useful expressions. **Vide et crede** (et KRAY-deh), "see and believe." **Vide infra** (IHN-frah), "see below," used by scholars to refer a reader to something that follows in a text. **Vide supra** (SUU-prah), "see above," a scholar's way of referring a reader to something that appears earlier in a text.

videlicet
wih-DAY-lih-keht
namely

Commonly abbreviated viz., which is expressed orally as "namely," not as "viz." *Videlicet*, literally "it is permitted to see," is also translated as "to wit."

video meliora proboque, deteriora sequor
WIH-day-oh meh-lee-OH-rah praw-BOH-kweh
day-teh-ree-OH-rah SEH-kwawr
even though I know better, I keep on doing the wrong thing

A line from Ovid's *Metamorphoses*, literally "I see the better way and approve it, but I follow the worse way," confirming what we know too well about recidivism.

vi et armis
wee et AHR-mees
by force of arms

vigilate et orate
wih-gih-LAH-teh et aw-RAH-teh
watch and pray

About all one can do in the nuclear age.

vincam aut moriar
WIHN-kahm owt MAW-ree-ahr
I will conquer or die

vincit qui patitur
WIHN-kiht kwee PAH-tih-tuur
patience wins out

Literally "he prevails who is patient."

vincit qui se vincit
WIHN-kiht kwee say WIHN-kiht
first we must learn to overcome our own bad habits

This advice, literally "he conquers who conquers himself," and perhaps appropriate for display in a psychotherapist's office, recognizes that most of us have traits or habits that are less than desirable. By changing our ways, we make it possible to win out in larger arenas. *Vincit qui se vincit* is an adaptation of one of Syrus's maxims, **bis** (bihs) **vincit qui se vincit in victoria** (ihn wih-KTOH-ree-ah), which has a narrower meaning, but one worth learning because it calls attention to the human tendency to gloat: "he conquers twice who conquers himself in victory."

vincit veritas
WIHN-kiht WAY-rih-tahs
truth wins out

Even though it may take a long time. This sanguine thought may also be expressed as **vincit omnia** (AWM-nee-ah) **veritas**, "truth conquers all things."

vinculum matrimonii
WIHN-kuu-luum mah-trih-MOH-nee-ee
the bond of matrimony

Vinculum may also be translated as "noose" or "chain."

virginibus puerisque canto
wihr-GIH-nih-buus poo-ehr-EES-kweh KAHN-toh
I chant to maidens and to boys

A line in Horace's *Odes*.

viribus totis
WEE-rih-buus TOH-tees
with all one's strength

viribus unitis
WEE-rih-buus oo-NEE-tees
with forces united

viri infelicis procul amici
WIH-ree ihn-FAY-lih-kihs PRAW-kuul ah-MEE-kee
success has many friends

Those who achieve eminence or wealth find suddenly that they are surrounded by friends, but when their fortunes have changed find just as suddenly that they are alone. *Viri infelicis procul amici*, literally "friends stay far away from an unfortunate man," affirms that fair-weather friends are friends we can rely on as long as we don't have to. (See FELICITAS HABET MULTOS AMICOS.)

vir sapit qui pauca loquitur
wihr SAH-piht kwee POW-kah LAW-kwih-tuur
know when to hold your tongue

Literally "that man is wise who talks little." (See CAVE QUID DICIS, QUANDO, ET CUI for another way of giving this same advice.)

virtus post nummos
WIHR-toos pawst NUUM-mohs
keep your eye on the bottom line

This cynical advice—one man's cynicism is another man's wisdom—freely adapted from one of Horace's *Epistles*, translates literally as "virtue after wealth." The full thought is **quaerenda pecunia primum est** (kwī-REN-dah peh-KOO-nee-ah PRIHM-uum est) **virtus post nummos**, which may be translated as "money is to be sought after first of all, virtue after wealth."

virtus probata florescit
WIHR-toos praw-BAH-tah floh-REH-skiht
grace under pressure

A maxim, literally "manly excellence flourishes in trial," suggesting that we learn our true character only when we put ourselves to the test and come out on top.

virtute et armis
wihr-TOO-teh et AHR-mees
by courage and arms

Motto of Mississippi.

virtutis fortuna comes
wihr-TOO-tihs fawr-TOO-nah KAW-mehs
good luck is the companion of courage

The suggestion is that good things don't just happen; we must prepare ourselves to grasp opportunity when it comes our way.

vis consili expers mole ruit sua
wees kawn-SIH-lee EK-spehrs MOH-leh ROO-iht
SOO-ah
discretion is the better part of valor

An observation from one of Horace's *Odes*, literally "force
without good sense falls by its own weight."

vis inertiae
wees ihn-EHR-tee-ī
the power of inactivity

It is to *vis inertiae* that we ascribe the willingness of many
people to put up with their troubles rather than change their
lives and risk encountering new and possibly more vexing troubles. With *inertiae* translated as "of inertia," *vis inertiae* explains why a plan set in motion is difficult to stop, and vice versa.

vita brevis, ars longa
WEE-tah BREH-wihs ahrs LAWN-gah
life is short, art is long

See ARS LONGA, VITA BREVIS.

vitam impendere vero
WEE-tahm ihm-PEN-deh-reh WAY-roh
to devote one's life to the truth

A noble resolve from Juvenal's *Satires*.

vitam regit fortuna non sapientia
WEE-tahm REH-giht fawr-TOO-nah nohn
sah-pee-EN-tee-ah
it's mostly a matter of luck

Literally "chance, not wisdom, governs human life."

vita non est vivere sed valere vita est

WEE-tah nohn est WEE-weh-reh sed wah-LAY-reh
WEE-tah est

life is more than merely staying alive

   One of Martial's epigrams, literally "life is not to live, but life
is to be strong, vigorous." Food for thought for all of us.

vivamus, mea Lesbia, atque amemus

wee-WAH-muus MAY-ah LEH-sbee-ah AHT-kweh
ah-MAY-muus

let's live it up

   Advice from Catullus, in one of his poems, literally "Lesbia
mine, let's live and love." (See CARPE DIEM.)

vivat

WEE-waht

long live . . .

   Vivat regina (ray-GEE-nah), "long live the queen." Vivat rex
(reks), "long live the king."

viva voce

WEE-wah WAW-keh

orally

   A *viva voce* (English pronunciation vī-və VOH-see), also a
"viva voce examination," is an oral examination. To respond
viva voce is to respond orally, rather than in writing. The Latin
phrase literally means "with the living voice."

vive hodie
WEE-weh HAW-dee-ay
live today

From one of Martial's epigrams, telling us in full that it is not wise to say I'll live tomorrow; tomorrow is for tomorrow's living. *Vive hodie*. (See CARPE DIEM for a fuller explanation.)

vivere parvo
WEE-weh-reh PAHR-woh
to live on little

Little income, that is.

vive ut vivas
WEE-weh uut WEE-wahs
live that you may live

Sound advice on how to conduct one's life, albeit contrary to that given in CARPE DIEM.

vive, vale
WEE-weh WAH-lay
farewell

Literally "live, be well," also given as **vive valeque** (wah-LAY-kweh), "live and be well."

vixere fortes ante Agamemnona
wee-KSAY-reh FAWR-tays AHN-teh
ah-gah-MEM-naw-nah
we don't have a monopoly on all that is good

This line from Horace's *Odes* tells us literally that "brave men lived before Agamemnon." The words that follow this line translate as "all unwept and unknown, lost in the distant night, since they lack a divine poet." Thus, Horace tells us that great acts of heroism, kindness, and the like have often been performed by unsung heroes—unsung in the sense that no record was made of their exploits—yet even though we know nothing of those acts, we must not assume they never happened. The public relations industry flourishes because it understands that perception of events may count for more than the events themselves.

vixit
WEE-ksiht
he or she has lived

A word found on tombstones, usually **vixit . . . annos** (AHN-nohs), "he or she lived (a certain number of) years."

viz.

Abbreviation of VIDELICET.

volens et potens
WAW-lens et PAW-tens
willing and able

volente Deo
waw-LEN-teh DAY-oh
God willing

See DEO VOLENTE.

volenti non fit iniuria (or injuria)
waw-LEN-tee nohn fiht ihn-YOO-ree-ah
to a willing person no wrong is done

The legal maxim we all know, for example, in the phrase "consenting adults."

volo, non valeo
WAW-loh nohn WAH-lay-oh
I am willing, but unable

voluptates commendat rarior usus
waw-luu-PTAH-tays kawm-MEN-daht RAH-ree-awr
OO-suus
all pleasure's no pleasure

Juvenal, in his *Satires*, counseling moderation in living the good life, literally "rare indulgence increases pleasures."

vox clamantis in deserto
wawks klah-MAHN-tihs ihn deh-SEHR-toh
the voice of one crying in the wilderness

Familiar words from various books of the New Testament, in Matthew continuing "prepare you the way of the Lord; make his paths straight." The motto of Dartmouth College, with apologies to the New Testament, is **vox clamans** (KLAH-mahns) **in deserto,** usually translated as "a voice crying in the wilderness." It must be pointed out that Isaiah had the same thought about 600 years before Matthew and the others, and the scholars who prepared the King James Version erred in translating Isaiah and so erred in the New Testament as well. What the Hebrew said was: "A voice crying, in the wilderness prepare ye the way of the Lord. . . ." That comma after "crying" makes all the difference in the world. Yet the error of the King James may be called a sublime mistranslation, since we will never discard so beautiful a metaphor.

vox et praeterea nihil
wawks et prī-TEH-ray-ah NIH-hihl
empty words

Plutarch's phrase, used to denote an empty threat. Plutarch tells a story of a man who plucks the feathers from a nightingale. Finding that its body sans plumage is pathetically small, he remarks, "*Vox et praeterea nihil*," literally "a voice and nothing more."

vox populi vox Dei
wawks PAW-puu-lee wawks DAY-ee
the voice of the people is the voice of God

Political leaders take heed, the wishes of the people are irresistible.

vulneratus non victus
wuul-neh-RAH-tuus nohn WIH-ktuus
bloodied but unbowed

Literally "wounded but not conquered."

vultus est index animi
WUUL-tuus est IHN-deks AH-nih-mee
the face is the mirror of the soul

Literally "the expression on one's face is a sign of the soul."

English Index

A

about, 80
about tastes there is no disputing, 97
above, 272
absolute divorce, 65
absolutely necessary, 262
absurd etymology, 175
acceptable person, 224
accommodation, 187
accomplice, 216
according to custom, 124
according to what is just and good, 120
accurately rendered, 291
acerbity, 252
acme, 193
actions speak louder than words, 128
admire nothing, 195
after childbirth, 229
after clouds, Phoebus, 229
after death, 228
after making the necessary changes, 189
after noon, 228
after this, therefore because of this, 228
again and again, 119
against, 292
against the best interests of society, 87
against the man, 22
agree, 84
agreement, 84
agreement of all, 85
agreement of rash men, 85
alas, the fleeting years glide by, 115
alliance between two states, 76
all or nothing, 63
all-out effort, 290
all people of that type, 143

all pleasure's no pleasure, 302
all's well that ends well, 260
all that glitters is not gold, 202
all that sort, 148
all that work and nothing to show for it, 217
all the more, 34
all things change, and we change with them, 211
all things yield to money, 220
all this sort, 143
all to one, 28
also known as, 37
altar, 41
altogether, 163
always faithful, 256
always ready, 256
always the same person, 256
always the same thing, 256
among other persons, 161
among other things, 161
and all that sort, 119
and even of several other things, 102
and everything of the kind, 119
and forever, brother, hail and farewell, 64
and other men, 118
and other people, 118
and others, 118
and other things, 118
and other women, 118
and so of similar people or things, 119
and so on, 118
and the rest, 119
and wife, 120
anew, 98
anger is brief madness, 166
annotations, 29
annually, 221
another day wasted, 106
another I, 39

with oars and sails, 247
with one's own hand, 180
with one voice, 284
without a day, 261
without anger, 261
without children, 262
without deception, 69
without delay, 262
without doubt, 261
without envy, 261
without help, 182
without issue, 262
without limit, 23
without place and date, 262
without prejudice, 262
without premeditation, 126
without preparation, 126
without saluting one's host, 158
without which not, 262
with pen running on, 93
with praise, 92
with privilege, 93
with sails and oars, 290
with strings attached, 30
with stronger reason, 34
with sword and plow, 116
with the hands and feet, 180
with the living voice, 299
with the name changed, 190
with the name changed, the story
    applies to you, 190
with the shield of thy good favor,
    thou hast encompassed us, 255
with thumb folded, 226
with thumb turned, 226
with united powers, 84
with what intention?, 240
with your permission, 215
woe to the solitary man, 288
woe to the vanquished, 288
woman is fickle and changeable, 290
a woman was the leader in the
    deed, 113
wonder at nothing, 195
wonderful to behold, 186
wonderful to relate, 186
wonders, 186
wooden block, 81
wool from an ass, 11
word for word, 152

word for word and letter for letter,
    291
word for word, letter for letter, and
    point for point, 291
a word is enough for a wise man,
    161, 291
words a foot and a half long, 258
a word to the wise, 160, 291
work conquers all things, 168, 212
work plan, 187
worlds apart, 280
the world wants to be deceived, 189
worth all of them, 160
worthless residue, 74
worthy of note, 202
wounded but not conquered, 303
written law, 170
written without care, 93

Y

yield not to misfortunes, but
    advance all the more boldly, 281
you also, Brutus, 120
you can't win 'em all, 38
you fall into Scylla in trying to avoid
    Charybdis, 151
you have arrived after the feast,
    228
you have lost oil, 209
you know as well as I that, 141
you may drive nature out with a
    pitchfork, but it will return, 190
you may have the body, 140
you must die so that I may live, 188
a young man's guardian, 94
your death, my life, 188
you're either for us or against us, 62
your good fortune, 233
you shall go safest in the middle
    course, 155
you too, 281
you've got to keep at it, 204
you've hit the nail right on the
    head, 247
you've touched the thing with a
    needle, 247
you've wasted your time, 209
you wake up one morning and find
    you are old, 136
you will go safest in the middle, 183

About the Author

Eugene Ehrlich is series coeditor of *Contemporary Studies in Literature*, as well as principal editor of the *Oxford American Dictionary*, *The Volume Library*, and the *NBC Handbook of Pronunciation*.

Among his many other books are *The Oxford Illustrated Literary Guide to the United States*, *English Grammar*, *Basic Grammar for Clear Writing*, *Writing and Researching*, and *A Concise Index to English*.

Name: _____

Find a Line of Symmetry

Study the example showing how to find a line of symmetry. Then solve problems 1–5.

Example

Which shape has more lines of symmetry—
a rectangle, an equilateral triangle, or a square?

 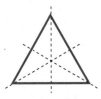 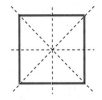

A rectangle has 2 lines of symmetry.

An equilateral triangle has 3 lines of symmetry.

A square has 4 lines of symmetry.

A square has more lines of symmetry than a rectangle and an equilateral triangle.

1 Circle the shapes below that have at least one line of symmetry.

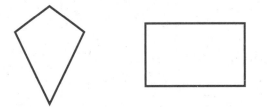

2 Circle the shape below that has a greater number of lines of symmetry.

 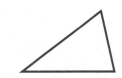

Vocabulary

line of symmetry a line dividing a shape into two matching parts.

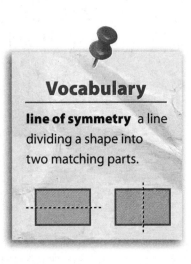

Solve.

3 Circle the shapes below that have exactly 4 lines of symmetry.

4 Look at the rectangle in problem 3. How many lines of symmetry does it have? Explain.

_____

_____

_____

_____

5 Choose *Yes* or *No* to tell whether the line drawn on each block letter is a line of symmetry.

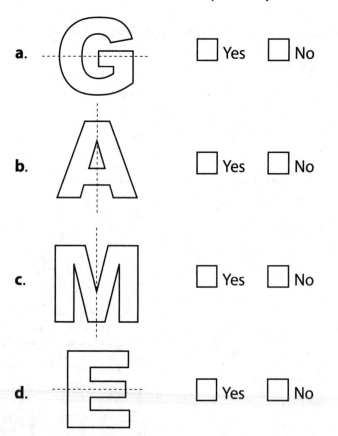

a. ☐ Yes ☐ No

b. ☐ Yes ☐ No

c. ☐ Yes ☐ No

d. ☐ Yes ☐ No

Name: _____

Draw a Line of Symmetry

Study the example showing how to draw a line of symmetry. Then solve problems 1–5.

Example

Draw all of the lines of symmetry for each star shape. How many lines of symmetry does each shape have? Where do all the lines of symmetry cross?

The 6-pointed star has 6 lines of symmetry.

The 5-pointed star has 5 lines of symmetry.

All the lines of symmetry cross at the center point of each shape.

1 Draw all the lines of symmetry on the tree shape below.

How many lines of symmetry does the tree shape have? _____

2 Draw all the lines of symmetry on the X shape below.

How many lines of symmetry does the X shape have? _____

Solve.

3 Draw all the lines of symmetry on each pentagon below. Write how many lines of symmetry each pentagon has.

_____ line(s) of symmetry _____ line(s) of symmetry

4 Titus drew a hexagon with 6 lines of symmetry. He says that all hexagons have 6 lines of symmetry. Use words and a drawing to explain why Titus's thinking is incorrect.

_____

_____

_____

_____

_____

5 Draw all the lines of symmetry that the design in each flag below has. Then write how many lines of symmetry that the design in each flag below has.

Line(s) of symmetry   Line(s) of symmetry

_____   _____

Name: _____

Symmetry

Solve the problems.

1 Which figure below shows a correct line of symmetry? Circle the letter for all that apply.

A ⬭

C ⬠

B 〰

D ➡

Does folding each shape on the line create two matching parts?

2 Part of a figure is shown below. Line *X* is the line of symmetry for the completed figure. What does the completed figure look like?

X

How does a matching part complete the figure?

A ♡

C

B ⬭

D

Leigh chose **C**. How did she get that answer?

_____

_____

_____

_____

Solve.

3 Draw all the lines of symmetry on the figure below. How many lines of symmetry are there?

Show your work.

Can you fold the figure in more than one way to show matching parts?

Solution: _____

4 Name a quadrilateral that always has the same number of lines of symmetry. Draw the shape and show the lines of symmetry. Explain why the number of lines of symmetry is always the same.

Show your work.

What are the different kinds of quadrilaterals? How many lines of symmetry do they have?

Solution: _____

_____

_____

_____

_____

_____

Unit 6 Game

Shape Round-Up

What you need: Recording Sheet, Game Board, Game Cards, 32 counters

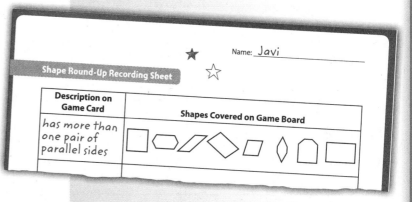

Directions

- Mix the Game Cards. Place them facedown in a stack.

- When it's your turn, draw a card and place counters on all of the shapes on your Game Board that match the description on the card.

- On your Recording Sheet, write the description from the Game Card and draw the shapes you covered on your Game Board. Then place the Game Card in a discard pile.

- Players take turns. Place only one counter on each space on the Game Board. If you use all the Game Cards, remix and reuse the cards in the discard pile.

- The winner is the first player to cover all the shapes on their Game Board.

> My Game Card reads "has more than one pair of parallel sides." I put counters on my Game Board over all the shapes with more than one pair of parallel sides.

Name: _____

Description on Game Card	Shapes Covered on Game Board

Shape Round-Up Game Board

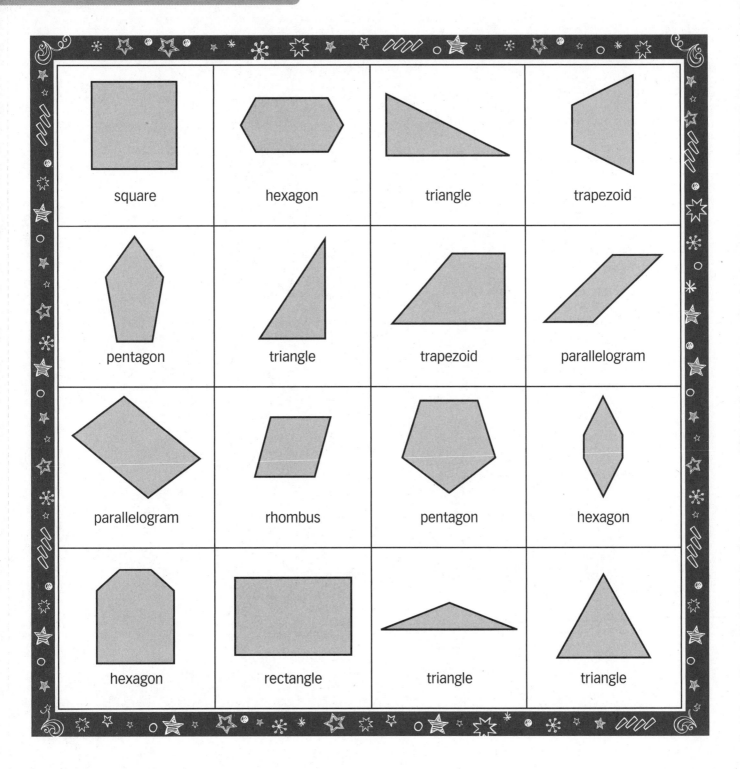

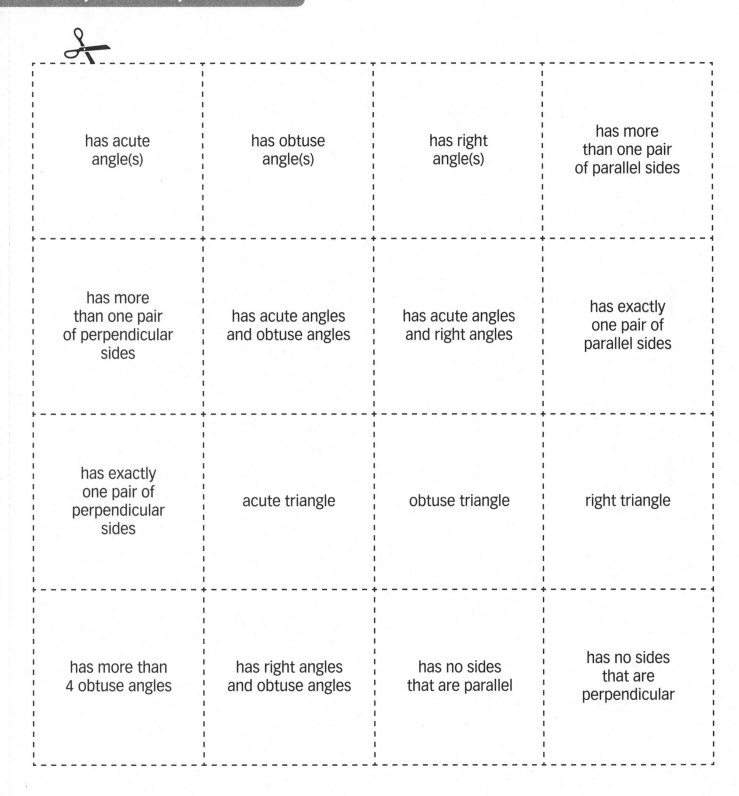

has acute angle(s)	has obtuse angle(s)	has right angle(s)	has more than one pair of parallel sides
has more than one pair of perpendicular sides	has acute angles and obtuse angles	has acute angles and right angles	has exactly one pair of parallel sides
has exactly one pair of perpendicular sides	acute triangle	obtuse triangle	right triangle
has more than 4 obtuse angles	has right angles and obtuse angles	has no sides that are parallel	has no sides that are perpendicular

Unit 6 Practice

Name: _____

Geometry

In this unit you learned to:	Lesson
draw and identify points, lines, line segments, rays, and perpendicular and parallel lines, for example: a plus sign has perpendicular lines.	31
draw and identify angles (right, acute, obtuse), for example: a square has 4 right angles.	31
classify two-dimensional figures based on sides and angles, for example: regular pentagons and hexagons have all obtuse angles.	32
draw and identify lines of symmetry, for example: a square has 4 lines of symmetry.	33

Use these skills to solve problems 1–4.

1 Tell whether each sentence is *True* or *False*.

   a. An acute angle has a larger opening than a right angle. ☐ True ☐ False

   b. Any shape with more than 4 sides has only obtuse angles. ☐ True ☐ False

   c. A triangle can have 1 right angle or 1 obtuse angle, but not both. ☐ True ☐ False

   d. An angle is formed by 2 rays. ☐ True ☐ False

2 Name each triangle below based on the kinds of angles it has and the length of its sides.

_____   _____   _____

Solve.

3 Compare the two triangles below. How are the triangles the same? How are they different?

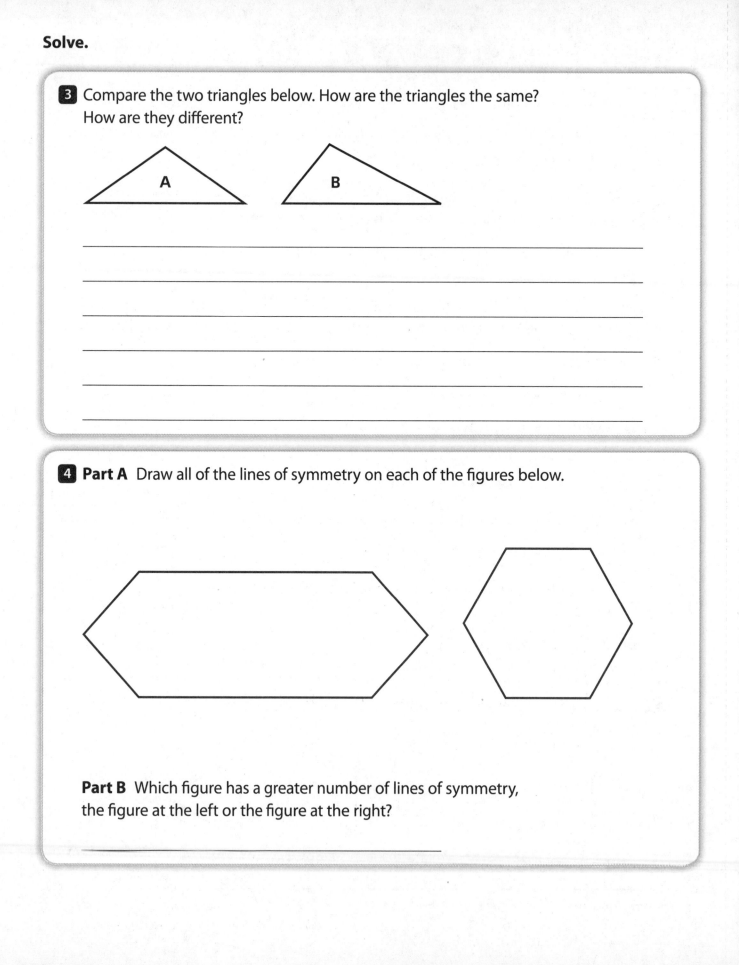

A

B

_____

_____

_____

_____

_____

4 **Part A** Draw all of the lines of symmetry on each of the figures below.

Part B Which figure has a greater number of lines of symmetry, the figure at the left or the figure at the right?

_____

Unit 6 Performance Task

Answer the questions and show all your work on separate paper.

Your math teacher has asked you to design a flower. The flower must be formed only from geometric shapes. Here is the example the teacher gives.

Create a design for a flower. You can use the shapes shown on the back of this page. You can also use other geometric shapes. Draw a picture of your flower. On a separate sheet of paper, list the names of all the different shapes you used. Also describe the properties of each shape.

Reflect on Mathematical Practices

After you complete the task, choose one of the following questions to answer.

1 Reason Mathematically How did you decide which shapes to use to create your flower design?

2 Be Precise How does your description of the properties of the shapes help someone understand what your flower design looks like?

Word Bank Here are some words that you might use in your answer.

triangle	angle	parallel
rectangle	equilateral	right
parallelogram	obtuse	side
acute	trapezoid	perpendicular

Models Here are some models that you might use to find the solution.

Sentence Starters Here are some sentence starters that might help explain your work.

I used _____ to make _____

The sides of the shape are _____

The angles are _____

The shape is _____

Unit 6 Vocabulary

Name: _____

My Examples

point

a single location in space

line segment

a straight row of points that starts at
one point and ends at another point

line

a straight row of points that goes on
forever in both directions

ray

a straight row of points that starts at
one point and goes on forever in one
direction

angle

a geometric shape formed by two rays (or lines or line segments) that meet at a common endpoint, called a vertex

parallel lines

two lines that are always the same distance apart and will never cross

perpendicular lines

two lines that cross at a 90° angle

equilateral triangle

a triangle that has all three sides with the same length

My Examples

isosceles triangle

a triangle that has two sides with the same length

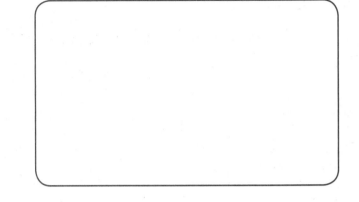

scalene triangle

a triangle that has no sides with the same length

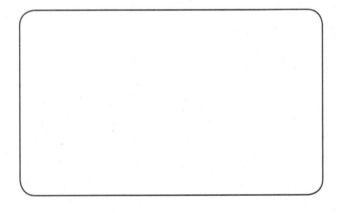

acute triangle

a triangle that has three acute angles

right triangle

a triangle that has one right angle

obtuse triangle

a triangle that has one obtuse angle

line of symmetry

a line dividing a shape into
two matching parts

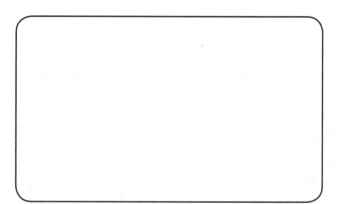

My Words

_____

_____

_____

_____

_____

_____

_____

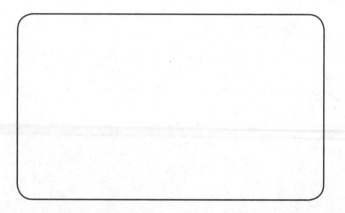

Fluency Table of Contents

Name: _____

Add within 10,000.

Form A

1 2,145
+ 653

2 5,260
+ 417

3 1,083
+ 2,513

4 2,864
+ 7,135

5 1,248
+ 532

6 3,709
+ 152

7 4,561
+ 1,054

8 5,726
+ 3,742

9 3,750
+ 456

10 2,538
+ 167

11 1,659
+ 3,291

12 4,806
+ 3,255

13 6,725
+ 385

14 5,218
+ 938

15 6,002
+ 2,999

16 8,375
+ 1,625

17 4,278
+ 3,956

18 9,407
+ 396

19 3,098
+ 2,574

20 2,710
+ 5,690

Multi-Digit Addition—Skills Practice

Name: _____

Add within 10,000.

1   1,247
   + 532

2   3,415
   + 243

3   1,068
   + 1,510

4   4,037
   + 5,062

5   2,653
   + 412

6   1,087
   + 637

7   1,960
   + 3,204

8   6,723
   + 1,238

9   4,058
   + 852

10   2,718
   + 534

11   3,605
   + 2,795

12   2,806
   + 6,294

13   6,725
   + 385

14   5,218
   + 938

15   7,538
   + 2,462

16   3,999
   + 4,006

17   7,092
   + 1,865

18   8,444
   + 565

19   5,146
   + 3,175

20   8,470
   + 1,525

Multi-Digit Addition—Skills Practice

Name: _____

Add within 100,000.

1   10,352
    + 1,430

2   16,164
    + 1,325

3   20,753
    + 10,104

4   50,618
    + 24,350

5   15,200
    +   999

6   32,145
    + 4,625

7   64,102
    + 17,254

8   24,390
    + 56,180

9   93,752
    +   598

10   46,250
    + 23,805

11   12,643
    + 52,794

12   54,622
    + 34,588

13   23,856
    + 15,246

14   47,423
    + 19,836

15   49,999
    + 3,999

16   90,187
    + 9,783

17   84,678
    + 6,395

18   27,329
    + 15,896

19   52,098
    + 28,107

20   48,365
    + 51,635

Name: _____

Add within 100,000.

Form B

1   10,943
  + 2,035

2   17,342
  + 1,340

3   12,453
  + 20,143

4   61,238
  + 24,501

5   34,210
  + 1,399

6   72,643
  + 8,142

7   15,920
  + 63,254

8   45,806
  + 54,159

9   94,627
  + 987

10   68,254
  + 2,438

11   26,513
  + 25,974

12   21,942
  + 38,657

13   23,658
  + 8,467

14   47,652
  + 27,836

15   29,999
  + 3,999

16   84,316
  + 15,684

17   74,895
  + 16,395

18   57,918
  + 25,896

19   42,968
  + 20,947

20   45,163
  + 27,989

Multi-Digit Addition—Repeated Reasoning

Name: _____

Find place value patterns in the tens.

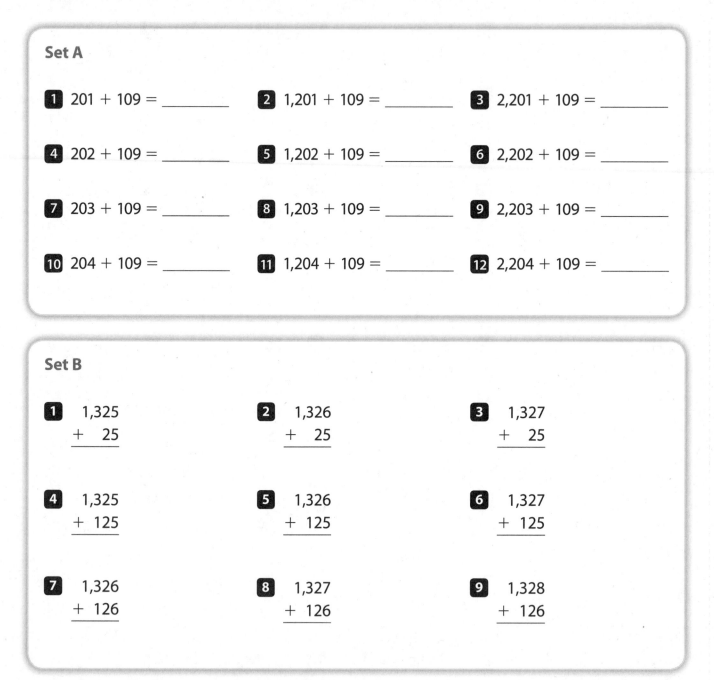

Set A

1 201 + 109 = _____

2 1,201 + 109 = _____

3 2,201 + 109 = _____

4 202 + 109 = _____

5 1,202 + 109 = _____

6 2,202 + 109 = _____

7 203 + 109 = _____

8 1,203 + 109 = _____

9 2,203 + 109 = _____

10 204 + 109 = _____

11 1,204 + 109 = _____

12 2,204 + 109 = _____

Set B

1 1,325
  + 25
  ‾‾‾‾‾

2 1,326
  + 25
  ‾‾‾‾‾

3 1,327
  + 25
  ‾‾‾‾‾

4 1,325
  + 125
  ‾‾‾‾‾

5 1,326
  + 125
  ‾‾‾‾‾

6 1,327
  + 125
  ‾‾‾‾‾

7 1,326
  + 126
  ‾‾‾‾‾

8 1,327
  + 126
  ‾‾‾‾‾

9 1,328
  + 126
  ‾‾‾‾‾

Describe a pattern you see in one of the sets of problems above.

_____

_____

_____

Multi-Digit Addition—Repeated Reasoning

Name: _____

Find place value patterns in the hundreds.

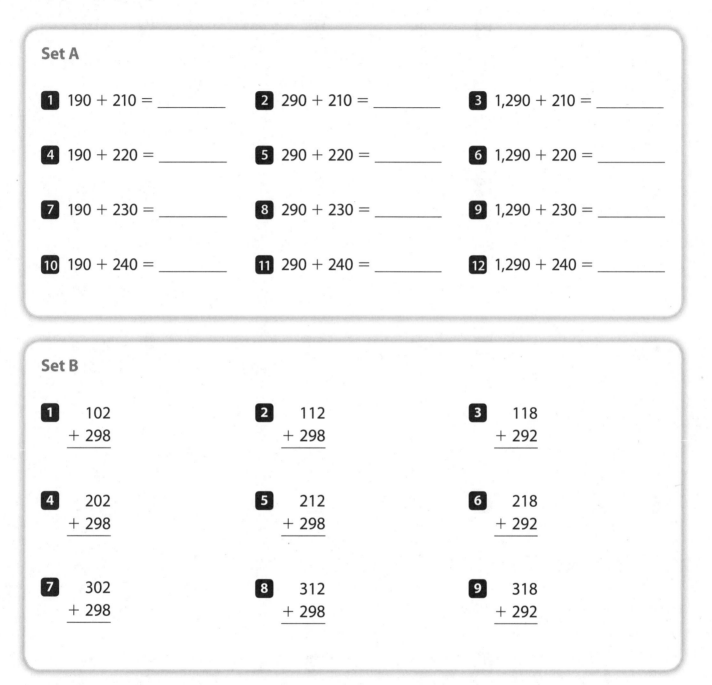

Set A

1 190 + 210 = _____

2 290 + 210 = _____

3 1,290 + 210 = _____

4 190 + 220 = _____

5 290 + 220 = _____

6 1,290 + 220 = _____

7 190 + 230 = _____

8 290 + 230 = _____

9 1,290 + 230 = _____

10 190 + 240 = _____

11 290 + 240 = _____

12 1,290 + 240 = _____

Set B

1   102
  + 298

2   112
  + 298

3   118
  + 292

4   202
  + 298

5   212
  + 298

6   218
  + 292

7   302
  + 298

8   312
  + 298

9   318
  + 292

Describe a pattern you see in one of the sets of problems above.

_____

_____

_____

Multi-Digit Subtraction—Skills Practice

Name: _____

Subtract within 10,000.

Form A

1　4,865
　　− 2,341

2　1,788
　　− 1,263

3　2,592
　　− 1,271

4　7,342
　　− 4,132

5　8,790
　　− 6,688

6　3,743
　　−　626

7　9,487
　　− 1,394

8　6,427
　　− 2,515

9　2,637
　　− 2,419

10　3,780
　　−　671

11　8,618
　　− 3,425

12　4,756
　　− 3,813

13　8,403
　　− 6,520

14　1,438
　　−　839

15　4,725
　　− 1,439

16　7,275
　　− 4,188

17　5,274
　　− 2,778

18　2,923
　　− 1,976

19　5,824
　　− 2,948

20　6,743
　　− 2,878

Multi-Digit Subtraction—Skills Practice

Name: _____

Subtract within 10,000.

Form B

1
   5,647
 − 3,210

2
   2,748
 −   312

3
   5,429
 − 4,003

4
   6,918
 − 4,105

5
   8,263
 − 1,453

6
   1,397
 − 1,239

7
   4,131
 − 2,051

8
   7,382
 − 2,581

9
   2,732
 − 1,108

10
   4,803
 −   615

11
   8,652
 − 3,481

12
   3,607
 − 2,801

13
   8,275
 − 2,391

14
   3,120
 − 1,052

15
   9,253
 −   198

16
   6,732
 − 5,587

17
   4,366
 − 1,568

18
   1,812
 −   945

19
   7,493
 − 2,594

20
   7,423
 − 2,846

Multi-Digit Subtraction—Skills Practice

Name: _____

Subtract within 100,000.

1   47,863
  −   251

2   19,038
  − 11,018

3   28,682
  − 3,270

4   76,429
  − 20,306

5   81,235
  − 20,017

6   36,725
  − 1,582

7   94,130
  − 20,125

8   64,728
  − 3,914

9   28,236
  − 8,915

10   58,623
  − 26,374

11   72,160
  − 2,087

12   38,412
  − 25,651

13   34,210
  − 8,105

14   10,714
  − 9,456

15   63,258
  − 21,399

16   40,805
  − 15,912

17   53,126
  − 45,928

18   80,052
  − 71,963

19   24,350
  − 9,582

20   100,000
  − 86,932

Multi-Digit Subtraction—Skills Practice

Name: _____

Subtract within 100,000.

1 53,641
  − 1,320

2 85,472
  − 82,302

3 93,245
  − 32,025

4 43,619
  − 20,301

5 30,582
  −   156

6 12,987
  − 2,793

7 82,056
  − 50,330

8 73,542
  − 25,402

9 27,810
  − 15,675

10 94,321
  − 4,255

11 65,852
  − 23,890

12 18,376
  − 8,953

13 15,008
  − 2,409

14 20,530
  − 19,790

15 99,325
  − 38,547

16 50,364
  − 37,148

17 36,825
  − 28,967

18 38,972
  − 19,999

19 45,000
  − 37,955

20 100,000
  − 23,871

Multi-Digit Subtraction— Repeated Reasoning

Name: _____

Find patterns in subtracting small numbers.

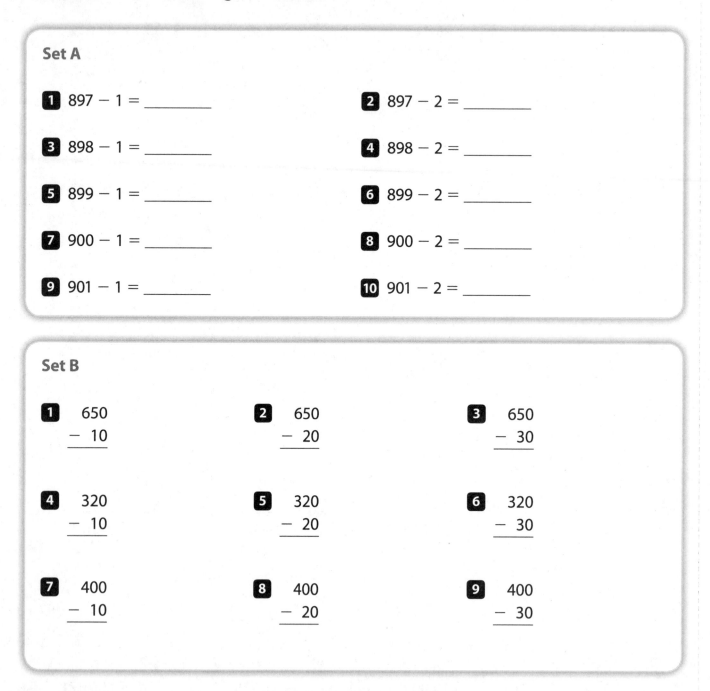

Set A

1 897 − 1 = _____

2 897 − 2 = _____

3 898 − 1 = _____

4 898 − 2 = _____

5 899 − 1 = _____

6 899 − 2 = _____

7 900 − 1 = _____

8 900 − 2 = _____

9 901 − 1 = _____

10 901 − 2 = _____

Set B

1　650
　 − 10
　_____

2　650
　 − 20
　_____

3　650
　 − 30
　_____

4　320
　 − 10
　_____

5　320
　 − 20
　_____

6　320
　 − 30
　_____

7　400
　 − 10
　_____

8　400
　 − 20
　_____

9　400
　 − 30
　_____

Describe a pattern you see in one of the sets of problems above.

_____

_____

_____

Multi-Digit Subtraction—Repeated Reasoning

Name: _____

Find place value patterns in subtracting hundreds.

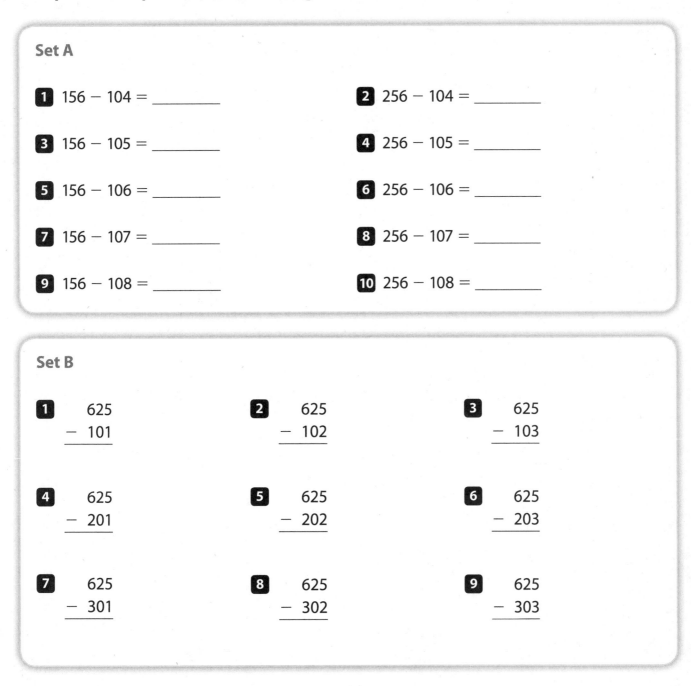

Set A

1 156 − 104 = _____

2 256 − 104 = _____

3 156 − 105 = _____

4 256 − 105 = _____

5 156 − 106 = _____

6 256 − 106 = _____

7 156 − 107 = _____

8 256 − 107 = _____

9 156 − 108 = _____

10 256 − 108 = _____

Set B

1
```
    625
−   101
_____
```

2
```
    625
−   102
_____
```

3
```
    625
−   103
_____
```

4
```
    625
−   201
_____
```

5
```
    625
−   202
_____
```

6
```
    625
−   203
_____
```

7
```
    625
−   301
_____
```

8
```
    625
−   302
_____
```

9
```
    625
−   303
_____
```

Describe a pattern you see in one of the sets of problems above.

_____

_____

_____

Fraction Addition—Skills Practice

Name: _____

Add fractions.

1 $\frac{1}{4} + \frac{1}{4} =$ _____

2 $\frac{1}{6} + \frac{1}{6} =$ _____

3 $\frac{1}{3} + \frac{2}{3} =$ _____

4 $\frac{1}{10} + \frac{2}{10} =$ _____

5 $\frac{1}{5} + \frac{3}{5} =$ _____

6 $\frac{5}{8} + \frac{2}{8} =$ _____

7 $\frac{3}{12} + \frac{5}{12} =$ _____

8 $\frac{5}{100} + \frac{5}{100} =$ _____

9 $\frac{6}{10} + \frac{3}{10} =$ _____

10 $\frac{4}{3} + \frac{1}{3} =$ _____

11 $\frac{4}{8} + \frac{5}{8} =$ _____

12 $\frac{1}{2} + \frac{1}{2} =$ _____

13 $\frac{2}{6} + \frac{5}{6} =$ _____

14 $\frac{3}{12} + \frac{7}{12} =$ _____

15 $\frac{80}{100} + \frac{8}{100} =$ _____

16 $\frac{1}{4} + \frac{4}{4} =$ _____

17 $\frac{3}{4} + \frac{5}{4} =$ _____

18 $\frac{2}{8} + \frac{3}{8} =$ _____

19 $\frac{8}{5} + \frac{2}{5} =$ _____

20 $\frac{8}{10} + \frac{3}{10} =$ _____

21 $\frac{1}{3} + \frac{2}{3} + \frac{1}{3} =$ _____

22 $\frac{4}{5} + \frac{2}{5} + \frac{3}{5} =$ _____

23 $\frac{2}{6} + \frac{1}{6} + \frac{2}{6} =$ _____

24 $\frac{5}{8} + \frac{2}{8} + \frac{1}{8} =$ _____

25 $\frac{2}{10} + \frac{1}{10} + \frac{5}{10} =$ _____

26 $\frac{1}{2} + \frac{1}{2} + \frac{1}{2} =$ _____

27 $\frac{7}{12} + \frac{1}{12} + \frac{3}{12} =$ _____

Fraction Addition—Skills Practice

Name: _____

Add fractions.   Form B

1 $\dfrac{1}{3} + \dfrac{1}{3} =$ _____

2 $\dfrac{1}{5} + \dfrac{2}{5} =$ _____

3 $\dfrac{1}{2} + \dfrac{1}{2} =$ _____

4 $\dfrac{3}{10} + \dfrac{2}{10} =$ _____

5 $\dfrac{2}{12} + \dfrac{5}{12} =$ _____

6 $\dfrac{2}{4} + \dfrac{1}{4} =$ _____

7 $\dfrac{3}{6} + \dfrac{2}{6} =$ _____

8 $\dfrac{2}{100} + \dfrac{8}{100} =$ _____

9 $\dfrac{60}{100} + \dfrac{30}{100} =$ _____

10 $\dfrac{9}{10} + \dfrac{3}{10} =$ _____

11 $\dfrac{3}{5} + \dfrac{4}{5} =$ _____

12 $\dfrac{5}{2} + \dfrac{1}{2} =$ _____

13 $\dfrac{3}{8} + \dfrac{2}{8} =$ _____

14 $\dfrac{4}{3} + \dfrac{1}{3} =$ _____

15 $\dfrac{30}{100} + \dfrac{300}{100} =$ _____

16 $\dfrac{4}{12} + \dfrac{5}{12} =$ _____

17 $\dfrac{7}{10} + \dfrac{2}{10} =$ _____

18 $\dfrac{2}{5} + \dfrac{3}{5} =$ _____

19 $\dfrac{3}{2} + \dfrac{4}{2} =$ _____

20 $\dfrac{5}{4} + \dfrac{2}{4} =$ _____

21 $\dfrac{3}{10} + \dfrac{5}{10} + \dfrac{1}{10} =$ _____

22 $\dfrac{1}{4} + \dfrac{2}{4} + \dfrac{3}{4} =$ _____

23 $\dfrac{2}{8} + \dfrac{1}{8} + \dfrac{4}{8} =$ _____

24 $\dfrac{2}{12} + \dfrac{3}{12} + \dfrac{5}{12} =$ _____

25 $\dfrac{1}{2} + \dfrac{1}{2} + \dfrac{1}{2} =$ _____

26 $\dfrac{9}{10} + \dfrac{3}{10} + \dfrac{1}{10} =$ _____

27 $\dfrac{4}{5} + \dfrac{3}{5} + \dfrac{2}{5} =$ _____

Fraction Addition—Skills Practice

Name: _____

Add mixed numbers.

Form A

1 $2\frac{1}{3} + \frac{1}{3} =$ _____

2 $2\frac{1}{5} + 1\frac{3}{5} =$ _____

3 $1\frac{1}{2} + 1\frac{1}{2} =$ _____

4 $2\frac{5}{12} + 3\frac{1}{12} =$ _____

5 $3\frac{2}{4} + 2\frac{1}{4} =$ _____

6 $\frac{5}{6} + 4\frac{1}{6} =$ _____

7 $3\frac{20}{100} + 4\frac{5}{100} =$ _____

8 $9\frac{2}{10} + 3\frac{7}{10} =$ _____

9 $2\frac{3}{5} + 4\frac{1}{5} =$ _____

10 $10\frac{3}{8} + 2\frac{3}{8} =$ _____

11 $9\frac{1}{3} + \frac{2}{3} =$ _____

12 $7\frac{10}{100} + \frac{7}{100} =$ _____

13 $5\frac{4}{10} + 1\frac{6}{10} =$ _____

14 $4\frac{2}{5} + 5\frac{4}{5} =$ _____

15 $3\frac{1}{2} + 4\frac{1}{2} =$ _____

16 $3\frac{5}{10} + 5\frac{1}{10} =$ _____

17 $6\frac{3}{4} + 4\frac{2}{4} =$ _____

18 $6\frac{2}{8} + 2\frac{5}{8} =$ _____

19 $\frac{8}{12} + 2\frac{7}{12} =$ _____

20 $3\frac{2}{10} + 4\frac{1}{10} =$ _____

21 $10\frac{1}{5} + 8\frac{3}{5} =$ _____

22 $5\frac{3}{4} + 2\frac{3}{4} =$ _____

23 $7\frac{90}{100} + 7\frac{10}{100} =$ _____

24 $6\frac{2}{3} + 4\frac{2}{3} =$ _____

Fraction Addition—Skills Practice

Name: _____

Add mixed numbers.

Form B

1 $2\frac{1}{4} + 3\frac{1}{4} =$ _____

2 $3\frac{4}{6} + 4\frac{1}{6} =$ _____

3 $2\frac{1}{3} + 6\frac{2}{3} =$ _____

4 $1\frac{4}{5} + 2\frac{3}{5} =$ _____

5 $5\frac{3}{8} + 7\frac{2}{8} =$ _____

6 $2\frac{3}{12} + 3\frac{9}{12} =$ _____

7 $6\frac{9}{10} + 3\frac{2}{10} =$ _____

8 $4\frac{2}{3} + 1\frac{2}{3} =$ _____

9 $4\frac{3}{8} + 5\frac{4}{8} =$ _____

10 $2\frac{5}{6} + 8\frac{4}{6} =$ _____

11 $1\frac{3}{12} + 6\frac{5}{12} =$ _____

12 $15\frac{80}{100} + 4\frac{20}{100} =$ _____

13 $5\frac{3}{4} + 6\frac{2}{4} =$ _____

14 $3\frac{1}{8} + 7\frac{4}{8} =$ _____

15 $8\frac{1}{5} + 7\frac{2}{5} =$ _____

16 $3\frac{2}{3} + 3\frac{2}{3} =$ _____

17 $3\frac{4}{5} + 5\frac{2}{5} =$ _____

18 $2\frac{5}{6} + 9\frac{3}{6} =$ _____

19 $7\frac{8}{10} + 5\frac{9}{10} =$ _____

20 $20\frac{1}{2} + 10\frac{1}{2} =$ _____

21 $7\frac{3}{12} + 2\frac{11}{12} =$ _____

22 $3\frac{7}{8} + 4\frac{5}{8} =$ _____

23 $\frac{32}{100} + 3\frac{55}{100} =$ _____

24 $3\frac{5}{6} + 8\frac{3}{6} =$ _____

Fraction Addition— Repeated Reasoning

Name: _____

Find patterns in adding fractions.

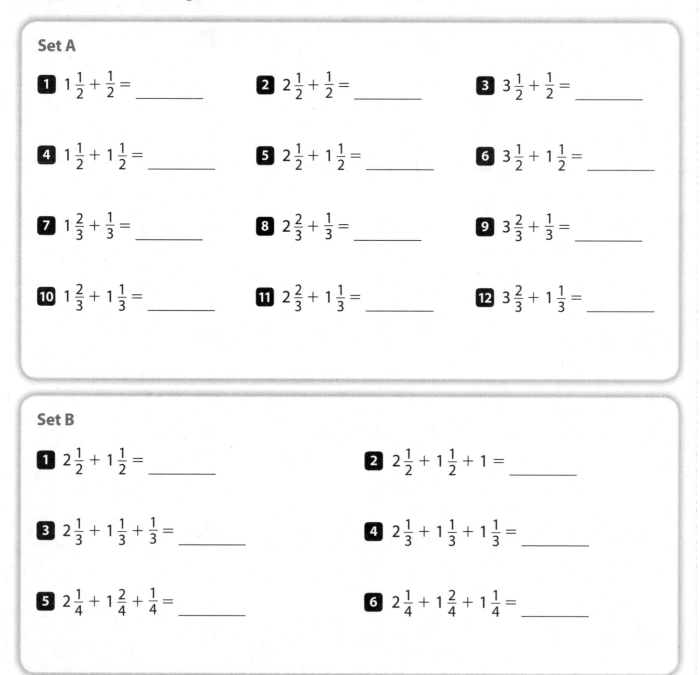

Set A

1 $1\frac{1}{2} + \frac{1}{2} =$ _____

2 $2\frac{1}{2} + \frac{1}{2} =$ _____

3 $3\frac{1}{2} + \frac{1}{2} =$ _____

4 $1\frac{1}{2} + 1\frac{1}{2} =$ _____

5 $2\frac{1}{2} + 1\frac{1}{2} =$ _____

6 $3\frac{1}{2} + 1\frac{1}{2} =$ _____

7 $1\frac{2}{3} + \frac{1}{3} =$ _____

8 $2\frac{2}{3} + \frac{1}{3} =$ _____

9 $3\frac{2}{3} + \frac{1}{3} =$ _____

10 $1\frac{2}{3} + 1\frac{1}{3} =$ _____

11 $2\frac{2}{3} + 1\frac{1}{3} =$ _____

12 $3\frac{2}{3} + 1\frac{1}{3} =$ _____

Set B

1 $2\frac{1}{2} + 1\frac{1}{2} =$ _____

2 $2\frac{1}{2} + 1\frac{1}{2} + 1 =$ _____

3 $2\frac{1}{3} + 1\frac{1}{3} + \frac{1}{3} =$ _____

4 $2\frac{1}{3} + 1\frac{1}{3} + 1\frac{1}{3} =$ _____

5 $2\frac{1}{4} + 1\frac{2}{4} + \frac{1}{4} =$ _____

6 $2\frac{1}{4} + 1\frac{2}{4} + 1\frac{1}{4} =$ _____

Describe a pattern you see in one of the sets of problems above.

_____

_____

_____

Fraction Subtraction—Skills Practice

Name: _____

Subtract fractions.

Form A

1 $\frac{3}{4} - \frac{1}{4} =$ _____

2 $\frac{5}{6} - \frac{1}{6} =$ _____

3 $\frac{2}{3} - \frac{1}{3} =$ _____

4 $\frac{7}{10} - \frac{3}{10} =$ _____

5 $\frac{4}{5} - \frac{3}{5} =$ _____

6 $\frac{5}{8} - \frac{2}{8} =$ _____

7 $\frac{13}{12} - \frac{5}{12} =$ _____

8 $\frac{50}{100} - \frac{5}{100} =$ _____

9 $\frac{6}{10} - \frac{3}{10} =$ _____

10 $\frac{5}{3} - \frac{1}{3} =$ _____

11 $\frac{10}{8} - \frac{5}{8} =$ _____

12 $\frac{5}{2} - \frac{1}{2} =$ _____

13 $\frac{9}{6} - \frac{1}{6} =$ _____

14 $\frac{7}{12} - \frac{3}{12} =$ _____

15 $\frac{80}{100} - \frac{20}{100} =$ _____

16 $\frac{7}{4} - \frac{4}{4} =$ _____

17 $\frac{7}{4} - \frac{3}{4} =$ _____

18 $\frac{7}{8} - \frac{1}{8} =$ _____

19 $\frac{8}{5} - \frac{2}{5} =$ _____

20 $\frac{8}{10} - \frac{3}{10} =$ _____

21 $\frac{6}{3} - \frac{2}{3} =$ _____

22 $\frac{4}{5} - \frac{2}{5} =$ _____

23 $\frac{7}{6} - \frac{5}{6} =$ _____

24 $\frac{10}{8} - \frac{3}{8} =$ _____

25 $\frac{12}{10} - \frac{5}{10} =$ _____

26 $\frac{3}{2} - \frac{3}{2} =$ _____

27 $\frac{6}{12} - \frac{3}{12} =$ _____

Fraction Subtraction—Skills Practice

Name: _____

Subtract fractions.

1 $\frac{3}{3} - \frac{1}{3} =$ _____

2 $\frac{5}{5} - \frac{2}{5} =$ _____

3 $\frac{1}{2} - \frac{1}{2} =$ _____

4 $\frac{6}{10} - \frac{2}{10} =$ _____

5 $\frac{11}{12} - \frac{5}{12} =$ _____

6 $\frac{5}{4} - \frac{1}{4} =$ _____

7 $\frac{7}{6} - \frac{3}{6} =$ _____

8 $\frac{12}{100} - \frac{8}{100} =$ _____

9 $\frac{60}{100} - \frac{30}{100} =$ _____

10 $\frac{12}{10} - \frac{3}{10} =$ _____

11 $\frac{13}{5} - \frac{4}{5} =$ _____

12 $\frac{6}{2} - \frac{1}{2} =$ _____

13 $\frac{7}{8} - \frac{1}{8} =$ _____

14 $\frac{5}{3} - \frac{1}{3} =$ _____

15 $\frac{56}{100} - \frac{6}{100} =$ _____

16 $\frac{15}{12} - \frac{3}{12} =$ _____

17 $\frac{7}{10} - \frac{2}{10} =$ _____

18 $\frac{7}{5} - \frac{3}{5} =$ _____

19 $\frac{4}{2} - \frac{3}{2} =$ _____

20 $\frac{7}{4} - \frac{2}{4} =$ _____

21 $\frac{30}{10} - \frac{5}{10} =$ _____

22 $\frac{10}{4} - \frac{2}{4} =$ _____

23 $\frac{7}{8} - \frac{4}{8} =$ _____

24 $\frac{12}{12} - \frac{3}{12} =$ _____

25 $\frac{7}{2} - \frac{5}{2} =$ _____

26 $\frac{9}{10} - \frac{3}{10} =$ _____

27 $\frac{8}{5} - \frac{1}{5} =$ _____

Fraction Subtraction—Skills Practice

Name: _____

Subtract mixed numbers.

Form A

1 $2\frac{1}{3} - \frac{1}{3} =$ _____

2 $2\frac{3}{5} - 1\frac{1}{5} =$ _____

3 $1\frac{1}{2} - \frac{3}{2} =$ _____

4 $4\frac{5}{12} - 1\frac{3}{12} =$ _____

5 $3\frac{2}{4} - 2\frac{1}{4} =$ _____

6 $4\frac{5}{6} - 3\frac{1}{6} =$ _____

7 $7\frac{15}{100} - 2\frac{5}{100} =$ _____

8 $8\frac{2}{10} - 3\frac{7}{10} =$ _____

9 $4\frac{1}{5} - 2\frac{3}{5} =$ _____

10 $10\frac{3}{8} - 2\frac{3}{8} =$ _____

11 $10\frac{1}{3} - \frac{2}{3} =$ _____

12 $2\frac{10}{100} - \frac{7}{100} =$ _____

13 $5\frac{6}{10} - 1\frac{3}{10} =$ _____

14 $6\frac{2}{5} - 5\frac{4}{5} =$ _____

15 $9\frac{1}{2} - 4\frac{1}{2} =$ _____

16 $7\frac{5}{10} - 5\frac{1}{10} =$ _____

17 $6\frac{3}{4} - 4\frac{2}{4} =$ _____

18 $6\frac{2}{8} - 2\frac{5}{8} =$ _____

19 $2\frac{8}{12} - 2\frac{7}{12} =$ _____

20 $6\frac{2}{10} - 4\frac{7}{10} =$ _____

21 $10\frac{1}{5} - 8\frac{4}{5} =$ _____

22 $5\frac{1}{4} - 2\frac{3}{4} =$ _____

23 $7\frac{90}{100} - 7\frac{10}{100} =$ _____

24 $6\frac{1}{3} - 4\frac{2}{3} =$ _____

Subtract mixed numbers.   **Form B**

1 $3\frac{2}{5} - \frac{1}{5} = $ _____

2 $6\frac{3}{4} - 1\frac{1}{4} = $ _____

3 $7\frac{1}{2} - \frac{1}{2} = $ _____

4 $4\frac{6}{10} - 1\frac{2}{10} = $ _____

5 $5\frac{2}{3} - 2\frac{1}{3} = $ _____

6 $4\frac{5}{6} - 3\frac{1}{6} = $ _____

7 $9\frac{20}{100} - 5\frac{2}{100} = $ _____

8 $8\frac{7}{10} - 3\frac{1}{10} = $ _____

9 $10\frac{4}{5} - 3\frac{1}{5} = $ _____

10 $1\frac{1}{8} - \frac{3}{8} = $ _____

11 $4\frac{1}{3} - \frac{3}{3} = $ _____

12 $8\frac{60}{100} - 2\frac{10}{100} = $ _____

13 $6\frac{5}{10} - 1\frac{9}{10} = $ _____

14 $8\frac{2}{5} - 5\frac{4}{5} = $ _____

15 $7\frac{1}{2} - 4\frac{1}{2} = $ _____

16 $5\frac{7}{10} - 3\frac{9}{10} = $ _____

17 $1\frac{3}{4} - \frac{2}{4} = $ _____

18 $16\frac{2}{8} - 12\frac{5}{8} = $ _____

19 $5\frac{3}{12} - 2\frac{7}{12} = $ _____

20 $7\frac{2}{10} - 2\frac{7}{10} = $ _____

21 $9\frac{1}{5} - 8\frac{4}{5} = $ _____

22 $3\frac{1}{4} - \frac{3}{4} = $ _____

23 $9\frac{70}{100} - 4\frac{10}{100} = $ _____

24 $14\frac{1}{3} - 9\frac{2}{3} = $ _____

Name: _____

Find patterns in subtracting fractions.

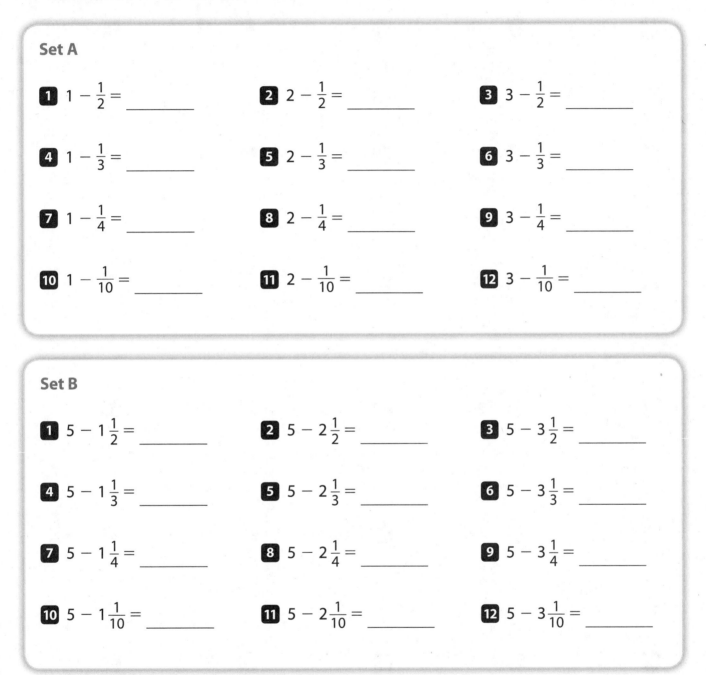

Set A

1 $1 - \frac{1}{2} =$ _____

2 $2 - \frac{1}{2} =$ _____

3 $3 - \frac{1}{2} =$ _____

4 $1 - \frac{1}{3} =$ _____

5 $2 - \frac{1}{3} =$ _____

6 $3 - \frac{1}{3} =$ _____

7 $1 - \frac{1}{4} =$ _____

8 $2 - \frac{1}{4} =$ _____

9 $3 - \frac{1}{4} =$ _____

10 $1 - \frac{1}{10} =$ _____

11 $2 - \frac{1}{10} =$ _____

12 $3 - \frac{1}{10} =$ _____

Set B

1 $5 - 1\frac{1}{2} =$ _____

2 $5 - 2\frac{1}{2} =$ _____

3 $5 - 3\frac{1}{2} =$ _____

4 $5 - 1\frac{1}{3} =$ _____

5 $5 - 2\frac{1}{3} =$ _____

6 $5 - 3\frac{1}{3} =$ _____

7 $5 - 1\frac{1}{4} =$ _____

8 $5 - 2\frac{1}{4} =$ _____

9 $5 - 3\frac{1}{4} =$ _____

10 $5 - 1\frac{1}{10} =$ _____

11 $5 - 2\frac{1}{10} =$ _____

12 $5 - 3\frac{1}{10} =$ _____

Describe a pattern you see in one of the sets of problems above.

_____

_____

_____

Multi-Digit Multiplication—Skills Practice

Name: _____

Multiply a 2-digit number by a 1-digit number.   **Form A**

1 12
   $\times$ 2

2 10
   $\times$ 3

3 21
   $\times$ 4

4 23
   $\times$ 1

5 33
   $\times$ 2

6 11
   $\times$ 8

7 35
   $\times$ 4

8 46
   $\times$ 5

9 51
   $\times$ 3

10 70
   $\times$ 5

11 10
   $\times$ 9

12 88
   $\times$ 4

13 78
   $\times$ 5

14 29
   $\times$ 6

15 61
   $\times$ 6

16 12
   $\times$ 7

17 26
   $\times$ 8

18 58
   $\times$ 9

19 81
   $\times$ 7

20 75
   $\times$ 3

21 72
   $\times$ 3

22 92
   $\times$ 3

23 49
   $\times$ 7

24 31
   $\times$ 6

25 56
   $\times$ 4

26 34
   $\times$ 6

27 58
   $\times$ 5

28 37
   $\times$ 7

29 64
   $\times$ 8

30 98
   $\times$ 9

Name: _____

Multiply a 2-digit number by a 1-digit number.

Form B

1 21
   $\times\ 2$

2 10
   $\times\ 6$

3 41
   $\times\ 3$

4 32
   $\times\ 1$

5 22
   $\times\ 4$

6 11
   $\times\ 7$

7 54
   $\times\ 9$

8 64
   $\times\ 5$

9 55
   $\times\ 8$

10 75
   $\times\ 5$

11 12
   $\times\ 9$

12 84
   $\times\ 8$

13 57
   $\times\ 4$

14 96
   $\times\ 7$

15 41
   $\times\ 6$

16 82
   $\times\ 7$

17 26
   $\times\ 5$

18 92
   $\times\ 6$

19 81
   $\times\ 3$

20 35
   $\times\ 7$

21 62
   $\times\ 8$

22 43
   $\times\ 8$

23 98
   $\times\ 2$

24 36
   $\times\ 9$

25 28
   $\times\ 4$

26 53
   $\times\ 4$

27 38
   $\times\ 5$

28 24
   $\times\ 7$

29 48
   $\times\ 3$

30 99
   $\times\ 9$

Name: _____

Multiply 2-digit numbers.

Form A

1   21
    × 35

2   18
    × 16

3   24
    × 12

4   32
    × 15

5   12
    × 37

6   11
    × 77

7   54
    × 92

8   64
    × 35

9   75
    × 28

10   43
    × 15

11   42
    × 96

12   40
    × 88

13   57
    × 64

14   96
    × 70

15   61
    × 54

16   82
    × 27

17   26
    × 45

18   82
    × 34

19   63
    × 36

20   35
    × 27

21   20
    × 16

22   41
    × 30

23   98
    × 20

24   36
    × 79

25   28
    × 49

Multi-Digit Multiplication

Name: _____

Multiply 2-digit numbers.

Form B

1 $\begin{array}{r} 12 \\ \times\, 53 \\ \hline \end{array}$ **2** $\begin{array}{r} 86 \\ \times\, 11 \\ \hline \end{array}$ **3** $\begin{array}{r} 55 \\ \times\, 43 \\ \hline \end{array}$ **4** $\begin{array}{r} 23 \\ \times\, 15 \\ \hline \end{array}$ **5** $\begin{array}{r} 12 \\ \times\, 83 \\ \hline \end{array}$

6 $\begin{array}{r} 11 \\ \times\, 66 \\ \hline \end{array}$ **7** $\begin{array}{r} 94 \\ \times\, 25 \\ \hline \end{array}$ **8** $\begin{array}{r} 46 \\ \times\, 53 \\ \hline \end{array}$ **9** $\begin{array}{r} 37 \\ \times\, 62 \\ \hline \end{array}$ **10** $\begin{array}{r} 78 \\ \times\, 18 \\ \hline \end{array}$

11 $\begin{array}{r} 24 \\ \times\, 96 \\ \hline \end{array}$ **12** $\begin{array}{r} 14 \\ \times\, 85 \\ \hline \end{array}$ **13** $\begin{array}{r} 74 \\ \times\, 36 \\ \hline \end{array}$ **14** $\begin{array}{r} 97 \\ \times\, 40 \\ \hline \end{array}$ **15** $\begin{array}{r} 41 \\ \times\, 56 \\ \hline \end{array}$

16 $\begin{array}{r} 92 \\ \times\, 57 \\ \hline \end{array}$ **17** $\begin{array}{r} 63 \\ \times\, 45 \\ \hline \end{array}$ **18** $\begin{array}{r} 52 \\ \times\, 27 \\ \hline \end{array}$ **19** $\begin{array}{r} 84 \\ \times\, 29 \\ \hline \end{array}$ **20** $\begin{array}{r} 99 \\ \times\, 34 \\ \hline \end{array}$

21 $\begin{array}{r} 50 \\ \times\, 26 \\ \hline \end{array}$ **22** $\begin{array}{r} 74 \\ \times\, 30 \\ \hline \end{array}$ **23** $\begin{array}{r} 89 \\ \times\, 40 \\ \hline \end{array}$ **24** $\begin{array}{r} 36 \\ \times\, 29 \\ \hline \end{array}$ **25** $\begin{array}{r} 98 \\ \times\, 90 \\ \hline \end{array}$

Multi-Digit Multiplication—Skills Practice

Name: _____

Multiply a 3-digit number by a 1-digit number. Form A

1 513
    × 2

2 120
    × 3

3 612
    × 4

4 711
    × 5

5 460
    × 3

6 325
    × 7

7 940
    × 5

8 518
    × 3

9 105
    × 9

10 862
    × 4

11 728
    × 5

12 429
    × 6

13 123
    × 7

14 256
    × 8

15 908
    × 9

16 381
    × 2

17 712
    × 3

18 923
    × 3

19 752
    × 7

20 310
    × 6

21 304
    × 6

22 502
    × 5

23 837
    × 6

24 604
    × 8

Multi-Digit Multiplication—Skills Practice

Name: _____

Multiply a 3-digit number by a 1-digit number.

Form B

1 100
× 7

2 421
× 3

3 324
× 1

4 202
× 4

5 504
× 9

6 614
× 5

7 945
× 8

8 157
× 5

9 624
× 8

10 457
× 3

11 967
× 4

12 804
× 6

13 250
× 4

14 512
× 9

15 381
× 5

16 336
× 7

17 843
× 2

18 938
× 6

19 362
× 9

20 278
× 4

21 308
× 5

22 724
× 7

23 548
× 3

24 909
× 9

Name: _____

Multiply a 4-digit number by a 1-digit number.   **Form A**

1   5,213
    ×   2

2   6,120
    ×   4

3   5,332
    ×   3

4   5,201
    ×   4

5   4,360
    ×   5

6   7,025
    ×   3

7   1,945
    ×   6

8   3,518
    ×   7

9   2,075
    ×   9

10   4,208
    ×   6

11   7,528
    ×   2

12   5,299
    ×   3

13   1,234
    ×   7

14   2,048
    ×   5

15   9,088
    ×   3

16   8,301
    ×   8

17   7,302
    ×   4

18   9,423
    ×   2

19   7,526
    ×   4

20   4,610
    ×   6

21   3,604
    ×   8

22   5,902
    ×   9

23   8,637
    ×   6

24   6,804
    ×   5

Multi-Digit Multiplication—Skills Practice

Name: _____

Multiply a 4-digit number by a 1-digit number.

1   4,130
  ×   2

2   5,212
  ×   4

3   3,023
  ×   3

4   1,200
  ×   4

5   5,170
  ×   5

6   6,047
  ×   8

7   2,593
  ×   6

8   8,350
  ×   7

9   3,084
  ×   9

10   2,708
  ×   6

11   8,925
  ×   2

12   7,599
  ×   3

13   9,423
  ×   4

14   2,048
  ×   5

15   4,625
  ×   7

16   5,304
  ×   8

17   2,730
  ×   3

18   9,067
  ×   2

19   7,199
  ×   4

20   5,402
  ×   7

21   6,521
  ×   8

22   3,207
  ×   9

23   8,022
  ×   6

24   4,635
  ×   5

Multi-Digit Multiplication— Repeated Reasoning

Name: _____

Find place value patterns.

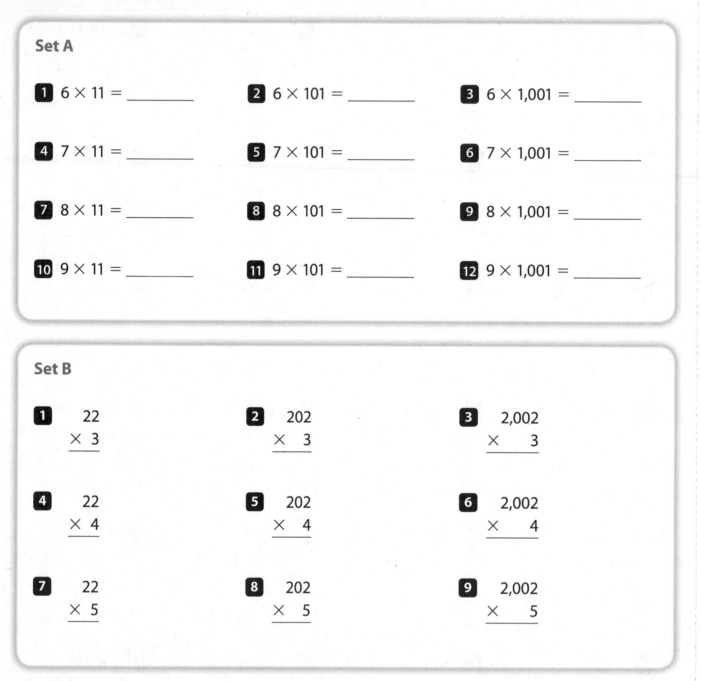

Set A

1 $6 \times 11 =$ _____

2 $6 \times 101 =$ _____

3 $6 \times 1,001 =$ _____

4 $7 \times 11 =$ _____

5 $7 \times 101 =$ _____

6 $7 \times 1,001 =$ _____

7 $8 \times 11 =$ _____

8 $8 \times 101 =$ _____

9 $8 \times 1,001 =$ _____

10 $9 \times 11 =$ _____

11 $9 \times 101 =$ _____

12 $9 \times 1,001 =$ _____

Set B

1
$$\begin{array}{r} 22 \\ \times\ 3 \\ \hline \end{array}$$

2
$$\begin{array}{r} 202 \\ \times\ 3 \\ \hline \end{array}$$

3
$$\begin{array}{r} 2,002 \\ \times\ \ \ 3 \\ \hline \end{array}$$

4
$$\begin{array}{r} 22 \\ \times\ 4 \\ \hline \end{array}$$

5
$$\begin{array}{r} 202 \\ \times\ 4 \\ \hline \end{array}$$

6
$$\begin{array}{r} 2,002 \\ \times\ \ \ 4 \\ \hline \end{array}$$

7
$$\begin{array}{r} 22 \\ \times\ 5 \\ \hline \end{array}$$

8
$$\begin{array}{r} 202 \\ \times\ 5 \\ \hline \end{array}$$

9
$$\begin{array}{r} 2,002 \\ \times\ \ \ 5 \\ \hline \end{array}$$

Describe a pattern you see in one of the sets of problems above.

_____

_____

_____

Multi-Digit Multiplication—
Repeated Reasoning

Name: _____

Find patterns multiplying by 98 and 99.

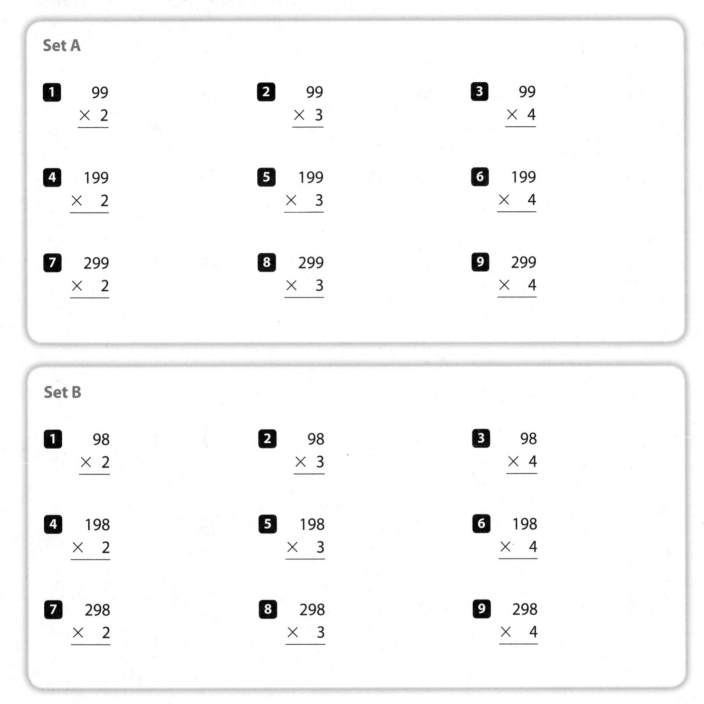

Set A

1   99
   × 2

2   99
   × 3

3   99
   × 4

4 199
   × 2

5 199
   × 3

6 199
   × 4

7 299
   × 2

8 299
   × 3

9 299
   × 4

Set B

1   98
   × 2

2   98
   × 3

3   98
   × 4

4 198
   × 2

5 198
   × 3

6 198
   × 4

7 298
   × 2

8 298
   × 3

9 298
   × 4

Describe a pattern you see in one of the sets of problems above.

_____

_____

_____

Multi-Digit Multiplication— Repeated Reasoning

Name: _____

Find patterns multiplying by near-hundreds.

Set A

1 101
     × 2

2 102
     × 2

3 103
     × 2

4 101
     × 3

5 102
     × 3

6 103
     × 3

7 101
     × 4

8 102
     × 4

9 103
     × 4

Set B

1 202
     × 2

2 202
     × 3

3 202
     × 4

4 203
     × 2

5 203
     × 3

6 203
     × 4

7 204
     × 2

8 204
     × 3

9 204
     × 4

Describe a pattern you see in one of the sets of problems above.

_____

_____

_____

Name: _____

Divide 2-digit dividends.

Form A

1 3)81 **2** 4)52 **3** 5)90 **4** 2)78

5 6)85 **6** 9)63 **7** 3)92 **8** 7)81

9 2)73 **10** 5)70 **11** 8)99 **12** 4)95

13 9)98 **14** 3)99 **15** 6)38 **16** 5)95

17 7)87 **18** 8)62 **19** 4)82 **20** 2)87

Divide 2-digit dividends.

1 2)54

2 3)50

3 4)34

4 5)55

5 6)77

6 7)91

7 8)97

8 9)95

9 2)89

10 3)94

11 4)83

12 5)78

13 6)90

14 7)50

15 8)80

16 9)87

17 2)38

18 3)94

19 4)99

20 5)94

Multi-Digit Division—Skills Practice

Name: _____

Divide 3-digit dividends. **Form A**

1 3)642

2 4)328

3 5)745

4 2)563

5 9)918

6 6)905

7 5)844

8 7)498

9 8)407

10 3)975

11 2)416

12 4)592

13 6)693

14 5)457

15 3)860

Name: _____

Divide 3-digit dividends.

Form B

1 3)741

2 4)508

3 5)354

4 2)705

5 7)936

6 6)648

7 5)820

8 7)149

9 8)916

10 3)960

11 2)613

12 4)887

13 6)738

14 5)432

15 3)722

Name: _____

Divide 4-digit dividends.

Form A

1 3)6,933   **2** 4)1,304   **3** 5)1,234

4 2)7,350   **5** 7)1,589   **6** 6)1,574

7 5)2,648   **8** 3)2,845   **9** 8)6,014

10 3)8,574   **11** 2)5,318   **12** 4)2,583

13 6)3,754   **14** 5)7,138   **15** 3)5,002

Multi-Digit Division—Skills Practice

Name: _____

Divide 4-digit dividends.

1 3)4,392

2 4)3,492

3 5)4,206

4 2)9,570

5 7)2,958

6 6)5,241

7 5)8,065

8 3)4,639

9 8)1,854

10 3)5,740

11 2)7,356

12 4)3,820

13 6)4,523

14 5)6,148

15 3)2,005

Multi-Digit Division—Repeated Reasoning

Name: _____

Find patterns in quotients.

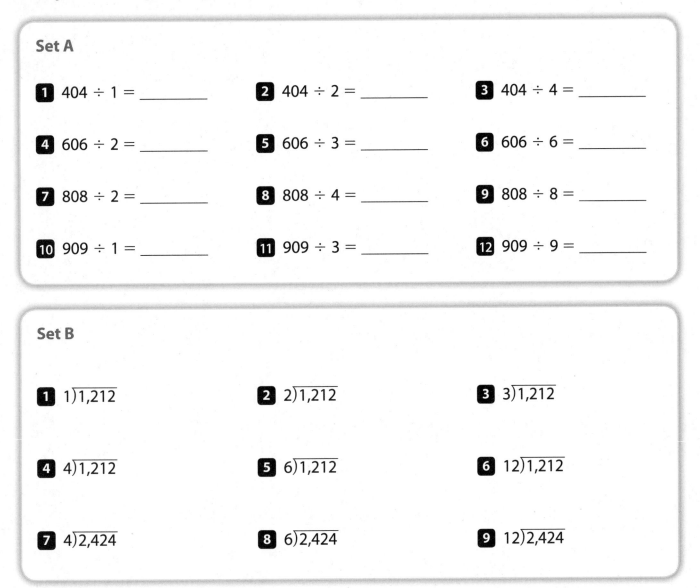

Set A

1 404 ÷ 1 = _____

2 404 ÷ 2 = _____

3 404 ÷ 4 = _____

4 606 ÷ 2 = _____

5 606 ÷ 3 = _____

6 606 ÷ 6 = _____

7 808 ÷ 2 = _____

8 808 ÷ 4 = _____

9 808 ÷ 8 = _____

10 909 ÷ 1 = _____

11 909 ÷ 3 = _____

12 909 ÷ 9 = _____

Set B

1 1)1,212

2 2)1,212

3 3)1,212

4 4)1,212

5 6)1,212

6 12)1,212

7 4)2,424

8 6)2,424

9 12)2,424

Describe a pattern you see in one of the sets of problems above.

_____

_____

_____